MINERALS, ROCKS
AND PRECIOUS STONES

D0525289

MINERALS, ROCKS
AND PRECIOUS STONES

Text by Jaroslav Bauer

Photographs by František Tvrz

BLITZ EDITIONS

549
1138121

Text by Jaroslav Bauer
Translated by Zdenka Náglová
Photographs by František Tvrz
Graphic design by Antonín Chmel

Designed and produced by Aventinum Publishing House, Prague, Czech Republic
This English edition published 1999 by Blitz Editions, an imprint of Bookmart Ltd.
Registered Number 2372865
Trading as Bookmart Limited
Desford Road, Enderby, Leicester LE9 5AD

ISBN 1-85605-443-8
Printed in the Czech Republic by Polygrafia, a.s., Prague
3/07/03/51-12

Contents

Preface   8

Introduction   10
Basic Terms   10

Minerals   12
Material Structure of Minerals   12
System of Mineral Classification   12
Origin of Minerals   13
   Magmatic Formation of Minerals   13
   Mineral Formation Caused by Weathering   14
   Mineral Formation Caused by Chemico-Sedimentary Processes 15
   Minerals and Rocks of Biological Origin   15
   Metamorphic Mineral Formation   15
External Form of Minerals   16
   Crystals   16
   Crystal Symmetry   16
   Appearance and Development of Crystals   18
   Aggregates   19
   Growth of Twin Crystals   20
   Crystal Faces   20
   Pseudomorphs   21

Physical Properties of Minerals   21
  Specific Gravity   21
  Properties of Cohesion   22
    Hardness   22
    Cleavage   24
    Fracture   24
    Other Physical Properties Dependent upon Cohesion   24
  Colour   25
  Streak   26
  Lustre   26
  Transparency   27
  Refraction of Light   27
  Luminescence   27
  Heat Conductivity   28
  Magnetism   28
Chemical Properties of Minerals   28
Identification of Minerals   29
  Process of Mineral Identification   29
  Examples of Mineral Identification   30
  Practical Advice for Collectors   31
  Where are Minerals to be Found?   32
  Collecting Equipment   32
  Field Work   34
  Preserving and Labelling Collected Specimens   35
Notes to the Identification Tables   36
Abbreviations   37

Minerals (Identification Tables and Plates)   39–167

Precious Stones   168
  Treatment of Precious Stones — Cutting Form   169
  Imitations and Synthetic Precious Stones   169
  Identification of Precious Stones   170

Rocks   172
  Classification of Rocks   172
  Structure and Texture of Rocks   174
  Identification of Rocks   174

Precious Stones and Rocks (Identification Tables and Plates) 175–191

Identification Tables according to Physical Properties   192–201

Index of Minerals   203

General Index   207

Localities of Minerals   208

List of Reference Books   215

Preface

As early as prehistoric times men knew how to make use of the various special properties of individual stones, ores and minerals; in other words, Stone Age man was the first mineralogist. In the course of time the use and importance of minerals for technical and scientific purposes has been increasing and modern industry still finds them essential as raw materials. The rich colour, perfect lustre and the regularity of form of crystal have long had a particular charm for man.

This book of 576 colour photographs is sure to appeal not only to mineral collectors, but also to laymen who appreciate the beauty of attractive stones. The wondrous world of nature lies open here to all those who are interested in discovering its hidden beauties. The photographic material was chosen from the taxonomic as well as the aesthetic point of view. The expert mineralogist will also find here unusual and rare specimens of minerals. The book is not meant to be used just for the purpose of easy identification of minerals. As it is intended for the layman, the author does not presuppose that the reader will know much about crystallography, chemistry or physics. Because many minerals may display a number of different characteristic forms, it is rather difficult even for an expert to classify them. For this reason typical features have been chosen which can either be recognized on sight or with the help of very simple tests.

The most striking feature of a mineral is its colour. It is, of course, not always the most reliable deciding factor. In this book the minerals have been divided according to their colour. Whenever a certain mineral occurs naturally in more than one colour, it is especially mentioned each time. To make it easier for the reader to use the book, individual colours are given in the form of coloured strips along the margins of the tables and plates.

The second important feature of a mineral is its lustre. This book divides minerals into metallic and non-metallic. The identification tables arrange the minerals according to their hardness as well as in the general mineralogical system. To enable more accurate identification to be made some other easily discernible features, such as streak, cleavage and transparency, are described.

Perfect models of crystals are only confusing for beginners, and cause them many difficulties later when they expect to find them in the field. For this reason drawings of crystals have not been included in the tables, but there is a summary of the main crystal forms on page 17 to illustrate the terms used in column five of the tables.

Precious stones and rocks are mentioned fairly briefly here. More detailed information may be found in numerous other books.

All the minerals described here form part of the excellent collection kept at the Technical University, Prague. Some of the specimens mentioned are from the Mineral Section of the National Museum, Prague.

Introduction

Basic Terms

Neither the apparently solid earth nor the porous soil under our feet are homogeneous. On the contrary, the upper layers of the earth's crust are composed of very different elements — in technical language, of heterogeneous building blocks. They are called *rocks*. At a closer glance it becomes evident that these are accumulations of minerals. *Minerals* must therefore be considered the basic constituents of rocks. In fact, rocks are generally mixtures of various sorts of minerals affected by natural processes. They form a heterogeneous yet geologically independent part of the earth's crust.

Although there are some rocks (such as marble, composed only of calcite crystals) which are chemically homogeneous but physically heterogeneous, other minerals can occur naturally which are chemically and physically homogeneous. Each one has a definite chemical composition. Apart from accidental inclusions and impurities, every mineral maintains the same character and composition regardless of where it is found.

Each mineral has special characteristic features and a typical and regular shape. Most are limited by plane faces, sharp edges and angles. Such minerals are called *crystals*. Their external regular shape is closely related to their internal structure. In other words, crystals are solids whose smallest parts, atoms, are arranged in a regular manner. The regularity of the external shape can be disturbed yet the orderliness and regularity of arrangement of the interior of the crystal remain unaltered.

Some minerals possess no geometrically regular shape. The internal organization of individual atoms is not always orderly, and the minerals are bounded by irregular faces. Such minerals are called *amorphous*, e.g. opals. Normally most amorphous minerals are easily subject to change and tend, sooner or later, to crystallize.

There are also the so-called *cryptocrystalline* minerals which outwardly resemble amorphous substances yet retain their inner crystalline structure, e.g. chalcedony.

All minerals are solid with one exception: mercury.

The majority of minerals occur in crystal form, yet not all minerals grow crystals.

Those minerals which contain elements important for industrial purposes and serve as raw materials for the extraction of these elements, are called *ores*.

Minerals

Material Structure of Minerals

The earth's crust is composed of various rocks whose separate constituents are minerals. Most are compounds of chemical elements. Some of them, however, are composed of a single element, such as copper, gold, sulphur, or carbon. The latter is better known in two forms as diamond and graphite. The basic element of the commonest mineral — quartz — is silica (SiO_2), a compound of silicon and oxygen. In many other minerals, on the other hand, the elements form complicated compounds. Most are of inorganic origin, but occasionally minerals with organic constituents are found, such as amber (fossil resin), or whewellite (calcium oxalate).

There are some 3,000 different minerals, composed of 92 chemical elements, from oxygen to uranium. Of the known minerals only a small number — some 40-50 — are generally rock-forming, e.g. quartz, felspar, mica, pyroxene, amphibole and olivine. These minerals form the major part of various rocks, and in consequence are called *rock-building minerals*.

System of Mineral Classification

As in all other branches of natural sciences, mineralogists have found it necessary and useful to arrange minerals in a system that is easy to understand, even though the figure of 3,000 known minerals is tiny in comparison with the tens of thousands of different plant and animal species in the world. It is convenient to arrange minerals according to their chemical composition and internal atomic lattice structure and almost all collections of minerals are arranged according to this system. It starts with the chemically simplest minerals, i.e. elements which are themselves minerals, and continues to more complicated compounds, while simultaneously considering the chemical relationship of individual minerals. This system is also recommended for arranging smaller private collections.

According to their crystallo-chemical properties minerals are usually grouped into nine natural classes corresponding to the mineralogical tables listed by H. Strunz:

1. Elements
2. Sulphides (selenides, tellurides, arsenides, antimonides, bismuthides)
3. Halides
4. Oxides, hydroxides
5. Nitrates, carbonates, borates
6. Sulphates (chromates, molybdates, wolframates)
7. Phosphates, arsenates, vanadates
8. Silicates
9. Organic substances

The Strunz classification system has been used to classify the minerals in this book.

Origin of Minerals

Magmatic Formation of Minerals

As the whole living world is in a continual state of change, so minerals also originate, grow and alter. Most of them are formed very deep down in the earth, where they are exposed to the effects of high pressures (thousands of atmospheres) and high temperatures (from approximately 900° to 1300°C). The earth's depths are composed of a glowing, liquid, molten silicate mass called *magma*. Because of the continuous movement of the earth's crust, parts of this magma have been driven upwards to cooler layers, where they gradually solidified forming agglomerations of rocks.

The magma is a molten mass, saturated with gases and water vapour and composed of different silicates and oxides. Its composition generally corresponds with the chemical properties of the rocks forming the earth's crust. Various currents keep the magma moving continuously, causing chemical reactions in its internal regions. Consequently new compounds arise, forming fresh minerals.

When the molten magma — which is constantly under pressure — reaches the upper, cooler levels of the earth's crust, its temperature falls. In the course of this cooling process the first minerals start to separate out, their number growing with the gradual cooling of the magma. The lighter minerals remain in the upper levels and the heavier ones sink slowly down again. This process is called *magmatic differentiation*. As a result, rich heavy mineral deposits are formed, such as those of magnetite and chromite.

During the next stage of crystallization the crystals start to grow. Minute cores become overgrown with crystals and the process continues as the magma cools.

In the final phase of crystallization the remainder of magma becomes more liquid. Its content of volatile components, such as gases and steam, is increasing. If some of the magma leaves the original mass it may form the so-called *pegmatites*, in which such minerals as mica, tourmaline and beryl are concentrated, together with others containing elements of rare earths, such as tin and tungsten ores. Finally the remainder of the magma cools off.

Part of the gases and vapour remains enclosed in the rocks and, like air-bubbles in a loaf, forms almond-shaped cavities. These cavities are a common phenomenon especially in basaltic rocks. At a later stage they often become filled with quartz, agate or chalcedony. The largest part of the gases and vapour escapes through rock fissures and cracks to the surface of the earth. Meanwhile the originally hot solution becomes cooler and new minerals appear in the form of crystals on the walls of the fissures. Well known minerals, such as quartz and calcite, originate at this stage and are known as *hydrothermal* minerals. If elements of heavy metals are present at this time ore veins are formed. The process of direct separation of specific ores, such as molybdenum, tungsten and tin ores, from hot gases and vapour, is called *pneumatolysis* or *pneumatolytic mineral formation*.

Just under the surface of the earth the steam changes into water but still contains many mineral substances. Together with surface water, which has seeped underground, it jets forth in the form of mineral springs. Cold as well as hot mineral springs give rise to various other minerals, such as aragonite or geyserite.

In places where hot solutions and gases escape through fissures and cracks in sedimentary rocks such as limestone, they dissolve the rocks giving rise to new secondary minerals. This is *metasomatic* mineral formation. Siderite-iron spar originates in this way.

Mineral Formation Caused by Weathering

On the surface of the earth all minerals and rocks are constantly subjected to the disturbing effects of various forces; this is called *weathering*. The effects of weathering are gradual, irrevocable and continuous. Rock surfaces are mechanically affected by changing temperature and by the shattering effects of frost. Chemical changes are caused by atmospheric oxygen, carbonic acid and water. Biological processes can also produce changes in rock surfaces.

The effects of weathering can cause profound changes in minerals; felspars change into kaolin, olivine into serpentine, and the golden-yellow pyrite into brown limonite. As a result of the weathering of pyrite sulphuric acid is liberated, which may affect the neighbouring calcite, changing it into gypsum or into a whole series of other sulphates. Opals are formed in a similar manner.

In this way several secondary minerals can originate from one mineral, e.g. malachite, azurite, or limonite from chalcopyrite. Dripstone caves are another product of weathering processes.

Mineral Formation Caused by Chemico-Sedimentary Processes

Various minerals are deposited from the sea water as a result of its evaporation, or of a change in its chemical composition. Rock salt, sylvine, gypsum, calcite and some iron ores, such as chamosite, also originate in this way.

Minerals and Rocks of Biological Origin

Apart from the effects of natural processes upon minerals and rocks, new minerals can be formed from mineral substances dissolved in water. Coral islands and limestone bodies are the product of living organisms. New minerals can also originate from the decomposed remnants of dead organisms, such as older or more recent deposits of phosphorite. Sulphur, salt-petre, pyrite and marcasite are also of biological origin.

Metamorphic Mineral Formation

The molten magma in the interior of the earth affects the individual layers of the crust by its temperature, pressure, and chemical reactions with various substances. This causes sedimentary rocks to change their appearance and their physical and chemical properties. This process, during which new secondary metamorphic rocks and minerals originate, is called *contact* metamorphism. Some sorts of mica, garnet and kyanite are formed in this way.

Summing up, it may be said that minerals originate under different conditions. In natural conditions a mineral seldom occurs by itself, almost always it is associated with several other minerals called the *accompanying* or *associated minerals*. Such a mineral assemblage is called *paragenesis*. Its formation is controlled by specific natural laws. A thorough knowledge of these helps in understanding the processes of mineral origin, and makes it possible to deduce from the occurrence of one mineral the probable existence of some other associated minerals.

External Form of Minerals

Halite (Rock salt) — model of lattice

Crystals

In the preceding section we have briefly explained the terms crystalline and amorphous. We have also mentioned the internal structure of crystals which depends upon the arrangement of their smallest particles, ions, atoms and molecules. They are arranged in a geometrical pattern forming the *crystal lattice* or the *space lattice*. Several types of lattices may be distinguished according to the arrangement of the crystal matter. Some minerals such as NaCl (rock salt) display comparatively simple space lattices, whereas in other minerals very complicated space lattices can be observed. The grouping of atoms inside a crystal is expressed by the arrangement of its external faces. As a geometrical body the crystal is bounded by faces, edges and angles of different size and form. Their mutual position and symmetry follow the same natural laws as the internal structure.

Internal structure of the crystal (grey balls — sodium, white balls — chlorine)

Every type of crystallized mineral shows typical angles at which individual faces intersect. These angles — called *space angles* — are identical in all crystals of one mineral irrespective of their size. This quality is defined by the Law of Constancy of Angle. It holds true, of course, only for identical adjoining faces.

Crystal Symmetry

One of the most striking features of crystals is the regularity of arrangement of the faces in juxtaposition with one another. This is called *crystal symmetry*. Listed below are the elements of symmetry:

1. The *plane of symmetry* divides the crystal into two symmetrical halves. For this reason it is often called the *mirror (reflection) plane*.
2. The *axis of symmetry* is an imaginary line passing through the centre of the crystal. Rotated about this axis through 360° the crystal returns to its original position. The axes of symmetry are divided into diad, triad, tetrad and hexad axes according to the number of times an identical face is displayed during rotation through 360°, i.e. a crystal which shows two identical faces during rotation is a diad, and so on.
3. The *centre of symmetry*: Each face of a crystal corresponds to a parallel, opposite face which is rotated through 180° about this imaginary centre.

There are in all 32 *crystal classes* in which the elements of symmetry are arranged

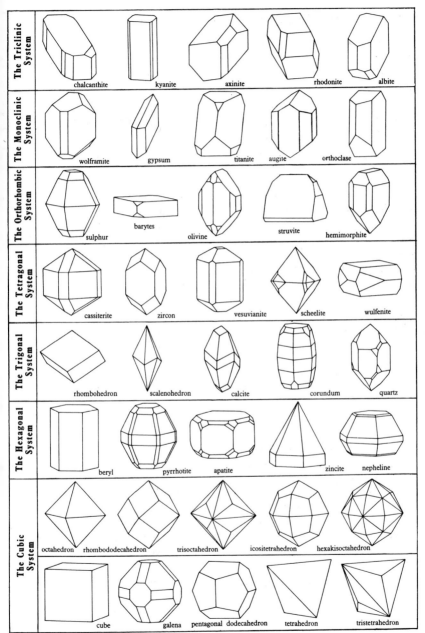

Examples of Crystal Forms of the Seven Crystal Systems

according to their number and kind. They are grouped into seven major divisions, the seven *Crystal Systems*. Common characteristic features of individual systems are the so-called *crystallographic axes*. As three-dimensional systems of coordinates they enable a precise determination of the location of every crystal face. The smallest number of symmetry elements is found in the triclinic system, followed in a progressive sequence by the monoclinic, orthorhombic, tetragonal, trigonal, hexagonal and cubic systems.

Some representatives of the large number of different crystal forms of the various systems are shown on the opposite page.

Most minerals belong to a single class and consequently also have a certain definite type of lattice. Some minerals of identical chemical composition, however, having originated under quite different conditions, can crystallize in two or more classes. Such minerals are called *polymorphs*. The individual crystal types in which polymorphic minerals occur are called *modifications*, e.g. diamond — graphite, calcite — aragonite, pyrite — marcasite, quartz — cristobalite — tridymite, rutile — brookite — anatase.

Appearance and Development of Crystals

The assemblage of all faces of a crystal is called the *form*. The relative width and length of these faces determine its shape which is called the *habit*. These may range from a pyramidal habit, in which all corners converge through columnar to tabular, acicular (needle-like), fibrous, tabular, plate-like or lamellar to the isometric habit with all faces equally developed.

Different habits of crystals with identical combinations of faces

Two crystals of identical form may have different habits and vice versa. The form as well as the habit of a crystal depend upon its chemical composition, but both of these can be affected by physical conditions prevailing at the time of crystal's origin, such as temperature, pressure, speed of growth and character of the environment. The drawing above shows the different habits in crystals of identical form.

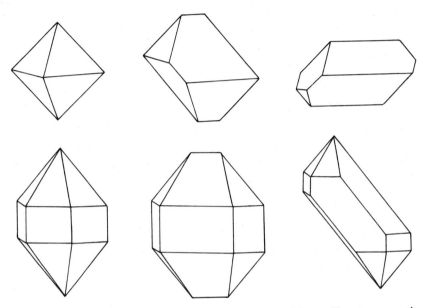

Crystal 'irregularities'. Left: ideal form, right: two distorted forms. Top row: magnetite crystals. Bottom row: quartz crystals

Crystals with even faces do not often occur naturally. However, they can originate in a soft, yielding environment, such as crystals of gypsum in soft clay. Crystals may also develop freely on the walls of caves. Such crystals always have well developed end faces. On the other hand, a one-way or irregular supply of new material in the course of the growth of a crystal can result in the most varied *distortions*. Such strangely developed forms can differ considerably from the ideal crystal forms as shown in the drawing on the preceding page. Nevertheless these 'irregularities' display angles of a constant value between similar faces.

Aggregates

Very often two individual crystals growing in a confined space have little room for the development of a new crystal. The result is an assemblage of interlocking crystals in irregular clumps called an *aggregate*. In rock crevices groups of crystals called *druses* or *geodes* grow from a common base in oval cavities. The appearance of these aggregates may differ according to their structure and morphology. On the fine internal surfaces of some limestones, skeletal and dendritic forms resembling fossil impressions of plants can sometimes be found. These so-called *dendrites* are manganese and iron oxides and hydroxides, and are entirely chemical in origin. They have nothing in common with fossils.

Growth of Twin Crystals

A characteristic feature of the growth of crystals in some minerals is the growth of *twin crystals* which is regulated by certain definite laws. In twin crystals re-entrant angles (interior angles greater than 180°) occur quite frequently, e.g. in cassiterite gypsum, and fluorite.

In some cases the growth of twin crystals results in a *pseudo-symmetry*, i.e. crystals of lower symmetry are twinned in such a way that they form a group of crystals of higher symmetry. For example, the orthorhombic aragonite often

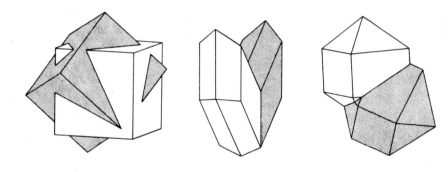

Twinned Crystals of (from left to right): fluorite, gypsum, cassiterite

grows columnar crystals of pseudo-hexagonal symmetry. The surface of such crystals is finely striated. This is called the *twinning striation*. Regular twinning of crystals in different ways is called *syntaxis* or *epitaxis*.

Crystal Faces

As mentioned before, crystals rarely have smooth even faces. More often their faces are considerably deformed and striated. Some minerals, such as pyrite, quartz, and tourmaline display such typical striations that they may serve as an important clue for identification.

Characteristic striation of (from left to right): pyrite, quartz, and tourmaline

Pseudomorphs

Pseudomorphs are unusual mineral formations. They are crystals which have borrowed their form from another type of crystal, e.g. externally they may resemble the pyrite crystal yet their composition corresponds to that of limonite. This is the result of a partial or complete exchange of chemical constituents.

Physical Properties of Minerals

The internal arrangement of atoms and their force of cohesion determines not only the external form and the symmetry of crystals, but a whole series of other important physical properties of minerals. According to the character of the particular structure, some physical properties in a certain mineral may vary according to the direction from which they are handled. Mica, for instance, can be split only in one direction. Consequently, we may say that crystals are *anisotropic* bodies, i.e. they show different physical properties in different directions. In amorphous materials, on the other hand, all physical properties are independent of the direction from which they are affected. Therefore amorphous materials are *isotropic*, i.e. they behave in the same way in all directions.

Every mineral has some typical physical properties. These are an important aid in identification.

Specific Gravity

The specific gravity of a mineral is the relative number indicating how many times heavier or lighter it is than the same amount of water. The exact determination of specific gravity requires special methods. The approximate specific gravity may be estimated by simply balancing the mineral in the hand and guessing its weight. Most minerals show the specific gravity of 2 to 4.

A little practice in the estimation of the weight of pieces of different minerals of similar size may help in acquiring the ability to distinguish between light minerals (specific gravity 1—2), medium-heavy minerals (specific gravity 2—4), heavy minerals (specific gravity 4—6), and very heavy minerals (specific gravity more than 6).

Properties of Cohesion

Other important properties of minerals depend upon the structure of their crystals and the direction in which the crystals are affected. These cohesion properties of crystals are called hardness, cleavage, fragility and tenacity (ability to resist damage).

Hardness

A crystal of calcite can be scratched quite easily with a knife. If we try the same with a quartz crystal the knife slides over its surface. The two minerals have a different hardness, or better still, scratch hardness. The term *scratch hardness* of a crystal face indicates its power of resistence to mechanical injuries.

For the determination of the hardness of minerals a *hardness scale* was established by Friedrich Mohs (1773—1839). It has ten grades in which each higher grade of mineral can always scratch the one just below it in hardness.

The set of standard minerals used as examples for the hardness tests is as follows:

1.	talc	6.	orthoclase felspar
2.	gypsum	7.	quartz
3.	calcite	8.	topaz
4.	fluorite	9.	corundum
5.	apatite	10.	diamond

These hardness tests can be applied only to fresh, unweathered minerals.

The hardness of a mineral can be determined quite easily. Minerals of the first grade can be scratched by the finger nail, and leave a soft greasy feel in the hand. Minerals of the second grade can also be damaged by the finger nail. A piece óf copper wire or a copper coin (hardness approx. 3) scratches minerals up to the hardness of 3. A pocket knife (hardness approx. 6) scratches minerals up to the hardness of 5. A good file scratches even quartz. Minerals of a hardness exceeding 6 can scratch window panes (hardness approx. 5). On the other hand minerals of grade 8—10 cannot be scratched by a file, and can be used in making sparks.

When determining the hardness of a mineral we proceed upwards from minerals of the lowest grades of the scale as long as we succeed in scratching them, each time trying the grade above for checking purposes. In the case of minerals embedded in rocks we proceed in the opposite way, i.e. we scratch the mineral to be tested with individual standard samples from the scale starting from the highest grade. After some practice it is quite easy to say whether the mineral scratches or only slides over the surface of another mineral. Usually the scratching is accompanied by a slight crackling sound.

Experience has shown that

1. the hardness of the mineral to be determined and the sample from the scale is identical if they do not damage each other;

2. the hardness of the mineral under determination and the scale sample is the same if they scratch each other. The angles and edges of a crystal are sometimes harder than its internal crystal or cleavage planes. Consequently, the edge of a gypsum crystal can scratch the cleavage plane of another gypsum crystal.

3. if the mineral under determination cannot scratch the mineral sample, but can itself be cut by it, it has a hardness somewhere between that of the sample and that of the next lower grade. In this case we consider the hardness to be of the lower grade adding a half-grade to it.

Although the determination of the hardness may seem to be quite easy, there are a number of factors which may be misleading. Thus the hardness of the same mineral may vary in different directions. It shows most clearly in the columnar kyanite. In the vertical direction kyanite shows the hardness 4-4.5 — it can be cut by a knife. Horizontally, however, it shows the hardness 6-7, and cannot be scratched by a knife. Scratch tests, therefore, must always be tried in different directions.

Sometimes soft aggregates are intergrown with some harder minerals, which make the hardness of the aggregate seem to be higher than it actually is. In such cases the hardness may show large differences, and a false identification may lead to completely wrong conclusions.

Different scratch hardness on kyanite

Other mistakes may arise if a piece of finely granular and thick aggregate is harder than the individual crystals of the same mineral. For instance, a compact piece of gypsum can be scratched by a finger nail only with difficulty. On the other hand, fibrous and porous aggregates often seem to have a lower hardness because of the blank spaces between individual grains. Chalk may easily be cut by a finger nail in spite of the fact that it has the hardness 3. Weathered pieces of minerals behave in a similar manner.

In earthy minerals, efflorescences, needle-shaped, fibrous and fine-grained aggregates, the exact determination of hardness by such simple methods is quite impossible. In these cases it is advisable to make use of some other characteristic identification feature of the mineral.

Cleavage

When hit with a hammer or pressed with a knife some crystallized minerals break apart along surfaces related to the internal crystal structure, resulting in smaller pieces of minerals with new smooth cleavage planes. Minerals tend to cleave along planes of least cohesion, and some may split in several directions, i.e. rock salt and galena into cubes, fluorspar into octahedra, and calcite into rhombohedral fragments. Other minerals, such as mica and gypsum possess a perfect cleavage only in one direction, in other directions cleavage being quite imperfect or completely absent.

The cleavage of transparent crystals is often indicated by the delicate cleavage rifts — apparent on closer inspection — running along the crystallographic planes. (See drawing)

Cleavage (left to right): galena, fluorite and calcite

Fracture

Some minerals, such as quartz and opal, do not cleave in any particular direction, but fracture irregularly instead. The appearance of the fractured surface may be even, uneven, conchoidal, subconchoidal or hackly (jagged). Metals and tough minerals have a hackly fracture. The type of fracture can also be used to distinguish between mineral species.

Other Physical Properties Dependent upon Cohesion

Brittle minerals such as pyrite, quartz and opal, crumble into small fragment with a crackling sound when hit with a hammer. *Soft* minerals like talc or graphite split into powder under a hammer blow.

Ductile or *malleable* minerals, such as native metals or argentite, can be flattened out into thin plates and no powder appears when they are scratched.

A thin plate of mica can be bent by the fingers. If the pressure is removed it returns to its original position. Such minerals are called *elastic*. Others, such as gypsum or antimonite, can be bent but they do not spring back to their original position. They are called *flexible*. On the basis of these properties we can easily distinguish between certain similar minerals, e.g. the elastic mica from flexible chlorite.

Colour

Some crystals have especially clear, brilliantly shining colours. It is no wonder that various colour shades have been named after them. We are familiar with emerald-green, ruby-red, turquoise or azure blue, amethyst-purple, and so on.

The colour of a mineral is often its most striking property, playing an important part in its identification. Yet it is not always a reliable clue or a characteristic feature of a particular mineral. There are several *idiochromatic* minerals which have their own and unchangeable colour, malachite is always green, graphite always black, and sulphur always yellow. In these minerals colour is a typical feature. There are, however, many other minerals which in their pure form are *colourless*, such as rock crystal (quartz), calcite, and rock salt. Yet if they contain any impurities they may be of quite different colours, such as blue salt, and yellow, pink, violet or brown quartz. Fluorspar can exist in almost all colour shades. Tourmaline, apatite and beryl also occur in many colours. The variable colours of these *allochromatic* minerals cannot be used for identification purposes as their colouring can be due to different impurities, pigments, mineral inclusions, and occasionally to small traces of other elements. The colouring may also be affected by radioactivity.

Some minerals change their colour with a change of illumination, e.g. alexandrite is green in sunlight whereas in artificial light it is violet. There are also minerals whose crystals change the intensity of their colour when held up to the light and turned around. For instance, when rotating a crystal of cordierite its colour changes from blue to yellow. Such minerals are called *pleochroic*. The change of colour is caused by the crystal's unequal absorption of light vibrating in different planes.

The colour of a mineral may sometimes be concealed under an encrustation. Numerous ores *tarnish* on the surface. Therefore their colour must always be tested on a fresh surface. The test is best carried out in a diffused light rather than in sunlight or artificial light.

The above-mentioned alexandrite changes its colour temporarily if exposed to the effects of light. Numerous precious stones lose their brilliant colours on continued exposure to the sun's rays. The emerald loses its rich green colour, and the amethyst and the rose quartz become paler in sunlight. Minerals containing silver also react sensitively to light, e.g. pyrargyrite and proustite. When exposed to the light they slowly become covered by a thin black film. In museum collections such minerals must be protected from the light. The deep-red realgar reacts in a similar way when it changes into the yellow orpiment in the presence of light. All these *changes of colour* take place only slowly.

A long time ago men learned how to speed up the natural processes of colour change. Yellow citrine may be obtained from the violet amethyst by heating. Diamonds, rubies and sapphires display richer colour shades under radioactive or ultraviolet rays. Radiation changes rock-crystal quartz into smoky quartz. Agates which are of an indistinct grey colour can be 'coloured' artificially by boiling in an aniline dye, in much the same way as textile fabrics are dyed.

Streak

Fortunately one characteristic — the *streak* of a mineral — is constant irrespective of colour variations. A mineral to be identified is rubbed on a piece of roughened or unglazed porcelain called a *streak plate*. It leaves behind a coloured scratch which is an important identification sign. We must not forget, however, that the hardness of the porcelain according to Mohs' scale is 6—6.5. Therefore minerals harder than this will produce only white porcelain powder. If we intend to determine the streak of a harder mineral we must either rub it to powder in a mortar or crush it with a hammer on a small anvil. The powder can then be rubbed on the streak plate. In this case only fresh unweathered minerals should be used.

Coloured minerals always produce a coloured streak which is a little lighter than the true colour of the mineral. Colourless and white minerals (of non-metallic lustre) need not be tested since their streak is always white. Similarly, discoloured minerals generally produce a white or light-grey streak. In this case the streak is likely to be discoloured as well. Its colour is indistinct since its intensity depends upon the proportion of pigment and other impurities. The greatest difference between the true colour and the streak of a mineral is shown by minerals of metallic lustre. Yellow pyrite produces a greenish-black streak, black haematite gives a red powder, black wolframite has a brown streak, and black cassiterite an almost colourless streak. Test results have shown that the determination of the streak is an important and simple means of identification. Naturally minerals producing a coloured streak are easier to identify than those producing a colourless or discoloured streak.

Lustre

Apart from the colour the *lustre* is also an important aid in the identification of minerals. It generally depends upon the amount and type of reflection and refraction of light as well as upon the quality of the mineral surfaces. There are minerals of *metallic* and of *non-metallic lustre*. A particular mineral does not always have the same lustre. It is therefore not always feasible to distinguish between metallic and non-metallic minerals. Some authors have introduced a supplementary term *submetallic lustre* for minerals which lack the full lustre of the metals.

Opaque ore minerals, such as pyrite, galena, etc., display a metallic lustre, and possess a good refractive capacity. With another large group of minerals, such as the dark sphalerite, cassiterite, rutile, etc., it is rather difficult to specify the type of lustre, therefore they appear several times in the accompanying tables. The lustre of non-metallic minerals may be subdivided, according to intensity and quality, as follows: 1. *Adamantine* or diamond lustre, occurs in transparent minerals of good refractive capacity; 2. *Vitreous*; 3. *Greasy*; 4. *Dull*, in minerals of low refractive capacity. Special kinds of lustre are either due to the structure of the aggregate or to a perfect cleavage. *Silky* lustre is often found in fibrous aggregates, such as asbestos. Some minerals composed of fine layers have a *pearly lustre*.

Transparency

The *transparency* of minerals varies greatly. A mineral is *transparent* when writing can be read through it. Rock crystal (quartz), rock salt and topaz are good examples. Impurities and inclusions can cause transparent minerals to lose some of their transparency and to become *translucent*. Minerals of metallic or of dull lustre are called *opaque*.

The structure of a mineral determines its degree of transparency. Finely granular aggregates, such as gypsum and mica, are opaque or merely translucent. But larger crystals of the same minerals are perfectly transparent. Under magnification thin sections of finely granular aggregates also become transparent.

Other physical properties of minerals can be mentioned only very briefly in this book. Those who would be interested in more detail are referred to the more comprehensive literature.

Refraction of Light

The *refraction of light* is an important optical property which remains constant for each mineral. Its exact determination requires special instruments called refractometers.

Double refraction occurs when a ray of light passing through an anisotropic crystalline substance is split into two. A piece of writing placed under such a mineral is seen twice. *Double refraction* is shown especially well by the colourless, transparent crystals of calcite.

Luminescence

Exposure in the dark to ultraviolet light elicits coloured luminescence from some minerals, such as scheelite and willemite. Others go on emitting light after having been subjected to certain conditions, such as heating, e.g. fluorite. This ability is called *thermoluminescence*. Another kind of luminescence, *triboluminescence* can be induced by crushing or rubbing some minerals.

Luminescence is particularly characteristic of certain minerals. It may therefore be applied in mineral identification as another simple supplementary factor.

Heat Conductivity

Taking a piece of copper in one hand, and a piece of amber in the other, we can feel that copper is colder. This is due to the different heat conductivity of the two substances. An experienced stone polisher is able to distinguish real gemstones from glass imitations in this way, feeling the stone against his cheek, since the skin on the cheeks is especially sensitive to warmth.

A similar category includes such *physiological properties* as the feel. Graphite and talc, for instance, feel greasy and smooth in the hand; chalk and kaolin feel dry and rough.

Minerals which are soluble in water, such as salt, sylvite, epsomite, etc., have a characteristic taste, being respectively saline, bitter, and sour.

Other minerals, such as sulphur, arsenopyrite, and fluorite can be identified by the characteristic odour especially when the minerals are struck or rubbed.

Magnetism

Pieces or powdered fragments of some minerals are attracted by a magnet, particularly when they contain a large amount of iron. In this way they can easily be distinguished from other minerals. Magnetite and pyrrhotite being themselves magnetic, attract iron dust. Other minerals, such as haematite, become magnetic as a result of heating.

Chemical Properties of Minerals

The identification of minerals by their chemical composition requires some special equipment and a thorough knowledge of analytical chemistry.

There is a simple chemical process which can be tried even by a layman; this is to remove carbonates from other similar minerals by means of dilute hydrochloric acid. By using a drop of this acid, white calcite can be distinguished from a similarly white piece of gypsum. The acid remains unchanged on the surface of gypsum yet it dissolves the calcite. Carbon dioxide is given off during this process, i.e. the drop changes into foam.

Identification of Minerals

The preceding sections have shown that it is not easy to identify positively a mineral at first sight. A reliable identification can be made either by using quantitative analysis, or by determining the internal crystal structure. For this a specially equipped laboratory is needed as well as the corresponding special knowledge.

Nevertheless a collector and admirer of minerals can identify many of them without any chemical analyses, from their external shape and physical properties. There are several identification clues which can be applied, based upon some typical mineral features. They include the morphological and the optical properties (refraction index, double refraction), the chemical composition (simple reaction tests), and the physical properties. Another way of identification is through the gradual elimination of the mineral species being considered in their class order. Common diagnostic features can only be used with typical mineral specimens. In other cases where it is necessary to employ all possible means of identification, or where only a few characteristics are really typical and reliable, their application would be too complicated. Amateur collectors are advised to pay attention only to those properties which may be recognized at first sight or by some very simple test.

Process of Mineral Identification

As a starting point for mineral identification, use a piece of fresh mineral broken off from a larger specimen. Testing should be very thorough and all properties recognizable by the naked eye or by means of a lens should be carefully recorded. Such a record may prove useful in cases when no explicit result has been achieved, and the identification of some properties may have to be repeated.

First note the external shape and appearance of the mineral, and in polycrystalline minerals note also the arrangement of crystals, the twinning and the symmetry. Determine the colour of the mineral and make sure by observing the streak that the mineral has not merely been tinged. The definition of the lustre may often seem rather complicated. It is therefore advisable to note down several different possibilities. The same applies to transparency. Hardness should be determined at first only approximately, more precise determination being possible at a later stage by means of the Mohs' Scale of Hardness. The more precisely the degree of hardness is determined, the more the search can be narrowed down to the correct place in the tables, to which the material under test is likely to belong.

Next, observe the presence or absence of cleavage, examine the cleavage planes where present, then test for brittleness, malleability, flexibility and elasticity. By weighing a mineral specimen in the hand we can estimate its specific gravity. With a smaller fragment of the mineral its solubility in water or hydrochloric acid can be tested. If the test specimen dissolves with effervescence in hydrochloric acid, it belongs to the carbonate class. Note also the paragenesis, i.e. the associated minerals, as these may be a guide to the identification of the specimen. On the basis of the observed properties we find the number of the mineral in the index on pp. 192—201, and under the same number in the identification tables a more detailed description of its properties will be found. To aid in identifying minerals existing in several colours, lustres and transparencies, they are included in the tables in several places.

Having finished the identification of the mineral check the results once more, comparing them with the data in the book. Ideally they should be identical. In practice the following situations may occur:

1. The mineral can be identified at first sight, but check the details once more to be certain.
2. Several minerals are very similar in their external shape. In successive tests examine their properties carefully and eliminate those that do not fit the description.
3. The mineral is completely unknown. In this case all its properties must be checked and eliminated in succession until a definite identification can be made. The more properties recognized, the easier the identification becomes.
4. It is impossible to identify the mineral with the aid of the tables. In such a case a mistake has probably been made somewhere. More attention should have been paid to similar minerals mentioned in the identification tables. Some seemingly unimportant feature may have been overlooked, or the mineral — whose identification might require some more complicated procedure — is not included in the tables at all.

Examples of Mineral Identification

Let us start from the fact that by means of the external features, such as lustre and colour, and with the aid of the tables, a preliminary conclusion has been reached according to which the mineral under investigation may belong to two or more mineral classes. The following section will show some examples of how to proceed in such a case, and which features should be selected to make identification easier.

The granular aggregates of magnetite and chromite look very similar. However they can be easily distinguished by the colour of their streak, which is black in magnetite and brown in chromite. Apart from this, magnetite is much more strongly magnetic than chromite.

If no crystal boundary is present, compact pyrite showing an iridescent surface, and chalcopyrite, are similar in appearance, the colour of their streak also being identical. They can be distinguished only by the degree of their hardness, i.e. pyrite is harder (6) than chalcopyrite (4.5).

Black sphalerite and black cassiterite display the same submetallic lustre. In this case also, they can be distinguished by their degree of hardness. The hardness of sphalerite is 3.5, and of cassiterite 6.5. A supplementary distinctive feature may be the frequent association of sphalerite with other sulphides, and of cassiterite with quartz and mica.

Chalk and kaolin can easily be distinguished chemically by using dilute hydrochloric acid. Chalk, as calcium carbonate, dissolves in it with effervescence.

Fluorite, amethyst and apatite can be recognized by the form of their crystals. However their coarsely granular aggregates are all of a similar violet colour. Amethyst is the hardest of the three minerals; it cannot be scratched by a knife, and is not cleavable. Fluorite shows a perfect cleavage, and when heated it becomes luminescent. Apatite is one degree harder than fluorite, and shows a different cleavage.

Augite, amphibole and tourmaline occur frequently in the form of black columnar crystals. Tourmaline may be identified by its poor cleavage and the typical striations on its prism faces. It occurs predominantly in acid igneous rocks. On the other hand, augite and amphibole often occur in basic igneous rocks. They can be distinguished from one another by the angle and quality of their cleavage planes. Augite has good cleavage at 90° angle, amphibole perfect cleavage planes at 55° and 125° angles.

Felspar, calcite, barytes and gypsum are often of a whitish colour, and all of them show a similarly perfect cleavage. Gypsum can be eliminated since it can be scratched by a finger nail, and felspar because it can be scratched by a knife. Barytes and calcite are of an identical hardness and differ only in weight, i.e. barytes is heavier. Calcite, on the other hand, readily dissolves with effervescence in dilute hydrochloric acid.

The few above-mentioned examples cannot, of course, fully illustrate all the problems of mineral identification. Nobody should be discouraged by initial bad luck, it is sometimes difficult even for an expert to identify some of the rarer minerals. In case of doubt every serious collector is sure to find assistance and advice from some experienced mineralogist. The best help, however, is our own perseverance and endurance.

Practical Advice for Collectors

Everyone starting a collection of minerals should determine in the first place what he is going to collect, and how his collection is to be set up. It is easiest to start first by collecting minerals and rocks occurring locally. Since the mineral richness of individual areas varies considerably, so will the extent of one's first collection. In any case the collector is advised to begin by making himself thoroughly acquainted with the geological conditions of his future collecting area. A good geological map, some special literature and the advice of other experienced collectors will all be helpful. Having this preliminary information the collector is ready to start a systematic collection of all mineral specimens which are typical of his locality.

Most probably in the initial stages each collector will pick up every possible mineral specimen within his reach. In the course of time, however, he is likely to replace some of the original pieces with better specimens, and he will be more aware of the aesthetic aspects of his collection. The value of a well organized and arranged mineral collection lies not only in the pleasure derived by the collector. It may serve later as research material for professional mineralogists. Frequently, an amateur collector possesses better specimens than a state museum.

Little by little one's collecting area can be enlarged and the collection expanded through exchange or purchase until one finally possesses a so-called systematic collection including samples of all attainable mineral types. Apart from the fact that a mineral collection is never complete it takes up much space in the home. He who has only a limited space for his hobby can establish a 'mini-collection' including only small but carefully selected and perfect specimens. An attractive collection can be made up of small individual crystals of only a few minerals, yet each displaying a different type of habit. A collection of important rock-building minerals or rocks in their most varied forms can also be interesting as well as instructive.

Where are Minerals to be Found?

Minerals cannot be planted like flowers. They are gained painstakingly after a long, patient search. Yet, it is this seeking and finding that brings the greatest pleasure to collectors. Where can they most easily be found?

First of all, any local stone quarries should be investigated very thoroughly as soon as possible after a blast. Do not forget, however, to ask the right authorities for permission! Abandoned quarries frequently yield a rich crop. The danger of falling stones should not be underestimated in the excitement of the moment. One should always proceed very cautiously, and carefully.

A large number of interesting minerals can also be found on heaps of mine refuse, but never enter abandoned shafts or caves alone. This is very dangerous even for an experienced collector.

A good opportunity for finding minerals and rocks arises, for instance, during the construction of roads, retaining dams and tunnels. In the course of sinking a well or digging a grave the changing composition of rocks with the increase in depth is clearly seen. Minerals can also be collected on the rocky banks of rivers and brooks, in rocky river beds or gravel pits. Interesting mineral specimens are also found on arable land or in stone debris along the roadside.

Collecting Equipment

The most useful tool in mineral collecting is a good geological hammer made of hard steel. There are pointed hammers and hammers with sharp edges diagonal

Equipment for mineral collectors. Above: UV-analyzation lamp for testing minerals by ultraviolet light. Right: stereoscopic prism lens for mineral identification and preparatory work. Below: pointed and flat chisels, geological hammers with pointed and with cutting edges.

to the handle (see illustration). The handle is usually 30 cm long, its approximate weight being 900 gm. To crush larger pieces of minerals we use a heavier, short hammer. For removing the superfluous remnants of rock and for the final trimming of the sample a small hammer (200 − 400 gm) similar to the geological hammer is normally used. The lighter the hammer, the longer the handle must be to give strength to the impact. As fundamental equipment, however, a single geological hammer will do.

Apart from the hammer, different chisels are needed (see illustration), i.e. pointed as well as flat. They should be made of good, hardened material. The ideal length is 20 cm. By means of the chisels specimens of minerals can be prized out of cracks and crevices without damage. They can also be used for breaking open quartz geodes.

Specimens are usually carried in a knapsack. It pays to buy a knapsack of a good quality with a supporting frame, since minerals are hard and very heavy. For wrapping the specimens to prevent them damaging each other, one can use newspaper, soft paper or cotton, the most brittle ones being placed in cardboard boxes. Each specimen should be provided with a small label (4 × 6 cm) indicating where it was found. Numbered labels, adhesive tapes, a notebook, pencils and some cards should always be at hand.

An indispensable aid in field work as well as at home is a lens, magnifying at least eight- to ten times. The exact identification of a mineral in situ is almost impossible, so it has to be taken home to be examined further. The following implements are essential: a lens, a hammer and some chisels, pincers for breaking off smaller pieces, an iron plate, and if possible a small grinding mortar. Other indispensable aids are: small streak plate of rough hard porcelain of about the size of a match box; a Mohs' Scale of Hardness (at least for the first 8 grades); a piece of broad glass; a knife with a steel tip; a magnet or magnetic needle; a steel needle; a piece of copper wire or a copper coin; a good file and a pair of forceps; a hermetically sealed bottle with dilute hydrochloric acid and a drop pipette.

Field Work

The same care that was used in collecting and treating the minerals must also be used in taking notes of all observed details before the minerals are packed for transport. Use plenty of paper − it is advisable to wrap every individual specimen carefully. Each must be provided with a label (or numbered tag) indicating where it was found, and then wrapped in another piece of paper. Never place the label directly on the mineral, it could be damaged during transport. The wrapping should be as tight as possible to prevent the specimens from moving and tearing the paper cover. Finally close the package by means of adhesive tape. Exposed crystal surfaces should be covered first with a layer of crumpled soft paper or a cotton plug, and then wrapped up in newspapers. Delicate mineral specimens should be embedded in cotton-wool and placed in cardboard boxes. The finest and most delicate minerals, such as the needle-shaped natrolite crystals cannot even stand the touch of cotton-wool. Such specimens are transported fastened with a piece of thread or a fine wire to the bottom of a cardboard box.

The number of individual labels (or tags) indicating the original locality should agree with the number in the notebook. Apart from the number the label should bear the date, the locality and the presumed mineral type. The description of the locality should preferably be more detailed, e.g. walls of a quarry, or refuse heap specimen, so that one could find the place again if need be. Moreover a mineral loses its value if its locality is unknown.

Preserving and Labelling Collected Specimens

After carefully unpacking the specimens at home they must be dusted and cleaned. Less delicate and larger pieces can be washed with water, soap and brush. Finer specimens are better cleaned with a fine brush. From needle-shaped crystals the dust can be simply blown off or they may be carefully rinsed in lukewarm water. Minerals which are soluble in water, such as salt, should be washed with petrol. Some sulphides, such as pyrite and marcasite, should not be treated with water, as this may cause them to decompose later. They are best cleaned with spirit. Crystals of gypsum are sensitive to soap which covers them with a whitish film. Minerals should never be exposed to direct sunlight to dry.

In order to mark a specimen a small label with a number can be affixed to the reverse side where it is least obtrusive. Or a small face of the mineral can be painted with white enamel and the number written in black Indian ink upon it.

Very small crystals are placed in glass tubes with their number fastened to the cork. Similarly, minerals soluble in water are kept in glass tubes which are sealed with wax or paraffin.

For an easily surveyed collection of minerals and rocks, special collection boxes with labels for marking the minerals are available. Every label should bear in its upper corner the name and the address of the collector, the number, and the date it was found. The middle part is reserved for the name of the mineral (in large letters) followed below by a short description (associated minerals, weight, size). Below left the locality is given, below right the manner in which it has been obtained.

A serious collector compiles a list — a catalogue — of his collection. The catalogue should contain the data on the labels and can be made more complete by including a more detailed description of the locality, references to special literature, conditions of exchange, and purchase or price. With larger collections it is also advisable to set up a card index of minerals in alphabetical order.

Every collection of minerals must be carefully protected from dust and humidity; excessive dryness and great variations in light and temperature can also be harmful.

Notes to the Identification Tables

The colour sequence of minerals: 1. colourless and white, 2. yellow, 3. orange, 4. red, 5. violet, 6. blue, 7. green, 8. brown, 9. grey, 10. black, 11. multicoloured.

In the identification tables the following terms are used for individual crystal systems: triclinic, monoclinic, orthorhombic, trigonal, tetragonal, hexagonal, cubic and amorphous minerals. Within the scope of individual colours, minerals of metallic lustre are indicated first, followed by those of non-metallic lustre. Within these two groups minerals are arranged according to their hardness from H 1 to H 10.

Abbreviations

assoc.	—	associated
chem.	—	chemical
deps.	—	deposits
diff.	—	different
nat.	—	native
No.	—	number
o.	—	other
phys.	—	physical
props.	—	properties
syst.	—	system
transluc.	—	translucent
transpar.	—	transparent

Minerals

Identification Tables and Plates

No.	Colour / Streak	Lustre / Transparency	Hardness / Specific Gravity	Cleavage / Fracture & o. Phys. Props.	Common Form, Aggregates / Crystalline Syst.	Occurrence / Assoc. Minerals / Similar Minerals	Name & Chem. Formula / Origin of Specimen
1	silver-white / –	metallic / opaque	liquid / 13.6	– / greasy	little drops / trigonal	in ore veins, in cinnabar deps. / cinnabarite / –	**nat. MERCURY** (Quicksilver) Hg / Idrija, Slovenia
2	tin-white, grey silver-white / grey	metallic / opaque	1.5 – 2 / 8.0 – 8.3	very good / brittle	tabular, lamellar, skeletal / monoclinic	in gold ore / sphalerite, pyrite, telluride / krennerite, nat. tellurium, calaverite	**SYLVANITE** AgAuTe$_4$ / Baia de Arieş, Romania
3	silver-white, greyish / grey	metallic / opaque	2 – 3 / 7.6 – 7.8	– / sectile, malleable	granular masses, crystals / orthorhombic, pseudotetragonal	in ore veins / selenium ores / clausthalite	**EUCAIRITE** Cu$_2$Se.Ag$_2$Se / Săcărâmb, Romania
4	silver-white, reddish / light grey, silver-white	metallic / opaque	2 – 2.5 / 9.7 – 9.8	very good / brittle, malleable	granular, compact, lamellar, dendritic / trigonal	in ore veins / – / niccolite, cobaltite, breithauptite	**nat. BISMUTH** Bi / Krupka, Czech Republic
5	silver-white, grey to opaque / silver-white & shining	metallic / opaque	2.5 – 3 / 10.1 to 11.1	– / hackly, malleable, ductile	compact, thread-like, platy, curling, mossy / cubic	in ore veins / argentite, pyrargyrite, proustite, galena, pyrite, barytes, siderite, fluorite, calcite, quartz / dyscrasite, nat. antimony	**nat. SILVER** Ag / Kongsberg on Lågenelf, Norway
6							**nat. SILVER** Ag / Příbram, Czech Republic
7	silver-white, yellowish / yellowish grey	metallic / opaque	2.5 – 3 / 8.6	very good / fragile	compact, granular, lamellar / orthorhombic	in gold veins / – / sylvanite, calaverite, nat. tellurium	**KRENNERITE** (Au,Ag)Te$_2$ / Săcărâmb, Romania
8	tin-white to grey / grey	metallic / opaque	3 – 3.5 / 6.6	good / –	finely granular to coarse-spathic masses, compact, reniform / trigonal	in arsenic-silver ore veins / arsenic, antimonite, sphalerite, siderite, calcite / –	**ALLEMON-TITE** As + Sb / Příbram, Czech Republic

No.	Colour / Streak	Lustre / Transparency	Hardness / Specific Gravity	Cleavage Fracture & o. Phys. Props.	Common Form, Aggregates / Crystalline Syst.	Occurrence / Assoc. Minerals / Similar Minerals	Name & Chem. Formula / Origin of Specimen
9	silver-white to steel-grey / silver-white	metallic / opaque	4—4.5 / 14—19	— / hackly, ductile, malleable	grains, lumps, lamellae / cubic	in placer deps. / chromite, magnetite, ilmenite / nat. iron	nat. **PLATINUM** Pt / Nizhni Tagil, Central Urals, Russia
10	tin-white / grey-black	metallic / opaque	5—5.5 / 7.4	clear, good / brittle	compact, granular, nodular, fibrous, short-columnar, needle-shaped / orthorhombic	in ore veins / arsenopyrite / arsenopyrite	**LÖLLINGITE** $FeAs_2$ / Złoty Stok, Poland
11	tin-white / greyish-black	metallic / opaque	5—5.5 / 7.1—7.4	good / brittle	needle-shaped, fibrous crystals, compact nodules / orthorhombic	in ore veins / arsenopyrite / arsenopyrite	Variety of löllingite **LEUCO-PYRITE** (löllingite with reduced content of As) / Złoty Stok, Poland
12	silver-white, steel-grey / greyish-black	metallic / opaque	5 / 6.7	good / brittle, uneven	compact, granular / cubic	in ore veins / gersdorffite, calcite, siderite / gersdorffite, smaltite, galena	**ULLMANNITE** NiSbS / Monte Narba, Sardinia, Italy
13	silver-white, steel-grey / greyish-black	metallic / opaque	5—5.5 / 5.6—6.2	very good / brittle	granular, compact, spathic / cubic	in ore veins / ullmannite, chalcopyrite, siderite, calcite / ullmannite	**GERSDORF-FITE** NiAsS (Grey Nickel Pyrites, Nickel Glance) / Harzgerode, Harz, Germany
14	tin-white to light steel-grey / greyish black	metallic / opaque	5.5—6 / 6.4—6.9	— / brittle, uneven; jointing due to zonality	compact, reniform, massive, finely granular / cubic	in silver-cobalt-nickel ore veins / silver, safflorite, niccolite / safflorite, gersdorffite, cf. No. 390	**CHLOAN-THITE** NiAs₃ (White Nickel) / Schneeberg, Ore Mountains, Germany
15	tin-white to grey / black	metallic / opaque	5.5—6 / 5.9—6.2	clear, good / brittle	short-columnar, tabular crystals, compact, granular, radial, fibrous / monoclinic, pseudoorthorhombic	in ore veins / galena, silver löllingite, chloanthite, skutterudite, cf. No. 389	**ARSENO-PYRITE** FeAsS (Arsenical Pyrite, Mispickel) / Freiberg, Ore Mountains, Germany
16	tin-white to grey / greyish-black	metallic / opaque	5.5—6 / 6.8	clear / brittle, uneven	cubic octahedral crystals, often bent, compact, reniform, massive, finely granular / cubic	in silver-cobalt-nickel ore veins / silver, safflorite, niccolite & o. / safflorite, löllingite, arsenopyrite, cf. No. 391	**SKUTTE-RUDITE** CoAs₃ (Smaltite) / Bou Azzer, Morocco

9	10
11	12
13	14
15	16

COLOURLESS AND WHITE MINERALS
OF NON-METALLIC LUSTRE

No.	Colour / Streak	Lustre / Transparency	Hardness / Specific Gravity	Cleavage / Fracture & o. Phys. Props.	Common Form, Aggregates / Crystalline Syst.	Occurrence / Assoc. Minerals / Similar Minerals	Name & Chem. Formula / Origin of Specimen
17	colourless, white-yellowish / white	greasy / transpar., transluc.	1.0 – 2 / 1.5	poor / con-choidal, soft, water-soluble	skeletal crystals, crusty, botryoidal, earthy, fibrous, compact / cubic	in burning coal piles, in volcanoes / — / —	AMMONIUM CHLORIDE NH_4Cl / Vesuvius, Italy
18	white, yellowish-white / white	dull / transluc.	1 – 2 / 1.7	— / powdery, earthy	nodular, compact, earthy, scaly / monoclinic	in clays, marls, sandstones, gypsum, chalk / — / alunite	ALUMINITE $Al_2[(OH)_4SO_4]$. $7H_2O$ / Chuchle, Czech Republic
19	white, grey-white, yellowish, brownish, greenish, pink / white	dull / macroscopically opaque	1 – 2 / 2 – 3	— / soft, friable, swelling in water	compact, massive, earthy, friable masses / monoclinic	in clays, in volcanic tuff / — / —	MONTMORIL-LONITE (Al,Mg) $[(OH)_2Si_4O_{10}]$. $(Na,Ca)_x$. $4H_2O$ / Kuzmice, Slovakia
20	white, grey, green, yellowish, brownish / white	pearly, greasy, dull / transluc., opaque	1 – 1.5 / 2.6 – 2.8	perfect / very soft, inelastic, flexible, greasy	lamellar crystals, scaly, massive, compact / monoclinic	alteration product of serpentine, in crystalline schists / chlorite, serpentine, magnetite, pyrite, dolomite, etc. / pyrophyllite, kaolinite	TALC Mg_3 $[(OH)_2Si_4O_{10}]$ (Soap-Stone, Steatite) / Providence, Rhode Island, USA
21	white, yellowish, greenish, bluish, reddish / white	pearly, dull / opaque	1 – 2 / 2.5 – 2.6	very good / soft, earthy	thin plates, fine-scaled, massive, loose, earthy / monoclinic	weathering product of felspars, in clays, as late formation in ore veins / quartz, mica / montmorillonite, pyrophyllite	KAOLINITE Al_4 $[(OH)_8Si_4O_{10}]$ / Podbořany, Czech Republic
22	white, yellowish grey-green, reddish / white	greasy / opaque	1 – 2 / 2.2 – 2.3	— / greasy	scaly, loose, earthy, massive, compact / monoclinic	as late formation in diff. rocks & serpentine / — / talc, pyrophyllite	SAPONITE $Mg_3[(OH)$ $AlSi_3O_{10}]$ nH_2O (Soap-Stone) / Faroes, Nólsoy, Denmark
23	white, grey, greenish, yellowish / white	pearly, dull / transluc.	1 – 2 / 2.6 – 2.9	perfect / soft, greasy	tabular crystals, rose-shaped, lamel-lar, scaly, massive / monoclinic	in quartz veins & ore veins, in slate clays / — / talc, kaolinite	PYRO-PHYLLITE Al_2 $[(OH)_2Si_4O_{10}]$ / Badin, North Carolina, USA
24	white, white-grey, yellowish, green-blue / white	dull / opaque	1.5 – 2 / 2.3	— / soft, floats on water	nodular masses, compact, massive, porous, earthy / orthorhombic	weathering product of serpentine / opal, chalcedony, magnesite, chlorite / —	SEPIOLITE Mg_4 $[(OH)_2Si_6O_{15}]$ $2H_2O + 4H_2O$ (Meerschaum) / Eskischehir, Turkey

Table 3

No.	Colour / Streak	Lustre / Transparency	Hardness / Specific Gravity	Cleavage / Fracture & o. / Phys. Props.	Common Form, Aggregates / Crystalline Syst.	Occurrence / Assoc. Minerals / Similar Minerals	Name & Chem. Formula / Origin of Specimen
25	colourless, white, yellowish, brownish / white	vitreous to dull / transpar., transluc.	1.5 – 2 / 2.2 – 2.3	very good / soft, brittle, water-soluble	granular, compact skeletal crystals / trigonal	isolated deps. / halite, mirabilite, epsomite, gypsum, clay / —	NITRO-NATRITE $NaNO_3$ (Chile Saltpetre, Soda Nitre) / Antofagasta, Chile
26	white / white	dull / opaque	1 – 2 / 2.6	— / earthy, porous	porous, earthy masses, loose / trigonal	organic sediments / clay, flint / kaolinite, montmorillonite, cf. No. 51 to 54, 170, 319	Calcite variety CHALK $CaCO_3$ / Heligoland
27	white, yellowish / white	silky, vitreous, pearly / transluc.	1.5 / 1.7	very good / soft, water-soluble	capillary, acicular crystals, reniform, fibrous, scaly, granular agg., crusts / triclinic	in ore veins, in coal piles, in clays / pyrite, melanterite / alunite	ALUNOGEN $Al_2[SO_4]_8 . 18H_2O$ (Keramohalite) / Bolzano, Italy
28	white, yellowish, pink, greenish / white	silky / transluc.	1.5 / 1.6 – 1.7	good / water-soluble	fibrous, acicular, capillary crystals, & agg. / monoclinic	in rocks as weathering product of sulphides / — / alunogen	APJOHNITE $MnAl_2[SO_4]_4 . 22H_2O$ (Manganese Alum) / Alum Cave, Tennessee, USA
29	colourless, whitish / white	vitreous / transpar., transluc.	1 – 2 / 1.6	— / brittle, conchoidal, water-soluble	fibrous, tubular agg., crusts; lamellar / cubic	in coal piles, in gypsum, clay, volcanoes / — / —	TSCHERMI-GITE $NH_4Al[SO_4]_2 . 12H_2O$ (Ammonium Alum) / Čermníky near Kadaň, Czech Republic
30	colourless, white / white	vitreous to dull / transpar., transluc.	1.5 – 2 / 1.4 – 1.5	good / conchoidal, water-soluble	tabular crystals, crusts, fibrous, earthy, granular, compact masses / monoclinic	as efflorescent crusts, in salt deps. / gypsum, halite, clay, marl / glauberite, glaserite	MIRABILITE $Na_2[SO_4] . 10H_2O$ (Glauber Salt) / Hallstatt, Salzkammergut, Austria
31	colourless, white, yellow, grey, red, brown / white	vitreous, silky, pearly / transpar., transluc.	1.5 – 2 / 2.3 – 2.4	very good / soft, inelastic, flexible	columnar, tabular, needle-shaped, often twinned crystals, loose crystals, in druses, coarse to fine-grained, fibrous, scaly, massive, compact, earthy / monoclinic	rocks in salt deps., weathering product of sulphides in sedimentary rocks, in ore deps. / anhydrite, aragonite, sulphur / anhydrite, mica, talc, kaolinite, cf. No. 132	GYPSUM $CaSO_4 . 2H_2O$ / Duchcov, Czech Republic
32							GYPSUM $CaSO_4 . 2H_2O$ / Prešov, Slovakia

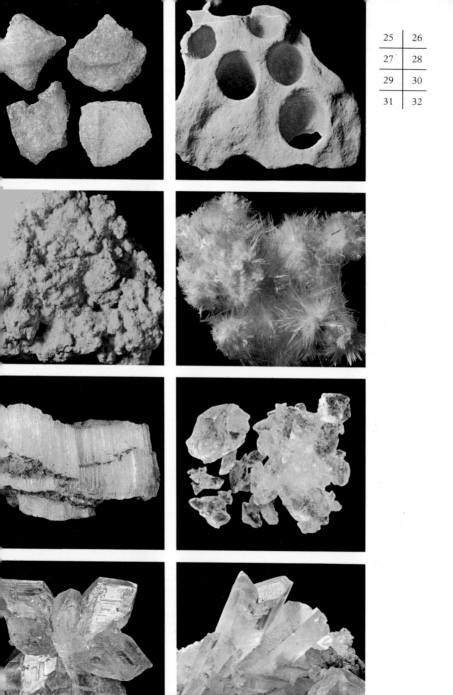

47

No.	Colour / Streak	Lustre / Transparency	Hardness / Specific Gravity	Cleavage / Fracture & o. / Phys. Props.	Common Form, Aggregates / Crystalline Syst.	Occurrence / Assoc. Minerals / Similar Minerals	Name & Chem. Formula / Origin of Specimen
33	colourless, white, yellow, blue, violet, reddish, orange / white	vitreous, transpar., transluc.	2 / 2.1 — 2.2	perfect, cube / soft to brittle, water-soluble	cubic crystals, coarse to fine-grained, compact, fibrous, massive / cubic	isolated deps., crusts in deserts, in volcanoes / anhydrite, gypsum, sylvite, dolomite & o. / sylvite, anhydrite, cf. No. 224	**ROCK SALT** NaCl (Halite) / Wieliczka near Cracow, Poland
34							**ROCK SALT** NaCl (Halite) / Dognecea, Romania
35	colourless, white, yellowish, grey / white	vitreous, greasy transpar., transluc.	2 / 1.9 — 2	very good, cube / soft to brittle, water-soluble	cubic, octahedral crystals, coarse to fine-grained, massive / cubic	sedimentary deps., as crusts in volcanoes / halite, anhydrite, carnallite, kainite & o. / rock salt	**SYLVITE** KCl / Stassfurt, Germany
36	colourless, white, greenish, yellowish, grey, red, brown / white	vitreous, greasy transpar., transluc.	2 / 1.6	— / conchoidal, brittle, fusible, water-soluble	thick-tabular crystals, coarsely-granular masses, fibrous, compact / orthorhombic	in rock salt / anhydrite, kainite, kieserite & o. / kainite	**CARNALLITE** KMgCl$_3$. 6H$_2$O / Stassfurt, Germany
37	colourless, white / white	vitreous to dull transluc.	2 / 1.8	clear / brittle, uneven, weathered	tabular crystals, with orthorhombic habit / monoclinic	in boron deps. / colemanite & o. boron minerals / —	**INYOITE** Ca[B$_3$O$_3$(OH)$_5$] . 4H$_2$O / Mount Blanco on Furnace Creek, California, USA
38	colourless, white, yellowish / white	dull transluc.	2 / 3.7	clear	very small octahedral crystals, crusts, needles, powdery, fibrous / cubic	as alteration product of arsenic minerals / — / —	**ARSENOLITE** As$_2$O$_3$ (White Arsenic) / Jáchymov, Czech Republic
39	colourless, grey, yellowish, brown, reddish, black / white, grey	adamantine, greasy transpar., transluc.	1.5 — 3 / 5.5 — 5.6	— / sectile, flexible, ductile	cubic, octahedral crystals, compact, horny crusts, as impregnations / cubic	in silver veins / silver, cerussite, calcite, barytes, limonite / bromargyrite	**KERARGYRITE** AgCl (Chlorargyrite, Horn Silver) / Zacatecas, Mexico
40	colourless, white, reddish, brown / white	adamantine, pearly, greasy transpar., transluc.	2.5 — 3 / 2.9	good / brittle, fissile	pseudocubic, short-columnar crystals, compact, granular, spathic, massive / monoclinic	in pegmatites / quartz, siderite, galena, pyrite & o. / anhydrite, barytes	**CRYOLITE** Na$_3$[AlF$_6$] / Ivigtut, Greenland

33	34
35	36
37	38
39	40

COLOURLESS AND WHITE MINERALS
OF NON-METALLIC LUSTRE

No.	Colour Streak	Lustre Trans-parency	Hard-ness Specific Gravity	Cleavage Fracture & o. Phys. Props.	Common Form, Aggregates Crystalline Syst.	Occurrence Assoc. Minerals Similar Minerals	Name & Chem. Formula Origin of Specimen
41	white, grey, yellowish ___ white	silky, dull transluc.	2—2.5 / 3.2—3.8	very good slightly brittle	cryptocrystalline, compact, reniform, massive, conchoidal, earthy, crusts monoclinic	weathering product in zinc deps. smithsonite, sphalerite smithsonite	**HYDRO-ZINCITE** $Zn[(OH)_3CO_3]_2$ (Zinc Bloom) San Giovanni Mine, Laorca, Sardinia
42	colourless, white, yellowish, grey ___ white	vitreous, dull transpar., transluc.	2—3 / 1.9	very good con-choidal, brittle, water-soluble	columnar, tabular crystals, rough planes, uneven monoclinic	eliminated from soda lakes, in clays — —	**GAYLUSSITE** $Na_2Ca(CO_3)_2 \cdot 5H_2O$ (Natrocalcite) Sangerhausen, Germany
43	colourless, white, grey, yellowish ___ white	vitreous, greasy, dull transpar., transluc.	2—2.5 / 1.7—1.8	clear soft, con-choidal, water-soluble	columnar, flat-tabular crystals, with dull crust; compact, earthy, powdery monoclinic	on edges of borax lakes halite, soda, mirabilite kernite	**BORAX** $Na_2[B_4O_5(OH)_4] \cdot 8H_2O$ (Tincal) Tibet
44	colourless, white, grey, yellowish, red ___ white	vitreous, greasy transpar., transluc.	2.5—3 / 2.7—2.8	very good brittle, con-choidal	tabular, columnar crystals, in druses, coarse spathic, compact, reniform, earthy monoclinic	in saline deps. natural potassium salts, anhydrite, gypsum mirabilite	**GLAUBERITE** $CaNa_2[SO_4]_2$ Villa Rubia de los Ojos, Spain
45	colourless, white, yellowish, reddish ___ white	vitreous, silky transpar., transluc.	2—2.5 / 1.6	very good non-hygro-scopic, water-soluble	needle-shaped, crystals, fibrous agg., earthy crusts orthorhombic	as weathering pro-duct in ore deps., efflorescent crusts in steppes, altera-tion product of kieserite — kieserite	**EPSOMITE** $Mg[SO_4] \cdot 7H_2O$ (Bitter Salt) Kremnica, Slovakia
46	colourless, white, yellowish, red, violet ___ white	vitreous transpar., transluc.	2.5—3 / 2.1	perfect infusible, water-soluble	thick-tabular pseudorhombic crystals, mostly finely granular, compact masses monoclinic	in salt deps. halite, carnallite, kieserite, anhydrite carnallite	**KAINITE** $KMg[ClSO_4] \cdot 3H_2O$ Stassfurt, Germany
47	white, grey-red, reddish-brown, yellowish ___ white	vitreous, pearly transpar., transluc.	2.5—3 / 3	very good uneven	small tabular & columnar crystals, compact, bo-tryoidal masses orthorhombic	in zinc ore deps. hemimorphite, vanadinite —	**HOPEITE** $Zn_3(PO_4)_2 \cdot 4H_2O$ Altenberg near Aachen, Germany
48	colourless, white, yellowish, reddish ___ white	vitreous, silky, dull transluc.	2—2.5 / 2.6	very good soft	fine needle-shaped, capillary crystals, powdery en-crustations; crusts; mammillary, bo-tryoidal, reniform, earthy, powdery monoclinic	efflorescent crusts on arsenic ores niccolite, chloan-thite, erythrite, annabergite —	**PHARMA-COLITE** $CaH[AsO_4] \cdot 4H_2O$ Jáchymov, Czech Republic

No.	Colour / Streak	Lustre / Transparency	Hardness / Specific Gravity	Cleavage / Fracture & o. / Phys. Props.	Common Form, Aggregates / Crystalline Syst.	Occurrence / Assoc. Minerals / Similar Minerals	Name & Chem. Formula / Origin of Specimen
49	white, grey, pink, brownish / white	adamantine, on cleavage planes pearly / transluc.	2.5 / 5.6−5.8	very good / brittle	needle-shaped, tabular, scaly crystals, compact, fibrous, radial, granular / orthorhombic	weathering product of antimony ores / antimonite, galena & o. / cerussite	VALENTINITE Sb_2O_3 (Antimony Bloom) / Cetinje, Montenegro, Yugoslavia
50	colourless / white	vitreous, pearly / transpar.	2.5 / 2.2	good / conchoidal	columnar, tabular crystals, often twinned in heart shape / monoclinic	in black coal seams, rare in ore deps. / — / calcite	WHEWELLITE $Ca[C_2O_4] . H_2O$ / Kladno, Czech Republic

No.	Colour / Streak	Lustre / Transparency	Hardness / Specific Gravity	Cleavage / Fracture & o. / Phys. Props.	Common Form, Aggregates / Crystalline Syst.	Occurrence / Assoc. Minerals / Similar Minerals	Name & Chem. Formula / Origin of Specimen
51							CALCITE $CaCO_3$ (Calcareous Spar) / Helgustadir, Reydarfjördur, Iceland
52	colourless, white, yellow, red, brownish / white	vitreous, pearly / transpar., transluc.	3 / 2.6−2.7	very good, rhombohedral / brittle	columnar, tabular, needle-shaped, rhombohedral, scalenohedral crystals, rich in planes; in druses; coarse to fine-grained, spathic, stalactitic, reniform, compact, massive / trigonal	very common as crystals, in rock-fissures, in ore veins, deposited at hot springs, as sinter formation, as sedimentary rocks / — / dolomite, magnesite, ankerite, aragonite, chabasite, barytes, cf. No. 26, 170, 319	CALCITE $CaCO_3$ (Calcareous Spar) / Cumberland, England
53							CALCITE $CaCO_3$ (Calcareous Spar) / Egremont, Cumberland, England
54							CALCITE $CaCO_3$ (Calcareous Spar) / St. Andreasberg, Germany
55	colourless, white, yellowish / white	vitreous, pearly / transpar., transluc.	3 / 2.7−2.8	very good / brittle	rhombohedral crystals, finely granular masses, compact / trigonal	mixed crystals of calcite & cerussite, in lead ore deps. / — / calcite	PLUMBO-CALCITE $(Pb,Ca)CO_3$ / Bleiberg, Carinthia, Austria
56	white, yellowish, grey / white	vitreous to dull / transpar., transluc.	3−3.5 / 4.2	good / brittle	columnar, tabular crystals, compact, botryoidal, granular, radial, lamellar, globular agg. & masses / orthorhombic, pseudohexagonal	in lead ore veins / galena, alstonite, barytes / cerussite, quartz	WITHERITE $BaCO_3$ / Alston Moor, Westmorland, England

No.	Colour / Streak	Lustre / Transparency	Hardness / Specific Gravity	Cleavage Fracture & o. Phys. Props.	Common Form, Aggregates / Crystalline Syst.	Occurrence Assoc. Minerals / Similar Minerals	Name & Chem. Formula / Origin of Specimen
57	colourless, white, grey, red, yellow, blue, brown / white	vitreous, pearly, greasy / transpar., transluc.	3 – 3.5 / 4.4	very good, brittle, conchoidal	thin- to thick-tabular, needle-shaped, pyramidal; lamellar, wisp-like, flabelliform, radial, reniform, granular agg.; massive, reniform, shelled / orthorhombic	frequent in ore veins, in fissures in sedimentary rocks, nodules in clays & marl / — / aragonite, calcite, anhydrite, felspars, cf. No. 144, 145, 234	**BARYTES** Ba(SO₄) (Heavy Spar) / Baia Sprie (Felsöbánya), Romania
58	colourless, white, grey, bluish, violet, reddish / white	vitreous, pearly / transpar., transluc.	3 – 3.5 / 2.8 – 3	very good, distinct cleavage cracks, brittle	tabular, columnar, cube-shaped crystals, spathic, fibrous, compact, botryoidal, granular, massive / orthorhombic	in salt deps., from gypsum due to loss of water, forms 'Snake Alabaster' in ore veins, exhalation product in lava / halite, gypsum / cryolite, gypsum barytes, calcite, cf. No. 190	**ANHYDRITE** Ca(SO₄) / Bochnia near Cracow, Poland
59	colourless, white, grey, yellow, reddish, brown / white	vitreous, pearly / transpar., transluc.	3.5 – 4 / 3	very good, rhombohedron / brittle, easily friable	rhombohedral, saddle-shaped crystals of twinned surface; coarse to fine-grained, spathic, massive, compact / trigonal	frequent in ore veins, as sedimentary rocks, metasomatic deps. in limestones / — / calcite, magnesite, cf. No. 151	**DOLOMITE** CaMg(CO₃)₂ / Banská Štiavnica, Slovakia
60	white, grey, yellowish, brownish / white	vitreous, pearly / —	3.5 – 4 / 3 – 3.1	very good, rhombohedron / brittle	rhombohedral, often twinned crystals, as in dolomite, compact, granular / trigonal	in siderite deps., in ore deps. / siderite, galena, sphalerite, quartz / siderite, breunnerite	**ANKERITE** CaFe[CO₃]₂ / Mlynky, Slovakia
61	colourless, white, yellow, grey, reddish, violet, blue, green, brown / white	vitreous, greasy / transpar., transluc.	3.5 – 4 / 2.9 – 3	indistinct conchoidal, brittle	prismatic, columnar crystals, often twinned, tubular-radiating, fragile agg. / orthorhombic	in rock-fissures, in ore deps., embedded in sulphur, as sinter formation / — / calcite, barytes, coelestine, strontianite, natrolite, topaz	**ARAGONITE** CaCO₃ / Hořenec, Czech Republic
62	white, yellowish / white	greasy / opaque	3.5 – 4 / 2.9 – 3	— exfoliation (scaling)	pea-like / orthorhombic	deposited at hot springs / — / —	**ARAGONITE** CaCO₃ (Pisolite, Pea Stone, Pea Grit) / Karlovy Vary, Czech Republic
63	white / white	dull / transluc.	3.5 – 4 / 2.9 – 3	— brittle	dendritic, ramifying agg. / orthorhombic	in siderite deps. / limonite / cf. No. 320, 485	**ARAGONITE** CaCO₃ (Flos Ferri) / Eisenerz, Styria, Austria
64	white, grey, yellow, green, pink / white	vitreous, greasy / transpar., transluc.	3.5 – 4 / 3.7	clear brittle	pointed, fragile, needle-shaped crystals, fibrous, compact, radial / orthorhombic	in ore veins, in marl / calcite / aragonite, calcite, barytes, coelestine, natrolite	**STRONTIANITE** SrCO₃ / Sendenhorst, Germany

No.	Colour / Streak	Lustre / Transparency	Hardness / Specific Gravity	Cleavage / Fracture & o. Phys. Props.	Common Form, Aggregates / Crystalline Syst.	Occurrence / Assoc. Minerals / Similar Minerals	Name & Chem. Formula / Origin of Specimen
65	white / white	dull / opaque	3.5 / 2.2	— / greasy	mammillary, nodular, radiating-columnar agg.; crusty, powdery / monoclinic	as weathering product of serpentine, embedded in volcanic tuffs / — / —	**HYDRO-MAGNESITE** Mg_5 $[OH(CO_3)_2]_2$. $4H_2O$ / Vesuvius, Italy
66	colourless, white, grey / white	vitreous / transpar., transluc.	3.5—4 / 2.4	very good / —	short- to long-columnar, tabular crystals, compact, granular, lamellar, massive / monoclinic	in clay & gypsum as nodules, lenses, in borax deps. / — / ulexite, pandermite, datolite	**COLEMA-NITE** Ca $[B_3O_4(OH)_3]$. H_2O / Death Valley, California, USA
67	colourless, white, grey, yellowish, reddish / white	vitreous / transluc.	3.5—4 / 2.7—2.8	good / brittle	rhombohedral, tabular crystals; tubular, fibrous, granular, compact, nodular, earthy / trigonal	isolated rocks, nodules in sedimentary rocks, in decomposed rocks / sulphide ores, aluminite	**ALUNITE** KAl_3 $[(OH)_6(SO_4)_2]$ (Alum Stone) / La Tolfa near Civitavecchia, Italy
68	white, yellow, green, brown, bluish / white	vitreous, silky / transluc.	3.5—4 / 2.3—2.4	good / brittle	fine-fibrous, radial bunches; semi-globular; mammillary, reniform agg. / orthorhombic	in fissures in sandstone, in silica schists, greywacke, quartzite / limonite, haematite, natrolite, prehnite, cf. No. 272	**WAVELLITE** Al_3 $[(OH)_3(PO_4)_2]$. $5H_2O$ / Cerhovice, Czech Republic
69	colourless, white, yellowish, bluish, brown / white	pearly, greasy to dull / opaque	3.5—4 / 1.9	exfoliation (scaling) / very brittle, conchoidal	shelly, globular, reniform, botryoidal structure / amorphous	in cavities in limonite deps. / — / chalcedony, some opals	**EVANSITE** $Al_3[(OH)_6PO_4]$. $6H_2O$ / Železník, Slovakia
70	white, yellowish, grey, reddish / white	vitreous, pearly, dull / transluc.	3.5—4 / 2.2—2.3	very good / less brittle, in the air dull & crumbly	long-columnar, needle-shaped crystals; tubular, compact, fibrous, earthy / monoclinic	in ore veins, in cavities & fissures in eruptive rocks / other zeolites, calcite, chlorite / felspars	**LAUMON-TITE** $Ca[AlSi_2O_6]_2$. $4H_2O$ (Fibrous Zeolite) / Peter's Point, New Scotland, Canada
71	colourless, white, grey, red, brown / white	vitreous, pearly / transpar., transluc.	3.5—4 / 2.2	very good / brittle	tabular, lamellar, short-columnar crystals, scaly, spathic, compact, flabelliform / monoclinic	in cavities & fissures in volcanic rocks, in ore deps., in crystalline schists / other zeolites / desmine, felspar, cf. No. 194	**HEULAN-DITE** $Ca[Al_2Si_7O_{18}]$. $6H_2O$ (Stilbite, Lamellar Zeolite) / Teigarhorn, Berufjördur, Iceland
72	white, reddish, yellowish, brownish / white	vitreous, pearly, silky / transpar., transluc.	3.5—4 / 2.1—2.2	very good / brittle	tabular, columnar, chip-shaped crystals; bundle-shaped bunches; radial agg. / monoclinic	in vesicles & druses in eruptive rocks, druses in granite, in alpine fissures, in ore deps. / other zeolites, calcite, quartz / other zeolites	**DESMINE** $Ca[Al_2Si_7O_{18}]$. $7H_2O$ (Stilbite, Bundle Zeolite) / Teigarhorn, Berufjördur, Iceland

No.	Colour / Streak	Lustre / Transparency	Hardness / Specific Gravity	Cleavage / Fracture & o. Phys. Props.	Common Form, Aggregates / Crystalline Syst.	Occurrence / Assoc. Minerals / Similar Minerals	Name & Chem. Formula / Origin of Specimen
73	colourless, yellow, green, violet, blue, pink / white	vitreous / transpar., transluc.	4 / 3 – 3.2	perfect, octahedron / conchoidal, brittle, shining when heated	cubic, octahedral crystals, coarsely to finely granular, spathic, massive, compact, radial, striated / cubic	frequent in rock fissures & ore veins, isolated masses, metasomatic in limestone, as cementing material in sandstones / — / barytes, apatite, amethyst, cf. No. 212, 233	**FLUORITE** CaF_2 (Fluor Spar, Blue John) / Pare in Val Sarentina, Italy
74	white, grey-yellow / white	vitreous, greasy / transluc.	4 – 4.5 / 3.6 – 3.7	good / —	pointed, pyramidal, short-columnar crystals; fibrous, granular, massive / orthorhombic	in lead ore deps. / witherite, baryto-calcite, galena / —	**ALSTONITE** $CaCO_3 + BaCO_3$ (Bromlite) / Alston Moor, England
75	colourless, white, reddish, yellowish / white	vitreous, / transpar., transluc.	4 – 4.5 / 2.1 – 2.2	good / brittle, striated cleavage planes	short-needle-shaped, thick-tabular crystals; pseudorhombic to pseudocubic polysynthetic twins / monoclinic	in cavities in volcanic rocks, in deep-sea deps. / analcime, chabazite / harmotome	**PHILLIPSITE** $KCa[Al_3Si_5O_{16}] \cdot 6H_2O$ (Cross Stone) / Vinařická hora, Czech Republic
76	colourless, white, grey, reddish, yellowish / white	vitreous / transpar., transluc.	4.5 / 2.4 – 2.5	good / brittle, smooth cleavage planes	thick-tabular, thick-columnar crystals; penetration twins as in phillipsite / monoclinic	in cavities in alkaline effusive rocks, in ore veins / barytes, calcite, galena, quartz / phillipsite	**HARMO-TOME** $Ba[Al_2Si_6O_{16}] \cdot 6H_2O$ (Cross Stone) / Strontian, Argyll, England
77	colourless, white, yellow, reddish / white	vitreous / transpar., transluc.	4 – 5 / 2 – 2.1	indistinct / brittle	cube-shaped, rhombohedral crystals; penetration twins, only in druses; no agg. / trigonal	in cavities in igneous rocks; in alpine clefts & ore veins / other zeolites, quartz, felspar / calcite, dolomite	**CHABAZITE** (Ca,Na_2) $[Al_2Si_4O_{12}] \cdot 6H_2O$ (Cubic Zeolite) / Řepčice, Czech Republic
78	colourless, white, yellowish, reddish, greenish / white	vitreous, / transpar., transluc.	4 / 2.1	poor, indistinct / brittle, conchoidal	thick-tabular crystals; penetration twins / orthorhombic	in cavities in basaltic rocks / chabazite	**LEVYNITE** $Ca[Al_2Si_4O_{12}] \cdot 6H_2O$ (Zeolite) / Benyevenagh, Ireland
79	colourless, white, bluish, greenish, yellowish, grey, brown / white	vitreous, pearly, silky / transpar., transluc.	4.5 – 5 / 3.3 – 3.5	very good / conchoidal, fibrous, brittle	tabular to needle-shaped, chip-shaped crystals; mammillary, reniform agg., crusts, massive / orthorhombic	in limestone & dolomite / galena, sphalerite, smithsonite, wulfenite, calcite, limonite / prehnite, smithsonite, chalcedony, opal, phosphorite	**HEMI-MORPHITE** Zn_4 $[(OH)_2Si_2O_7] \cdot H_2O$ (Silicate of Zinc, Galmei, Calamine) / Nerchinsk, Transbaikal, Russia
80	colourless, white, yellowish, grey / white	vitreous, silky / transluc.	4.5 – 5 / 2.8	very good / brittle	thick-tabular, needle-shaped, capillary, compact, spathic, tubular to fibrous, lamellar / monoclinic	in contact-metamorphic limestones in crystalline schists / quartz, garnet, vesuvianite, pyroxene, pektolite, tremolite	**WOLLA-STONITE** $Ca_3[Si_3O_9]$ (Table Spar) / Mirsk, Poland

No.	Colour / Streak	Lustre / Transparency	Hardness / Specific Gravity	Cleavage Fracture & o. Phys. Props.	Common Form, Aggregates / Crystalline Syst.	Occurrence / Assoc. Minerals / Similar Minerals	Name & Chem. Formula / Origin of Specimen
81	colourless, white, yellowish, reddish, brown / white	vitreous, greasy / transluc.	5 / 2.9–3	indistinct / brittle	thick-tabular, columnar crystals; radial agg. / orthorhombic	in weathering zone of lead deps. / — / aragonite	**TARNO-WITZITE** (Pb,Ca)CO₃ / Tsumeb, South-West Africa
82	white, whitish-grey / white	greasy, dull / opaque	5 / 3.1	indistinct / con-choidal, brittle	columnar, hexagonal crystals; coarsely granular masses / hexagonal	large crystals in apatite veins in phosphate-pegmatites / — / cf. No. 158, 214, 281	**APATITE** here **HYDROXYL-APATITE** Ca₅[OH(PO₄)₃] / Snarum, Norway
83	white, greyish / white	vitreous, silky, pearly / transluc.	5 / 2.8	very good / very brittle	needle-shaped, long-columnar crystals; fibrous agg., compact, massive, reniform, radiating / triclinic	in fissures in igneous rocks / zeolite, calcite, tremolite, wollastonite	**PECTOLITE** Ca₂NaH[Si₃O₉] / Bergen Hill (Tunnel), New Jersey, USA
84	colourless, white, greyish, yellowish / white	vitreous, silky / transluc.	5 / 2.2–2.4	good / brittle	acicular, capillary crystals; radial, fine-fibrous, semi-globular agg., compact, massive, earthy / monoclinic	in fissures & cavities, in basic igneous rocks / other zeolites, calcite, natrolite, thomsonite	**MESOLITE** Na₂Ca₂ [Al₂Si₃O₁₀] . 8H₂O (Zeolite) / Hauenštejn, Czech Republic
85	colourless, white, yellow, grey, reddish / white	greasy, vitreous / transpar., transluc.	5–5.5 / 3–3.1	— / con-choidal	short-columnar crystals with longitudinal striation, mostly compact / monoclinic	hydrothermal formation in quartz veins, in vesuvian lavas / quartz, magnesite, siderite, barytes, apatite / —	**WAGNERITE** Mg₂[F PO₄] / Werfen, Salzburg, Austria
86	colourless, white, greyish, yellowish / white	vitreous, greasy / transpar., transluc.	5–5.5 / 2.9–3	indistinct / con-choidal	thick-tabular, short-columnar crystals, compact, granular, reniform, massive, crusty / monoclinic	in druses & fissures in basic igneous rocks, in granitic veins, in ore deps. / — / danburite, colemanite, zeolite	**DATOLITE** CaB[OH SiO₄] / Seiser Alm, South Tyrol Austria
87	colourless, white, dim, green-grey, grey, blue / white	vitreous, pearly / transpar., transluc.	5–6 / 2.7	good to clear / con-choidal brittle	short-prismatic, thick-columnar, tubular crystals; granular, fibrous, radial, massive / tetragonal	in metamorphic rocks, as volcanic ejecta / garnet, epidote, vesuvianite, pyroxene, felspars, spodumene, cf. No. 421	Scapolite variety **MEIONITE** Ca₈ [(Cl₂,SO₄,CO₃)₂ (Al₂Si₂O₈)₆] / Vesuvius, Italy
88	colourless, white, yellowish, reddish, pink, red / white	vitreous, silky / transpar., transluc.	5–5.5 / 2.2–2.4	very good / brittle	columnar, acicular, capillary crystals; radial, reniform, con-centric, shelled, fibrous, compact, massive, powdery / orthorhombic	in cavities in igneous rocks, in fissures in granites & crystalline schists / other zeolites, calcite, aragonite, scolezite, thomsonite, meso-lite, wavellite, cf. No. 199	**NATROLITE** Na₂Al₂Si₃O₁₀ . 2H₂O (Fibrous Zeolite) / Česká Lípa, Czech Republic

No.	Colour Streak	Lustre Transparency	Hardness Specific Gravity	Cleavage Fracture & o. Phys. Props.	Common Form, Aggregates Crystalline Syst.	Occurrence Assoc. Minerals Similar Minerals	Name & Chem. Formula Origin of Specimen
89	colourless, white, yellowish, reddish, grey — white	vitreous, dull — transpar., transluc.	5—5.5 — 2.1—2.3	— con-choidal, uneven	isolated grown up crystals; druses; also compact, granular, massive, earthy — cubic	in vesicles & fissures in basic igneous rocks, in ore veins — zeolite, calcite — leucite, sodalite, garnet	**ANALCITE** Na[AlSi$_2$O$_6$] . H$_2$O — Seiser Alm, South Tyrol, Austria
90	white, yellowish, reddish, greenish, brown — white	vitreous — transpar., transluc.	5—5.5 — 2.2—2.4	good brittle	acicular, short-columnar, thick-tabular crystals; reniform, globular, nodular agg.; radial, tubular bunches; compact — orthorhombic	in vesicles in basic igneous rocks, in vesuvian lavas — other zeolites, analcite, calcite — natrolite, prehnite	**THOMSONITE** NaCa$_2$ [Al$_2$(Al,Si) Si$_2$O$_{10}$]$_2$. 6H$_2$O (Comptonite, Fibrous Zeolite) — Doubice, Czech Republic
91	colourless, white, yellowish, brownish — white	vitreous, silky — transpar., transluc.	5—5.5 — 2.1—2.4	very good brittle, con-choidal	columnar, needle-shaped to capillary crystals; bunchy, radial, fibrous agg.; also compact — monoclinic	in cavities & fissures in volcanic rocks, in cracks in granite & syenite, in crystalline schists, in alpine cracks — other zeolites, calcite — thomsonite, aragonite	**SCOLEZITE** Ca[Al$_2$Si$_3$O$_{10}$] . 3H$_2$O (Fibrous Zeolite) — Teigarhorn, Berufjördur, Iceland
92	colourless, white, grey — white	vitreous, greasy to dull — transluc., mostly dull, opaque	5.5—6 — 2.5	— con-choidal	isometric, rounded, embedded crystals; seldom grown up, granular agg. — tetragonal to pseudocubic	constituent of volcanic rocks, in vesuvian lavas & ashes — — analcite, sodalite, garnet	**LEUCITE** K[AlSi$_2$O$_6$] — Ariccia, Italy
93	colourless, white, blue, grey, greenish — white	vitreous, greasy — transpar., transluc.	5.5—6 — 2.3—2.5	good con-choidal	seldom isometric crystals; mostly compact, granular agg. — cubic	constituent of diff. igneous rocks, in volcanic ejecta — — leucite, analcite, hauyne, nosean, lazurite, cf. No. 237	**SODALITE** Na$_8$ [Cl$_2$(AlSiO$_4$)$_6$] — Vesuvius, Italy
94	colourless, white, grey, yellow, dark-green — white	vitreous — transpar., transluc.	6 — 3.7—3.9	very good —	octahedral, cubic, grown up & embedded crystals; compact, granular — cubic	in metamorphosed limestones & dolomites, in volcanic ejecta — — —	**PERICLASE** MgO — Monte Somma, Vesuvius, Italy
95	colourless, water-clear, white — white	vitreous — transpar., transluc.	5.5—6 — 2.1	— con-choidal	botryoidal, reniform, conical, platy, massive, crusty — amorphous	in cracks & cavities in volcanic rocks, in ore veins, deposited at hot springs — — —	**HYALITE** SiO$_2$. nH$_2$O (Glassy Opal) — Valeč, Czech Republic
96	white, enamel-like — white	dull opaque	5.5—6 — 1.9—2	— con-choidal	reniform, botry-oidal, massive, porcellanic — amorphous	in vesicles & cavities in basalt rocks — —	Opal variety **KASCHO-LONG** SiO$_2$. nH$_2$O — Hüttenberg, Carinthia, Austria,

COLOURLESS AND WHITE MINERALS
OF NON-METALLIC LUSTRE

Hardness 5 — 6

No.	Colour / Streak	Lustre / Transparency	Hardness / Specific Gravity	Cleavage Fracture & o. Phys. Props.	Common Form, Aggregates / Crystalline Syst.	Occurrence / Assoc. Minerals / Similar Minerals	Name & Chem. Formula / Origin of Specimen
97	milk-white, yellowish-white / white	dull / opaque	5—6 (also softer) / 2.1—2.3	— / conchoidal	veins, nodules, opaline / amorphous	base opal containing alum, in hornstones or jasper / —	ALUMOCALCITE $SiO_2 \cdot nH_2O + Al_2O_3$ / Eibenstock, Ore Mountains, Germany
98	colourless, greenish, yellowish / white	vitreous / transpar.	6 / 2.6	— / conchoidal, brittle	columnar, hexagonal, grown up crystals / hexagonal	in pegmatites, in fissures in granites / smoky quartz, adularia, apatite, titanite / aquamarine	MILARITE KCa_2 $[(Be,Al)Si_4O_{10}]_3$ / Val Giuv, Graubünden, Switzerland
99	colourless, white / white	vitreous, pearly / transpar., transluc.	6 / 2.5	very good / —	tabular crystals, frequent twin striation / monoclinic	in fissures in syenite / zeolite / zeolite, felspar	EUDIDYMITE $NaBe$ $[OH Si_3O_7]$ / Langesundsfjord, Norway
100	white, reddish, yellowish / white	vitreous, pearly / transluc.	6 / 2.6	very good / brittle, uneven	thick-tabular, columnar, acicular crystals, often with twin striation; compact, granular, radial, spathic / monoclinic	as rock constituents in granites, syenites, pegmatites, in crystalline schists, in fissures in gneiss, in ore veins / — / barytes	ALBITE $Na[AlSi_3O_8]$ (Felspar Family) / Intschitobel near Amsteg, Switzerland
101	colourless, white, greenish / white	vitreous, pearly / transpar., transluc.	6 / 2.5	very good / brittle	only grown up thick-tabular crystals, often covered with green chlorite dust / monoclinic	in druses in alpine cracks, in ore veins / quartz, albite, pericline, titanite, chlorite / —	ADULARIA $K[AlSi_3O_8]$ (Felspar Family) / Grimsel, Switzerland
102	colourless, white, grey-white, reddish / white	vitreous, pearly / transpar., transluc., dim	6 / 2.7	very good / brittle	tabular, short-columnar, embedded & grown up crystals; massive, granular / triclinic	rock constituents in metamorphic limestone & dolomite, in ore deps., in volcanic ejecta / — / cf. No. 204	ANORTHITE $Ca[Al_2Si_2O_8]$ (Felspar Family) / Monte Somma, Vesuvius, Italy
103	colourless, white, greenish, reddish, yellowish / white	vitreous, pearly / transpar., transluc., opaque	6 / 2.6—2.7	very good / brittle	tabular crystals; massive, granular agg.; compact, granular, massive / triclinic	rock constituent in diorites, andesites, syenites, in cordierite-gneiss / — / —	ANDESINE Constituent of $Na[AlSi_3O_8]$ $Ca[Al_2Si_2O_8]$ (albite + anorthite) (Felspar Family) / Esterel, France
104	colourless, white, green / white	vitreous, pearly / transpar., transluc.	6 / 2.6	very good / brittle	grown up twinned plagioclases; columnar, thick-tabular crystals; no agg. / triclinic	in druses in alpine cracks / quartz, adularia, titanite, rutile, anatase, chlorite / —	PERICLINE $Na[AlSi_3O_8] \pm$ K,Ca (Felspar Family) / Rothenkopf, Zillertal, Tyrol, Austria

No. 97 — 104

Table 1

No.	Colour / Streak	Lustre / Transparency	Hardness / Specific Gravity	Cleavage Fracture & o. Phys. Props.	Common Form, Aggregates / Crystalline Syst.	Occurrence / Assoc. Minerals / Similar Minerals	Name & Chem. Formula / Origin of Specimen
105	colourless, whitish, bluish — white	pearly, vitreous with bright bluish shine transluc.	6 / 2.5 – ? 6	very good brittle	thick-tabular, wide-columnar crystals; spathic / monoclinic	due to differentiation of pale milky adularia or sanidine / — / —	**MOONSTONE** $K[(Si,Al)_4O_8]$ (Felspar Family) / Kandy, Sri Lanka
106	white, yellow, brown — whitish	vitreous transluc.	6 – 6.5 / 3.1 – 3.2	indistinct —	small, short-columnar crystals, rich in planes; compact, granular agg. / orthorhombic	in contact metamorphic deps., in volcanic ejecta, in ore deps. / — / cancrinite	**HUMITE** $Mg_7(OH,F)_2(SiO_4)_3$ / Monte Somma, Vesuvius, Italy
107	colourless, white, yellowish, reddish, violet, grey — white	vitreous, pearly transpar., transluc.	6.5 – 7 / 3.3 – 3.5	very good, lamellar conchoidal, very brittle	tabular, wide-columnar, foliaceous, acicular crystals; compact, lamellar, radial, tubular, scaly / orthorhombic	constituent in bauxite, in crystalline schists / kyanite, corundum, magnetite, calcite, serpentine / gypsum	**DIASPORE** α-AlOOH / Banská Štiavnica, Slovakia
108	colourless, yellowish-white, greenish, grey — white	vitreous transpar., transluc.	6.5 – 7 / 3.1 – 3.2	very good brittle	wide-tubular, columnar, thick-tabular, spathic / monoclinic	in pegmatites / lepidolite, quartz, albite, tourmaline, beryl / felspars, scapolite	**SPODUMENE** $LiAl[Si_2O_6]$ / Chesterfield, South Carolina, USA
109	colourless — white	vitreous, greasy transpar.	7 / 2.6	— conchoidal	columnar to needle-shaped grown up crystals in druses / trigonal	in druses & fissures in magmatic rocks & crystalline schists, in ore veins / albite, titanite, rutile & o. / phenakite, topaz, beryl	**QUARTZ** SiO_2 (Rock Crystal) / Bourg d'Oisans, Dauphiné, France
110	milk-white, also differently coloured — white	vitreous, greasy transpar., transluc.	7 / 2.6	— conchoidal	columnar, embedded & grown up crystals; mostly horizontally striated, coarsely to finely granular / trigonal	very frequent constituent of diff. rocks, in ore veins / — / —	**QUARTZ** SiO_2 (Milky Quartz) / Ratibořice, Czech Republic
111	white, yellowish, reddish, grey, brownish — white	vitreous transluc., opaque	7 / 2.6	— conchoidal	radiating-columnar agg. / trigonal	quartz variety with morphological peculiarities, in vesicles in basalts / — / —	**ASTERIATED QUARTZ** SiO_2 / Peřimov, Czech Republic
112	white, grey, yellow, red, brown, greenish, blackish — white	greasy, waxy transluc., opaque	5.5 – 6.5 / 1.9 – 2.5	— conchoidal, brittle	veins, nodules, concretions, filling of cavities, disseminated, compact, botryoidal, nodular, reniform / amorphous	product of decomposition of many rocks, in ore veins, deposited at hot springs / — / —	**OPAL** $SiO_2 \cdot nH_2O$ / Madeira, Portugal

No.	Colour / Streak	Lustre / Transparency	Hardness / Specific Gravity	Cleavage Fracture & o. Phys. Props.	Common Form, Aggregates / Crystalline Syst.	Occurrence / Assoc. Minerals / Similar Minerals	Name & Chem. Formula / Origin of Specimen
113	colourless, white, yellowish, grey / white	vitreous, pearly, also dull / transpar., transluc.	7 / 2.2	indistinct / brittle	thin-tabular crystals, flabelliform twins & triplets / orthorhombic	in cavities in trachyte, andesite, porphyry / —	**TRIDYMITE** SiO_2 / Colli Euganei, Italy
114	colourless, grey, yellowish, greenish, bluish / white	vitreous, greasy or adamantine / transpar., transluc.	7 / 2.9−3	— / conchoidal	cube-shaped embedded crystals; compact, massive, fibrous nodules / orthorhombic, pseudotetragonal	in potash salt deps. / embedded in gypsum, anhydrite, carnallite / —	**BORACITE** $Mg_3[Cl\,B_7O_{13}]$ (Stassfurtite) / Lüneburg, Germany
115	colourless, grey-white, yellowish / white	vitreous / transpar., transluc.	7.5 / 2.3	very good / brittle	thick-tabular, vertically striated, many-planed crystals / orthorhombic	in syenites & pegmatites in Norway & Madagascar / —	**HAMBERGITE** $Be_2[(OH,F)\,BO_3]$ / Imalo, Madagascar
116	colourless, white, yellow, pink, brown / white	vitreous / transpar., transluc.	7.5−8 / 3	less clear to good / brittle, conchoidal	hexagonal, quartz-like, short-columnar, grown up crystals / trigonal	in beryllium-pegmatites, in cracks in granite & mica slates, in tin ore deps. / beryl, apatite, topaz, tourmaline, quartz / quartz, topaz	**PHENAKITE** $Be_2[SiO_4]$ / San Miguel di Piracicaba, Minas Gerais, Brazil
117	colourless, yellow, blue, green, red, reddish / white	vitreous / transpar., transluc.	8 / 3.5−3.6	very good / uneven, conchoidal	short- to long-columnar crystals with orthorhombic outline, as impregnation; compact, massive, felspar-like / orthorhombic	pneumatolytic structure, in pegmatites, granites, in tin ore veins, in placers of precious stones / — / phenakite, quartz, corundum, beryl, aragonite, cf. No. 168, 523	**TOPAZ** $Al_2[F_2SiO_4]$ / Tonokamiyama, Japan
118	colourless, yellow, green, blue, red, black, grey / white	adamantine, greasy, also dull / transpar., transluc., opaque	10 / 3.5	very good / conchoidal, brittle	octahedral, cubic, dodecahedral crystals; bulbous & striated planes frequent; granular, radiate, globular agg. / cubic	embedded in ultrabasic rocks, in conglomerates, loose crystals in placers, in river sands / — / cf. No. 513	**DIAMOND** C / Kimberley, South Africa

YELLOW MINERALS OF METALLIC LUSTRE

Hardness 2.5 − 3

No.	Colour / Streak	Lustre / Transparency	Hardness / Specific Gravity	Cleavage Fracture & o. Phys. Props.	Common Form, Aggregates / Crystalline Syst.	Occurrence / Assoc. Minerals / Similar Minerals	Name & Chem. Formula / Origin of Specimen
119	gold-yellow, light yellow, brownish, mustard-yellow	metallic / opaque	2.5−3 / 14.5 to 19.3	— / ductile, malleable, flexible, hackly	compact, sheets, grains, dendritic skeleta; octahedral, cubic, dodecahedral crystals rare; feather-shaped, arborescent, filiform, capillary, platy agg., mossy / cubic	in hydrothermal veins in volcanic rocks, lamellar, granular & nodular in placers / quartz, pyrites, galena, arseno-pyrite, antimonite, gold-telluride / pyrites, chalcopyrite, marcasite	nat. **GOLD** Au / Roșia Montană, Romania
120	yellow, golden, shining						nat. **GOLD** Au / Jílové, Czech Republic

Table with numbers: 113 | 114 / 115 | 116 / 117 | 118 / 119 | 120

113	114
115	116
117	118
119	120

69

No.	Colour / Streak	Lustre / Transparency	Hardness / Specific Gravity	Cleavage / Fracture & o. / Phys. Props.	Common Form, Aggregates / Crystalline Syst.	Occurrence / Assoc. Minerals / Similar Minerals	Name & Chem. Formula / Origin of Specimen
121	gold-yellow, light yellow, mustard-yellow, brownish	metallic / opaque	2.5 − 3 / 14.5 to 19.3	— / ductile, malleable, flexible, hackly	sheets, plates, grains, compact, dendritic skeleta; rarely octahedral, cube-like, dodecahedral crystals; feather-shaped, arborescent, filiform, capillary, platy agg., mossy / cubic	in hydrothermal veins, in volcanic rocks, lamellar, granular, in lumps in placers / quartz, pyrites, galena, arsenopyrite, antimonite, gold-telluride / pyrites, chalcopyrite, marcasite	nat. GOLD Au / Křepice, Czech Republic
122	yellow, golden, shining						nat. GOLD Au / Roșia Montană, Romania
123	speiss-yellow, brass-yellow, brownish / greyish-black	metallic / opaque	3 − 3.5 / 5.5	very good / brittle	acicular, capillary crystals in bunches; radiate, fibrous agg.; granular, compact / trigonal	in ore veins, filling cracks in coal seams / siderite, chalcopyrite, barytes, fluorite, calcite / —	MILLERITE NiS (Hair Pyrites) / Kladno, Czech Republic
124	brass-yellow, often tarnished / greenish-black to black	metallic / opaque	3.5 − 4 / 4.1 − 4.3	indistinct / soft, brittle, uneven	isometric crystals; octahedral & tetrahedral; often striated; compact, reniform, finely granular, massive / tetragonal, pseudocubic	very frequent in diff. ore deps. / pyrites, galena, sphalerite, carbonate, quartz / pyrites, gold, marcasite	CHALCO-PYRITE CuFeS$_2$ (Copper Pyrites) / Freiberg, Ore Mountains, Germany

Hardness 4 − 6.5

No.	Colour / Streak	Lustre / Transparency	Hardness / Specific Gravity	Cleavage / Fracture & o. / Phys. Props.	Common Form, Aggregates / Crystalline Syst.	Occurrence / Assoc. Minerals / Similar Minerals	Name & Chem. Formula / Origin of Specimen
125	gold-yellow, brass-yellow, occasionally tarnished	metallic / opaque	6 − 6.5 / 4.8 − 5	indistinct / conchoidal, brittle	well-developed embedded & grown up octahedral, cube-like, pentagondo-decahedral crystals; cube planes often striated; compact, granular, reniform, nodular, closely packed fibres, radiate, massive / cubic	very frequent in sulphidic ore deps., in sedimentary rocks, as mixture in magmatic rocks, crystalline schists, in coals, as petrifaction medium in sedimentary rocks / — / marcasite, chalcopyrite, gold, pyrrhotite	PYRITES FeS$_2$ (Sulphuric Pyrites, Iron Pyrites) / Rio Marina, Elba, Italy
126	greenish-black						PYRITES FeS$_2$ (Sulphuric Pyrites, Iron Pyrites) / Tavistock, Devon, England
127	brass-yellow to greenish / greenish-black	metallic / opaque	6 − 6.5 / 4.8 − 4.9	indistinct / brittle, in damp air weathers easily	tabular, short-columnar, acicular, chip-shaped crystals; pectiniform, fibrous agg.; massive, compact, reniform, nodular, radial, globular, stratified / orthorhombic	with pyrites in ore deps., in lignites, marls, clays, not in igneous rocks, less frequent than pyrites / — / pyrites, chalcopyrite, pyrrhotite, gold	MARCASITE FeS$_2$ (Spear Pyrites) / Komořany, Czech Republic
128	yellow-brown, dark-brown, occasionally tarnished / grey-black	metallic / opaque	4 / 4.6	clear (fissile) / brittle, uneven	thick-tabular to short-columnar crystals; rose-shaped agg.; disseminated, compact, granular, massive / hexagonal	in basic igneous rocks, in metamorphic rocks, in crystalline schists, in pegmatites, in ore veins / pyrites, magnetite, chalcopyrite & o. / pyrites, chalcopyrite, marcasite, cf. No. 308	PYRRHO-TITE (Pyrrhotine) FeS (Magnetic Pyrites) / Herja (Chiuzbaia, Kisbánya), Romania

No.	Colour / Streak	Lustre / Transparency	Hardness / Specific Gravity	Cleavage Fracture & o. Phys. Props.	Common Form, Aggregates / Crystalline Syst.	Occurrence / Assoc. Minerals / Similar Minerals	Name & Chem. Formula / Origin of Specimen
129	yellow, orange-yellow, yellow-brown,	adamantine, greasy	1 — 2.5 / 2	indistinct very brittle, con-choidal, easily inflam-mable, burns with blue flame	pyramidal, tabular, many-planed crystals; compact, lamellar, massive, granular, reniform, earthy, powdery	in sedimentary limestones & marls; as sublimate in volcanoes & hot springs, on coal piles	nat. SULPHUR S / Cianciana, Sicily, Italy
130	brownish / straw-yellow	transpar., transluc.			orthorhombic	calcite, aragonite, gypsum, anhydrite, rock salt / —	nat. SULPHUR S / Agrigento, Sicily, Italy
131	yellow, lemon-yellow / lemon-yellow	adamantine, greasy, vitreous, pearly / transpar., transluc.	1.5 — 2 / 3.4 — 3.5	very good sectile, soft, flexible	lamellar, columnar, tabular, short-prismatic crystals; compact, platy, tubular, radial, reniform, nodular / monoclinic	in ore veins, dis-seminated in clays, marls, on volcanoes, at hot springs / realgar, antimonite, sphalerite, pyrites / —	ORPIMENT As_2S_3 (Tinsel) / Allchar near Mrežičko, Macedonia
132	yellow, brownish / white	silky, pearly / transluc.	1.5 — 2 / 2.3 — 2.4	very good soft	coarse to fine-fibrous, parallel agg. / monoclinic	in cracks in sedi-mentary rocks, in salt deps. / — / cf. No. 31, 32	SELENITE $Ca[SO_4] \cdot 2H_2O$ (Satin Spar) / Yekaterinburg, Central Urals, Russia
133	sulphur-yellow, lemon-yellow, orange-yellow / yellow	dull, silky / transluc.	1 — 3 / 2.5	good / —	capillary, acicular, lamellar, tabular crystals; compact, fine-fibrous, scaly, powdery, earthy; flabelliform encrustations, efflorescences / monoclinic	decomposition product of uranium minerals besides other uranium micas / — / uranophane	ZIPPEITE $[6UO_2 \, 3(OH)_2 \, 3SO_4] \cdot 12H_2O + 3H_2O$ (Uran Ochre) / Jáchymov, Czech Republic
134	yellowish-white, straw-yellow / yellowish, straw-yellow	dull, silky / transluc.	2 / 4 — 4.5	clear / —	efflorescences, en-crustations, fibrous, earthy, radial, disseminated / orthorhombic	weathering product of molybdenite & other molybdenum minerals / — / different ochres	MOLYBDITE MoO_3 or $Fe_2(MoO_4)_3 \cdot 7H_2O$ (Molybdenum Ochre) / Buena Vista, Colorado, USA
135	reddish, yellow, orange, yellowish-brown / straw-yellow	dull opaque	2.5 — 3 / 3.9 — 4.5	— con-choidal	compact, massive, reniform, dissemi-nated, gummous, loose, earthy / amorphous	weathering product of uraninite / — / —	GUMMITE $(Pb,Ca,Ba)U_3[O_8 \, SiO_4] \cdot 5H_2O$ (Uranium Ochre) / Flat Rock Mine, Carolina, USA
136	yellowish-green, dirty yellow, light yellowish / pale yellow	pearly / transpar., transluc.	2 — 3 / 3.5	very good —	foliated, needle-shaped, scaly crystals; lamellar, radial, bunchy agg.; crusty / tetragonal	in pegmatites, in quartz veins / uranium minerals autunite, cf. No. 138, 260	URANO-CIRCITE $Ba[UO_2 \, PO_4]_2 \cdot 8H_2O$ (Uranium Mica) / Falkenstein, Vogtland, Germany

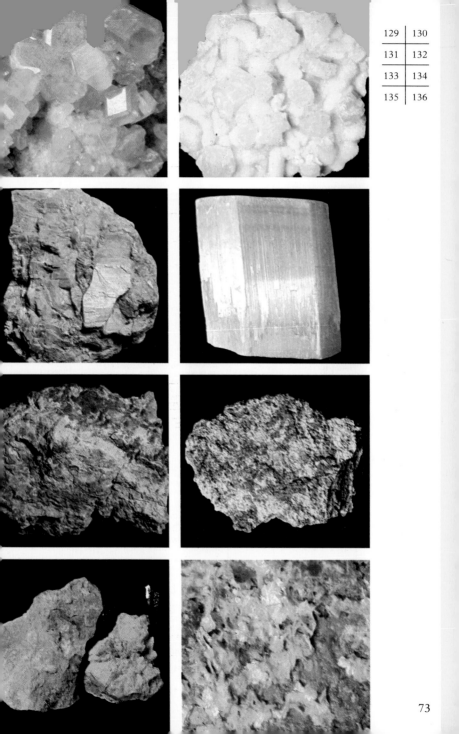

129	130
131	132
133	134
135	136

No.	Colour / Streak	Lustre / Transparency	Hardness / Specific Gravity	Cleavage Fracture & o. / Phys. Props.	Common Form, Aggregates / Crystalline Syst.	Occurrence Assoc. Minerals / Similar Minerals	Name & Chem. Formula / Origin of Specimen
137	light yellow, greenish-yellow / pale yellow, greenish-yellow	vitreous, pearly transluc.	2.5 / 2.5	very good / —	thin, tabular, micaceous crystals; fine-scaly agg.; earthy, encrustations / triclinic, pseudohexagonal	weathering product of uranium minerals / — / —	SCHROECK-INGERITE NaCa$_3$[UO$_2$ F SO$_4$ (CO$_3$)$_3$] . 10H$_2$O (Uranium Mica) / Jáchymov, Czech Republic
138	sulphur-yellow, lemon-yellow, yellowish-green, greenish-yellow / yellowish, greenish	pearly, vitreous transluc.	2—2.5 / 3—3.2	very good soft	thin- to thick-tabular, grown up crystals; scaly clusters, lamellar agg.; massive, earthy / tetragonal	as secondary uranium mineral in granites & pegmatites, in cracks, in uranium ore veins / quartz, fluorite / other uranium micas, cf. No. 260	AUTUNITE Ca[UO$_2$ PO$_4$]$_2$. 10H$_2$O (Lime Uranite) / Sabugal, Portugal
139	colourless, white, yellow, greenish, brown, apple-green / white	silky transluc.	2.5 / 1.8—2	— water-soluble	capillary, fibrous, acicular crystals / monoclinic	weathering product of pyrites in ore deps., in lignites / — / apjohnite	HALO-TRICHITE FeAl$_2$[SO$_4$]$_4$. 22H$_2$O (Iron Alum, Feather-Alum, Hair Salt) / Dubník, Slovakia
140	honey-yellow, orange, brownish, yellowish-white / whitish	greasy transpar., transluc., dull	2—2.5 / 1—1.1	— con-choidal, brittle, electric when rubbed	gravel, pebbles, plates, banded, drop-shaped, disseminated / amorphous	fossil resin in sedimentary rocks / — / cf. No. 552	AMBER C$_{12}$H$_{20}$O (Succinite) / Klaipeda, Lithuania
141	straw-yellow, orange-yellow, brownish / whitish	greasy transluc., opaque	2—2.5 / 1	— brittle, con-choidal	disseminated, massive, banded, nodular, stratified / amorphous	amber-like fossil resin from brown coal, lignite / — / —	WALCHO-VITE (C$_{15}$H$_{20}$O)$_4$ / Valchov, Czech Republic
142	colourless, yellow, red, brown, green, grey, black / white, yellow, brown	adamantine, greasy, almost metallic transpar. to opaque	3.5—4 / 3.9—4.2	very good, rhombo-dodeca-hedron brittle	tetrahedral, dode-cahedral, cubic, often twinned crystals; coarse to fine-grained, massive, compact, fibrous, shelled-reniform masses / cubic	in ore veins, hydro-thermal, pneumato-lytic, also sedimentary / galena, chalco-pyrite, quartz & o. / tetrahedrite, cassiterite, garnet, cf. No. 191, 315, 445	SPHALERITE ZnS (Blende, Black Jack) / Banská Štiavnica, Slovakia
143	yellow, orange, brown / yellow	ada-mantine, (only crystals), dull transluc.	3—3.5 / 4.9—5	good brittle	rarely short-co-lumnar crystals; mostly as powdery coating; massive, earthy / hexagonal	in weathering zone of zinc deps. / sphalerite, galena, smithsonite / zippeite, bismutite	GREEN-OCKITE CdS / Bishoptown near Paisley, Scotland
144	colourless, white, yellow, grey, red, blue, brown / white	vitreous, greasy, pearly transpar., transluc.	3—3.5 / 4.4	very good less brittle, con-choidal	thin- to thick-tabu-lar, columnar, needle-shaped, py-ramidal, lamellar, radiated, reniform, granular agg.; / orthorhombic	in ore veins, in cracks in sedimentary rocks / — / aragonite, calcite, cf. No. 57, 145, 234	BARYTES Ba[SO$_4$] (Heavy Spar) / Baia Sprie (Felsöbánya), Romania

No.	Colour / Streak	Lustre / Transparency	Hardness / Specific Gravity	Cleavage Fracture & o. Phys. Props.	Common Form, Aggregates / Crystalline Syst.	Occurrence Assoc. Minerals / Similar Minerals	Name & Chem. Formula / Origin of Specimen
145	colourless, white, yellow, red, grey, blue, brown / white	vitreous, pearly, greasy / transpar., transluc.	3—3.5 / 4.4	very good less brittle, conchoidal	tabular, columnar, lamellar crystals, also massive, granular / orthorhombic	very common in ore veins / — / cf. No. 57, 144, 234	**BARYTES** $Ba[SO_4]$ (Heavy Spar) / Příbram, Czech Republic
146	white, yellow, orange, brown, greenish, grey / white	adamantine, greasy / transluc.	3.5 / 7.1	good brittle, conchoidal	columnar, thick-tabular, barrel-shaped, needle-shaped; botryoidal, reniform agg.; earthy, crusty / hexagonal	in lead & manganese ore deps. / arsenic ores, limonite wad, psilomelane, quartz / pyromorphite, cf. No. 174	**MIMETESITE** $Pb_5[Cl(AsO_4)_3]$ (Mimetite) / Johanngeorgenstadt, Ore Mountains, Germany
147	yellow, orange-yellow, brownish / white	adamantine, greasy / transluc.	3.5—4 / 7—7.2	— brittle	botryoidal, reniform coatings; compact, globular agg. / hexagonal	arsenical pyromorphite of Nussière / — / —	Variety of pyromorphite **NUSSIERITE** $Pb_5Cl(PO_4)_3 + As$ / Beaujeu, Dep. Rhône, France
148	yellow, ochre-yellow, brown / straw-yellow	silky, resinous / transluc.	3—4 / 2.3—2.8	— brittle	acicular, capillary crystals; fibrous, radial agg.; reniform, globular, compact, earthy / hexagonal	in iron ore veins / haematite, siderite, limonite / different ochres	**KAKOXEN** (Cacoxenite) $Fe_4[(OH) PO_4]_3 . 12H_2O$ / Hrbek, Czech Republic
149	yellow, green-yellow / light yellow	dull / transluc., opaque	4 / 4.4—4.5	very good —	tabular, lamellar crystals; flabelliform agg.; powdery, earthy, reniform, botryoidal coatings / monoclinic	impregnation in sandstones & limestones, secondary uranium mineral / — / autunite	**CARNOTITE** $(K,Na,Ca,Pb)_2[(UO_2)_2 V_2O_8] . 3H_2O$ / Sabugal, Portugal
150	yellow, greenish-yellow to brown / light yellow	vitreous, pearly, dull / transluc.	3—4 / 4.6	very good —	small pyramidal crystals; mostly compact, earthy, crusty / orthorhombic	secondary uranium mineral / curite & torbernite / —	**SODDITE** $(UO_2)_{16}[(OH)_{20} Si_6O_{17}] . 8H_2O$ / Shinkolobwe, Katanga (now Shaba), Congo
151	white, yellow, reddish, brown / white	vitreous, pearly / transpar., transluc.	3.5—4 / 3	very good brittle, easily friable	rhombohedral crystals; coarsely to finely granular, spathic, massive / trigonal	in ore veins, metasomatic from limestone / — / cf. No. 59	**DOLOMITE** $CaMg[CO_3]_2$ / Banská Štiavnica, Slovakia
152	white, yellow, light brown, brown / white	vitreous, pearly / transluc.	4 / 3.4	good brittle	flat, lentiform, rhombohedral crystals; also massive, spathic, granular / trigonal	mixed crystals between magnesite & siderite, in siderite ore deps. / — / siderite, magnesite, ankerite	**MESITITE** $(Fe,Mg)CO_3$ (Mesitine Spar) / Traversella, Piedmont, Italy

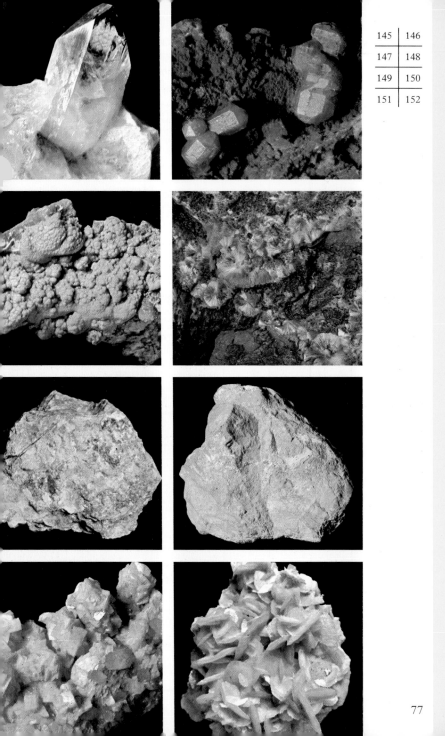

145	146
147	148
149	150
151	152

77

No.	Colour / Streak	Lustre / Transparency	Hardness / Specific Gravity	Cleavage Fracture & o. Phys. Props.	Common Form, Aggregates / Crystalline Syst.	Occurrence / Assoc. Minerals / Similar Minerals	Name & Chem. Formula / Origin of Specimen
153	white, yellow, grey, greenish / white	vitreous / transpar., transluc.	4 / 3.7	very good / brittle	small prismatic crystals in druses; granular, tubular agg.; spathic, massive / monoclinic	in ore veins / barytes, galena, fluorite, quartz / —	**BARYTO-CALCITE** $BaCa[CO_3]_2$ / Alston Moor, Westmorland, England
154	whitish, yellow, yellow-brown, brown-red / yellowish, brownish	dull / opaque	5.5−6 / 4.1−5.8	− / −	earthy crusts, powdery, compact masses, coatings, encrustations / cubic	weathering product of antimonite & o. antimony ores / — / other ochres	**ROMEITE** $(Ca,NaH)\,Sb_2O_6$ (O,OH,F) (Antimony Ochre) / St. Marcel, Piedmont, Italy
155	honey-yellow, ochre-yellow / white	greasy, resinous / transluc.., opaque	5.5−6 / 1.9−2.5	− / conchoidal, brittle	solid masses, veins, nodular / amorphous	opal displaying annual ring marking	**WOOD OPAL** $SiO_2 \cdot nH_2O$ / Clover Creek, Lincoln Co., Idaho, USA
156	yellow, red-orange, brown-yellow, orange-yellow	ada-mantine, dull / transluc.	4−5 / 7.2	good / −	columnar, needle-shaped crystals; mostly compact, massive, granular, acicular, compact / orthorhombic	as alteration product of uranium ores & o. uranium minerals / — / —	**CURITE** $3PbO \cdot 8UO_3 \cdot 4H_2O$ / Shinkolobwe, Katanga (now Shaba), Congo
157	white, yellow, brown, greenish, reddish / white	ada-mantine, greasy / transpar., transluc.	4.5−5 / 5.9−6.1	clear / brittle, con-choidal	pseudooctahedral, pyramidal, tabular, grown up & em-bedded crystals; compact, granular, crusty, as impre-gnation / tetragonal	in pegmatites, in tin deps., in meta-somatic limestone & dolomite, in lead veins / wolframite, molyb-denite, quartz & o. / anglesite, cerussite	**SCHEELITE** $Ca[WO]_4$ (Calcium Tung-state) / Obří důl, Giant Mountains, Czech Republic
158	colourless, white, yellow, greenish, violet, red / white	vitreous, greasy / transpar., transluc.	5 / 3.1	clear / con-choidal, brittle	hexangular, tabular, short- to long-columnar, many-planed crystals; compact, reniform, botryoidal, nodular, globular, massive, radial, granular / hexagonal	as constituent in magmatic rocks, in cracks, in crystal-line schists, in pegmatic-pneu-matolytic veins, in sedimentary deps. / — / beryl, quartz, nepheline, felspars, cf. No. 82, 214, 281	**APATITE** $Ca_5[F(PO_4)_3]$ / Durango, Mexico
159	whitish, yellowish, greenish / white	greasy / transluc.	4−4.5 / 2.8−3.1	− / con-choidal	radial, fibrous, nodular, globular, botryoidal agg.; coatings, crusty, earthy / hexagonal	in cracks in weath-ered basalt rocks / chalcedony	**STAFFELITE** $Ca_5[F(PO_4, CO_3OH)_3]$ (Francolite) / Staffel/Lahn, Germany
160	white, yellowish, greenish, greyish / white	dull / opaque	4.5 / 2.5	− / brittle	semi-globular agg., reniform crusts / orthorhombic	in cracks & cavities of sedimentary rocks & sedi-mentary iron ores / wavellite / —	**BARRAN-DITE** $(Al,Fe)PO_4 \cdot 2H_2O$ (Aluminiferous Strengite) / Zbirov, Czech Republic

No.	Colour / Streak	Lustre / Transparency	Hardness / Specific Gravity	Cleavage Fracture & o. Phys. Props.	Common Form, Aggregates / Crystalline Syst.	Occurrence Assoc. Minerals / Similar Minerals	Name & Chem. Formula / Origin of Specimen
161	colourless, white, yellow, brownish / white	vitreous transpar., transluc.	5.5—7 / 2.2	— / conchoidal, brittle	subvitreous, amorphous, agglomerated grains of sand, compact / amorphous	natural silica glass melted in volcanoes & thunderbolts (fulgurite), in meteorite craters / — / —	**LECHATE-LIERITE** SiO_2 / Lybian Desert
162	white, yellow, brown, reddish greenish, black / white	vitreous, greasy, adamantine transpar., transluc.	5—5.5 / 3.4—3.6	clear / conchoidal, brittle	columnar, wedge-shaped, tabular, needle-shaped crystals; rarely compact, granular / monoclinic	in alpine cracks, in crystalline schists, in magnesite deps., embedded in syenite & phonolite, as constituent of magmatic rocks / — / axinite, cf. No. 339, 463	**TITANITE** $CaTi[OSiO_4]$ (Sphene) / Tavetsch, Bündner Oberland, Switzerland
163	straw-yellow, yellow-green, yellow-brown / white	silky transluc.	5—5.5 / 2.9	good, clear brittle	fine-fibrous, capillary, fibrous bunches, entangled agg., compact, radiate / orthorhombic	in druses in tin ore deps., in crystalline schists, in quartz / — / —	**CARPHOLITE** $MnAl_2$ $[(OH)_4 Si_2O_6]$ / Horní Slavkov, Czech Republic
164	yellowish, grey, whitish / white	vitreous, pearly transluc., opaque	4.5—7 / 3.5—3.7	very good brittle	tubular, needle-shaped, lamellar agg. / triclinic	cyanite in colourless to yellowish, radial entangled agg. / — / sillimanite	Cyanite variety **RHAETIZITE** $Al_2[OSiO_4]$ (Disthene) / Alto Adige, Italy
165	yellow, white, grey, green / white	vitreous, greasy transpar., transluc., dim	6—7 / 3.2—3.3	good, clear conchoidal	prismatic, thick-tabular, short-columnar crystals; massive, granular, nodular / orthorhombic	constituent in basic rocks, in volcanic ejecta, in metamorphosed limestones / — / —	**FORSTERITE** $Mg_2[SiO_4]$ / Monte Somma, Vesuvius, Italy
166	honey-yellow, brown, green / white	greasy, vitreous transluc., opaque, dim	6—6.5 / 3.1—3.2	poor, indistinct conchoidal	tetrahedral embedded & grown up crystals; globular agg. / cubic	in ore deps., in syenite-pegmatites nepheline, sodalite, garnet, epidote / vesuvianite, hessonite	**HELVITE** $(Mn,Fe,Zn)_8$ $[S_2 (BeSiO_4)_6]$ / Schwarzenberg, Ore Mountains, Germany

No.	Colour / Streak	Lustre / Transparency	Hardness / Specific Gravity	Cleavage Fracture & o. Phys. Props.	Common Form, Aggregates / Crystalline Syst.	Occurrence Assoc. Minerals / Similar Minerals	Name & Chem. Formula / Origin of Specimen
167	yellowish, yellow / white	vitreous, greasy transpar.	7 / 2.6	— / conchoidal	columnar, grown up crystals & druses / trigonal	colour variety of quartz / — / cf. No. 109	**CITRINE** SiO_2 / Rio Grande do Sul, Brazil
168	straw-yellow, yellowish, greenish / white	vitreous transluc.	8 / 3.5	very good conchoidal	parallel-radial, tubular agg. / orthorhombic	tubular topaz in tin ore deps. / wolframite, zinnwaldite, quartz, cassiterite & o. / aragonite, cf. No. 117	Topaz variety **PYCNITE** $Al_2[F_2 SiO_4]$ / Altenberg, Ore Mountains, Germany

161	162
163	164
165	166
167	168

81

No.	Colour / Streak	Lustre / Transparency	Hardness / Specific Gravity	Cleavage Fracture & o. Phys. Props.	Common Form, Aggregates / Crystalline Syst.	Occurrence / Assoc. Minerals / Similar Minerals	Name & Chem. Formula / Origin of Specimen
169	orange, light brown, brownish-black / yellow	greasy / opaque	2.5 / 1.8—2	— / conchoidal	globular, reniform nodules & masses / amorphous	in weathering zones of iron ore deps. / — / diadochite	DELVAUXITE $Fe_2(OH)_3\,PO_4$. 3.5 H_2O / Nučice, Czech Republic
170	orange, brownish / white	dull / transluc.	3 / 2.6—2.7	good / brittle	botryoidal, stalactitic agg. / trigonal	in fissures & cavities in sedimentary limestones / — / —	CALCITE $CaCO_3$ (Calc-spar) / Mořina, Czech Republic
171	yellowish, orange, red, grey, brown, green / white	ada-mantine, greasy / transluc.	3 / 7.9—8.3	indistinct / brittle to soft, con-choidal	pyramidal, short-columnar crystals; bundle-shaped, globular / tetragonal	in tin ore deps. / cassiterite, scheelite, wolframite, quartz & o. / scheelite, cf. No. 323	STOLZITE $Pb[WO_4]$ / Cínovec, Czech Republic
172	orange, yellow, red, grey, greenish / white, light grey	ada-mantine, greasy / transpar., transluc.	3 / 6.5—6.9	clear / brittle to soft, con-choidal	tabular, short-columnar, cube-shaped, pyramidal, grown up crystals; compact, granular, crusty / tetragonal	in oxidation zone of lead ore deps. / sphalerite, siderite, hydrozincite, smithsonite, galena, anglesite, calcite, dolomite / tabular, yellow barytes	WULFENITE $Pb[MoO_4]$ (Yellow Lead Ore) / Mežica, Slovenia
173							WULFENITE $Pb[MoO_4]$ (Yellow Lead Ore) / Los Lamentos, Mexico
174	orange, yellow, brown, whitish, grey, greenish / white	ada-mantine, greasy / transluc.	3.5—4 / 7.1	good / brittle, uneven	columnar, ventri-cular, barrel-shaped, needle-shaped, thick-tabular crystals; botryoidal, reni-form, earthy, crusty, encrusta-tions, coatings / hexagonal	in lead ore deps. / arsenic ores, galena, cerussite, mimete-site, limo-nite, descloizite & o. / pyromorphite, vanadinite, cf. No. 146	MIMETESITE $Pb_6[Cl\,(AsO_4)_3]$ (Mimetite) / Dry Gill Mine, Cumberland, England
175	orange, yellow, brown, green / yellow	ada-mantine, greasy / transluc.	3.5 / 7.2	good / brittle, con-choidal	barrel-shaped, ventricular, thick-tabular, grown up crystals; in semi-globular agg. / hexagonal	in lead ore deps., cf. No. 327 / — / —	Mimetesite variety KAMPYLITE Pb_5 $[Cl\,(As,P)\,O_4]_3$ (Phosphomime-tite) / Příbram, Czech Republic
						Hardness 7—8	
176	orange, yellowish, red, brownish / white	vitreous to greasy / transpar., transluc.	7—7.5 / 4.2	— / brittle, con-choidal to splintery	icositetrahedral, almost globular crystals; compact, massive / cubic	in granites, pegma-tites, in crystalline schists / — / other garnets, sphalerite, zircon	SPESSAR-TITE $Mn_3Al_2[SiO_4]_3$ (Garnet Family) / Takovaya River, Central Urals, Russia

No.	Colour / Streak	Lustre / Transparency	Hardness / Specific Gravity	Cleavage Fracture & o. Phys. Props.	Common Form, Aggregates / Crystalline Syst.	Occurrence Assoc. Minerals / Similar Minerals	Name & Chem. Formula / Origin of Specimen
177	copper-red, brown to black, weathered crust	metallic / opaque	2.5—3 / 8.5—9	— / very ductile, malleable, sectile, flexible, hackly	cube-shaped, octa-hedral, tubular, tabular crystals; strongly distorted, dendritic, platy, fili-form, mossy, arbo-rescent, ramifying, compact, in clumps, sheets, plates, encrustations / cubic	in basalt & porphy-ritic rocks, in lime-stone veins / cuprite, chalcocite, malachite, azurite, calcite, analcime, limonite, quartz & o.	nat. **COPPER** Cu / Houghton Co., Michigan, USA
178	/ copper-red					—	nat. **COPPER** Cu / Moldova, Banat, Romania
179	reddish, reddish-white, silver-grey / black	metallic / opaque	5 / 8	— / brittle	small, thin-tabular crystals; mostly compact, tubular, finely granular, fibrous / tetragonal	in silver-nickel-cobalt ore veins / niccolite, chloan-thite, bornite, chalcocite / niccolite, rammelsbergite	**MAUCHE-RITE** Ni_3As_2 / Eisleben, Harz, Germany
180	reddish, light copper-red, grey, brownish / brown-black	metallic / opaque	5.5 / 7.7—7.8	— / brittle, con-choidal	mostly compact, disseminated, bo-tryoidal, reniform, granular, massive, knitted / hexagonal	in silver-nickel-cobalt ore veins / chloanthite, bis-muth, silver, arse-nic, rammelsbergite, safflorite, anna-bergite, barytes / maucherite	**NICCOLITE** NiAs (Arsenical Nickel) / Schladming, Styria, Austria

No.	Colour / Streak	Lustre / Transparency	Hardness / Specific Gravity	Cleavage Fracture & o. Phys. Props.	Common Form, Aggregates / Crystalline Syst.	Occurrence Assoc. Minerals / Similar Minerals	Name & Chem. Formula / Origin of Specimen
181	red, reddish-orange / yellow-orange	ada-mantine, greasy / transpar., transluc.	1.5—2 / 3.5—3.6	good soft to brittle, sectile, decom-poses in the light	short- to long-columnar, needle-shaped crystals; in druses; compact, granular, massive, disseminated, as encrustations / monoclinic	in ore veins, in marls, limestone, dolomite, in volca-noes & at hot springs / orpiment, arsenic & lead ores, antimonite / cinnabarite, crocoite	**REALGAR** As_4S_4 / Baia Sprie (Felsőbánya), Romania
182	cherry-red, purple-red / cherry-red, brown-red	ada-mantine / transluc.	1—1.5 / 4.6	very good flexible	capillary, needle-shaped crystals; radial, bunchy, radiate-fibrous agg., disseminated / triclinic	in ore veins / antimonite, ber-thierite, valentinite, quartz / —	**KERMESITE** Sb_2S_2O (Red Antimony, Pyrantimonite) / Bräunsdorf, Germany
183	deep red, orange, light yellow	vitreous / transpar., transluc.	1.5—2 / 2—2.1	very good brittle	short-columnar crystals; granular, compact, botry-oidal, bundle-shaped agg. / monoclinic	in ore veins in weathering zones / — / realgar, cinnabarite	**BOTRYOGEN** MgFe $[OH (SO_4)_2]$. $7H_2O$ / Redington Mine, California, USA
184	scarlet-red, grey to black / scarlet-red	ada-mantine to dull / transpar., transluc., opaque	2—2.5 / 8.1	good splintery, uneven	thin- to thick-tabu-lar, cube-shaped, short-columnar, polymorphous crystals; compact, granular, massive, fibrous, earthy, disseminated / trigonal	in hydrothermal veins, as impregna-tion in sedimentary rocks, at thermal springs / quicksilver, chalco-pyrite, pyrites, galena, carbonates, opal / realgar, rutile, crocoite, proustite, botryogen	**CINNA-BARITE** HgS (Cinnabar) / Tržić, Slovenia

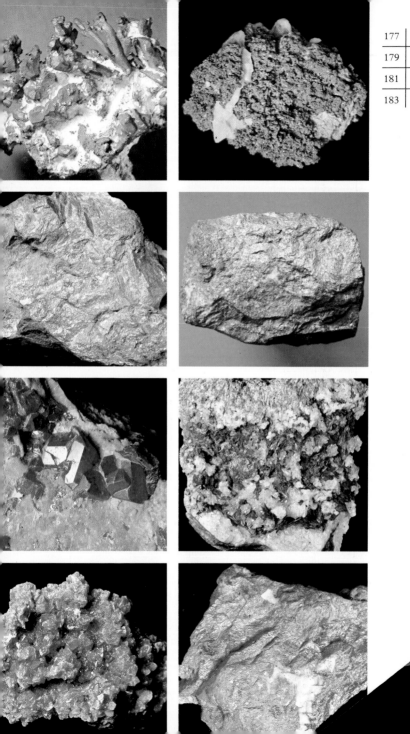

No.	Colour / Streak	Lustre / Transparency	Hardness / Specific Gravity	Cleavage / Fracture & o. / Phys. Props.	Common Form, Aggregates / Crystalline Syst.	Occurrence / Assoc. Minerals / Similar Minerals	Name & Chem. Formula / Origin of Specimen
185	cinnabar-red, lead-grey / brick-red, yellowish-red	ada-mantine / transpar., transluc.	2.5 / 5.5	good / splintery, con-choidal	prismatic, fragile, columnar, rhombo-hedral crystals; compact, massive, dendritic, as coat-ings, encrustations / trigonal	in silver-lead ore veins / silver, argentite, arsenic, chloanthite, galena, pyrites, barytes, fluorspar, pyrargyrite, cinna-barite	PROUSTITE Ag_3AsS_3 (Light Red Silver Ore) / Jáchymov, Czech Republic
186	dark red, reddish-lead-grey, black / dark red, brown-red	ada-mantine, metallic, dull / transluc.	2.5 — 3 / 5.8	very good / splintery, con-choidal	prismatic, thick-tabular, fragile, needle-shaped to capillary crystals; compact, granular, disseminated / trigonal	in silver-lead ore veins / proustite / proustite, cuprite, cinnabarite	PYRAR-GYRITE Ag_3SbS_3 (Dark Red Silver Ore) / St. Andreasberg, Harz, Germany
187	brick-red / orange-yellow	greasy, dull / opaque	2 — 3 / 8.9 — 9.2	— / earthy, uneven	only compact, fibrous, finely granular, earthy, disseminated, en-crustations / tetragonal	weathering product of galena, cerus-site & o. / lead minerals / — / cinnabarite, realgar	MINIUM Pb_3O_4 (Red Oxide of Lead) / Niedermendig, Eifel, Germany
188	red, yellowish, red-orange / yellow, orange-yellow	ada-mantine, greasy / transpar., transluc.	2.5 — 3 / 5.9 — 6	good / soft, uneven	long-columnar to needle-shaped crystals; sometimes hollow showing longitudinal stria-tion; in druses; also compact / monoclinic	in oxidation zone of ore veins / galena, limonite, quartz / realgar, cinnabarite	CROCOITE $Pb[CrO_4]$ (Red Lead Ore) / Dundas, Tasmania, Australia
189	red, red-brown / whitish	vitreous, pearly / transpar., transluc.	2.5 / 2.8 — 3.2	very good / soft to brittle	pseudohexagonal thin- to thick-tabu-lar, embedded crystals / monoclinic	product of decom-position of biotite, as insets in basaltic rocks & tuffs / — / —	Biotite variety RUBELLAN $K(Mg,Fe,Mn)_3$ $[(OH,F)_2 Al\ Si_3 O_{10}]$ / Laacher See, Eifel, Germany

No.	Colour / Streak	Lustre / Transparency	Hardness / Specific Gravity	Cleavage / Fracture & o. / Phys. Props.	Common Form, Aggregates / Crystalline Syst.	Occurrence / Assoc. Minerals / Similar Minerals	Name & Chem. Formula / Origin of Specimen
190	reddish, violet, bluish, white, grey, colourless / white	vitreous, pearly / transpar., transluc.	3 — 3.5 / 2.8 — 3	very good / brittle, distinct cleavage cracks	tabular, short-columnar, cube-shaped crystals; spathic, fibrous, compact, botryoid-al, granular, massive / orthorhombic	in ore veins, in salt deps. / halite, gypsum, dolomite / cryolite, gypsum, barytes, calcite, cf. No. 58	ANHYDRITE $Ca[SO_4]$ / Hallein near Salzburg, Austria
191	red-yellow, brown, green, black, colourless / white, yellow, brown	ada-mantine, greasy, almost metallic / transpar. to opaque	3.5 — 4 / 3.9 — 4.2	very good, rhombo-dodeca-hedron / brittle	tetrahedral, dode-cahedral, cubic crystals; coarse to fine-grained, mas-sive, compact, fibrous / cubic	in ore veins / galena, chalco-pyrite & o. / — / cf. No. 142, 315, 445	SPHALERITE ZnS (Zinc Blende) / Cumberland, England
	e-red, erry- w	vitreous / transluc.	3.5 — 4 / 3.3 — 3.6	very good, rhombo-hedron / brittle	lentiform, rhombo-hedral crystals; often recurved, saddle-shaped agg., compact, granular, spathic, massive, botryoidal / trigonal	in ore veins, in iron ore deps., in lime-stones & argillace-ous slates / haematite, limonite / rhodonite, quartz	RHODO-CHROSITE $MnCO_3$ (Manganese Spar) / Săcărâmb, Romania

Table 2

No.	Colour / Streak	Lustre / Transparency	Hardness / Specific Gravity	Cleavage / Fracture & o. / Phys. Props.	Common Form, Aggregates / Crystalline Syst.	Occurrence / Assoc. Minerals / Similar Minerals	Name & Chem. Formula / Origin of Specimen
193	rose-red, pink, reddish, yellowish, white / white	vitreous, pearly / transluc.	3.5−4 / 2.7	good / brittle	rhombohedral, lentiform, recurved crystals; globular, botryoidal agg.; compact / trigonal	manganiferous mixed crystals of calcite family, in ore veins / − / −	**MANGAN-CALCITE** $CaCO_3 \pm MnCO_3$ / Banská Štiavnica, Slovakia
194	brick-red, light pink / white	pearly, vitreous, dull / transluc.	3.5−4 / 2.1−2.2	very good / brittle	tabular crystals in druses; rose-shaped agg. / monoclinic	in vesicles & cracks in basalt rocks, in ore deps. / calcite, quartz, other zeolites / cf. No. 71	**HEULANDITE** $Ca[Al_2Si_7O_{18}] \cdot 6H_2O$ (Stellerite, Zeolite Family) / Kilpatrick near Dumbarton, Scotland
195	reddish-lead-grey, red-brown, cochineal-red / brownish-red	ada-mantine, sub-metallic / opaque	4 / 6.1	clear / brittle, uneven	octahedral, cubic, dodecahedral crystals; compact, massive, granular, earthy, dissemi-nated / cubic	as oxidation pro-duct of copper ores / copper, malachite, azurite, limonite / cinnabarite, proustite, haematite	**CUPRITE** Cu_2O (Red Oxides of Copper) / Bisbee, Arizona, USA
196	luminous-red, cochineal-red / brownish-red	ada-mantine / transluc.	4 / 6.1	good / −	fibrous, capillary, acicular crystals; bunchy, interlacing / cubic	needle-shaped cuprite / − / −	Cuprite variety **CHALCO-TRICHITE** Cu_2O (Copper Protoxide) / Huel Basset, Cornwall, England

No.	Colour / Streak	Lustre / Transparency	Hardness / Specific Gravity	Cleavage / Fracture & o. / Phys. Props.	Common Form, Aggregates / Crystalline Syst.	Occurrence / Assoc. Minerals / Similar Minerals	Name & Chem. Formula / Origin of Specimen
197	dark red, reddish-yellow, red-brown / orange-yellow, brownish-yellow	ada-mantine, sub-metallic / transluc., opaque	4.5−5 / 5.4−5.7	very good / brittle	mostly granular, compact, spathic, lamellar / hexagonal	in metamorphic limestones / franklinite, calcite, willemite, rhodonite, garnet / rutile, cinnabarite	**ZINCITE** ZnO (Red Oxide of Zinc) / Franklin, New Jersey, USA
198	yellow, red-brown, brown to black / yellow, brownish-yellow	metallic, ada-mantine to dull / transpar., transluc.	5.5−6 / 3.9−4.2	poor / subcon-choidal	flat, thin-tabular, pyramidal, only grown up crystals / orthorhombic	in alpine cracks / quartz, anatase, adular, titanite & o. / rutile, ilmenite	**BROOKITE** TiO_2 / Snowdon, North Wales
199	red, pink, white, yellowish / white	vitreous / transpar., transluc.	5−5.5 / 2.2−2.4	very good / brittle	short-columnar, needle-shaped, capillary crystals in druses / orthorhombic	in cavities in igneous rocks / other zeolites, cal-cite, apophyllite & o. / cf. No. 88	**NATROLITE** $Na_2[Al_2Si_3O_{10}] \cdot 2H_2O$ (Zeolite Family) / Ústí nad Labem, Czech Republic
200	flesh-red, rose-red, raspberry-red, reddish-brown / whitish	vitreous, pearly / transluc.	5.5−6.5 / 3.4−3.6	good / uneven	columnar, thick-tabular to needle-shaped crystals; compact, granular, coarse-spathic, massive, often stained black / triclinic	in manganese ore deps., in lead-zinc ore veins / magnetite, haus-mannite & o. / dialogite	**RHODONITE** $CaMn_4[Si_5O_{15}]$ (Manganese Spar, Fowlerite) / Franklin, New Jersey, USA

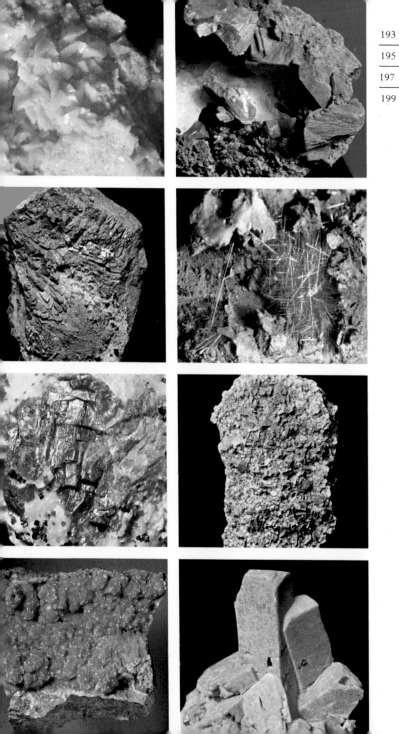

193	194
195	196
197	198
199	200

No.	Colour / Streak	Lustre / Transparency	Hardness / Specific Gravity	Cleavage Fracture & o. / Phys. Props.	Common Form, Aggregates / Crystalline Syst.	Occurrence / Assoc. Minerals / Similar Minerals	Name & Chem. Formula / Origin of Specimen
201	red-brown, grey, black / blood-red, red-brown	sub-metallic, dull / opaque	5—6.5 / 5.2—5.3	— / scaly slacking, fibrous	compact, massive, fibrous, haematitic, reniform, stalactitic, with fibrous fracture / trigonal	in ore veins, in various rocks / cinnabarite, proustite, cuprite, cf. No. 435—437 / —	Haematite variety **RED HAEMATITE** Fe_2O_3 / Blatno, Czech Republic
202	brick-red / white	vitreous / transpar., transluc.	6 / 2.1	— / con-choidal	veins-nodules, fil-lings of cavities, compact, bo-tryoidal, reniform / amorphous	in fissures & cracks in porphyritic trachyte / — / —	Opal variety **FIRE-OPAL** $SiO_2 . nH_2O$ / Zimapan, Mexico
203	yellow, red, brown-red, brownish-black / yellowish-brown, brown-red	ada-mantine, sub-metallic, greasy / transluc., opaque	6—6.5 / 4.2—4.3	good / uneven, con-choidal	thick-columnar, needle-shaped crystals; often heart-shaped & reniform twins; longitudinal stria-tion, compact, granular, tubular, disseminated, de-tached grains / tetragonal	in pegmatites, in alpine cracks / titanite, anatase, brookite, felspar, apatite, quartz, ilmenite, zincite, cassiterite, zircon, tourmaline	**RUTILE** TiO_2 / Alto Adige, Italy
204	reddish, grey-white, white, colourless / white	vitreous, pearly / transpar., transluc.	6 / 2.7	very good / brittle	tabular, short-columnar grown up & embedded crystals; massive, granular / triclinic	rock constituent in diff. rocks, in ore deps. / — / other felspars, cf. No. 102	**ANORTHITE** $Ca[Al_2Si_2O_8]$ (Felspar Family) / Toal della Foja, Trentino, Italy
205	reddish, brownish, grey, white, yellowish, colourless / white	vitreous, pearly / transluc., transpar.	6—6.5 / 2.5	very good / brittle, uneven	short-columnar, bench-shaped, in thick plates em-bedded & grown up crystals; often twinned; spathic masses, finely granular, massive / monoclinic	main constituent of many rocks, in granite druses, in pegmatites, in alpine cracks & crystalline schists, in ore veins / other felspars, spodumene cf. No. 346	**ORTHO-CLASE** $K[AlSi_3O_8]$ (Felspar Family) / Strzegom, Silesia, Poland
							Hardness 6 — 7.5
206	reddish, brown, grey, white, green / white	vitreous, silky / transluc.	6—7 / 3.2	very good / brittle	columnar, needle-shaped crystals; fine-fibrous, wisp-like agg.; radial, tubular, compact / orthorhombic	in crystalline schists, granulites, eclogites, in con-tact-metamorphic rocks / — / cyanite	**SILLI-MANITE** $Al_2[OSiO_4]$ (Fibrolite) / Goyamin Pool, Australia
207	red, reddish, brown / white, reddish	vitreous / opaque	7 / 2.6	— / brittle, con-choidal	columnar, grown up crystals with druse-shaped hae-matite coating / trigonal	quartz coloured with iron oxide / — / —	Quartz variety **EISENKIESEL** SiO_2 (Ferruginous Quartz) / Cínovec, Czech Republic
208	red, pink, violet / white	vitreous, greasy / transpar., transluc.	7—7.5 / 3—3.2	— / uneven	columnar to needle-shaped crystals; radiating agg.; tubular, compact / trigonal	in pegmatites, granites / lepidolite, indigo-lite, quartz & o. cf. No. 220	**RUBELLITE** Na,Li,Mg_3Al_6 $[(OH)_3(BO_3)_3$ $Si_6O_{18}]$ / Rožná, Czech Republic

No.	Colour / Streak	Lustre / Transparency	Hardness / Specific Gravity	Cleavage / Fracture & o. / Phys. Props.	Common Form, Aggregates / Crystalline Syst.	Occurrence / Assoc. Minerals / Similar Minerals	Name & Chem. Formula / Origin of Specimen
209	blue, violet, greenish, black / colourless, changing immediately to indigo blue	vitreous, pearly, sub-metallic / transluc., opaque	1.5 — 2 / 2.6 — 2.7	very good / soft, thin laminae, flexible	long-columnar, needle-shaped, tabular, chip-shaped crystals; compact, reniform, globular, radial, earthy, powdery / monoclinic	in clays, peat, in fossil shells / limonite / lazulite	**VIVIANITE** $Fe_3[PO_4]_2 \cdot 8H_2O$ (Blue Iron Earth) / Bodenmais, Bavarian Forest, Germany
210	reddish, pink, violet, grey / reddish, rose-red	ada-mantine, pearly / transluc.	1.5 — 2.5 / 3.0	very good / soft	needle-shaped, scaly, lamellar crystals; in bunchy, stellate clusters; earthy encrusta-tions / monoclinic	decomposition product of cobalt ores / pharmacolite & o. / —	**ERYTHRITE** $Co_3(AsO_4)_2 \cdot 8H_2O$ (Cobalt Bloom) / Schneeberg, Ore Mountains, Germany
							Hardness 2.5 — 4
211	violet, pale red, reddish-grey, greenish, white / whitish, light pink	pearly / transpar., transluc.	2.5 — 4 / 2.8 — 2.9	very good / soft, laminae elastic, flexible	lamellar, pseudo-hexagonal crystals; scaly, compact, finely granular / monoclinic	in pegmatites & granites in tin ore deps. / rubellite, topaz, beryllium, spodumene / zinnwaldite	**LEPIDOLITE** $KLi_2Al[(OH,F)_2Si_4O_{10}]$ (Lithium Mica) / Maharitra, Madagascar
212	violet, yellow, green, blue, pink, colourless / white	vitreous / transpar., transluc.	4 / 3.0 — 3.2	perfect / con-choidal, brittle	cubic, octahedral crystals; coarsely to finely granular, spathic, massive, compact, striated / cubic	in ore veins, in rock fissures / — / apatite, amethyst, cf. No. 73, 233	**FLUORITE** CaF_2 (Fluor Spar) / Alston Moor, Westmorland, England
							Hardness 4 — 7
213	colourless, white, reddish, violet, greenish / white	vitreous, pearly / transpar., transluc.	4 — 5 / 2.3 — 2.4	very good / brittle, uneven	short-columnar, tabular, pyramidal crystals; compact, granular, lamellar, massive / tetragonal	in druses in cavities in basaltic rocks, in ore veins, in magnetite ore deps. / analcime, natrolite, calcite	**APOPHYL-LITE** $KCa_4[F(Si_4O_{10})_2] \cdot 8H_2O$ / St. Andreas-berg, Harz, Germany
214	colourless, white, yellow, violet, green / white	vitreous, greasy / transpar., transluc.	5 / 3.1	clear / brittle, con-choidal	hexagonal, short- to long-columnar crystals; compact, massive, granular / hexagonal	as constituent in magmatic rocks, in ore veins / — / cf. No. 158, 281	**APATITE** $Ca_5[F(PO_4)_3]$ / Horni Slavkov, Czech Republic
215	dark violet, blue-violet / white, grey	vitreous, greasy / transluc., opaque	5 — 6 / 3.2	good / —	foliaceous, granu-lar-radiating, fine-fibrous masses / monoclinic	violet or blue manganiferous variation of dio-pside / — / —	Diopside variety **VIOLANE** $CaMg[Si_2O_6] \pm Mn,Fe$ / St. Marcel, Piedmont, Italy
216	red-violet, blue, greenish / white	silky / transluc.	7 / 3.4	clear / —	in compact pieces, thin-columnar, needle-shaped, parallel-fibrous / orthorhombic	in pegmatite veins, in gneiss, in granulites / cyanite, cordierite / cyanite	**DUMOR-TIERITE** $(Al,Fe)_7[O_3BO_3(SiO_4)_3]$ / Yuma, Arizona, USA

No.	Colour<hr>Streak	Lustre<hr>Transparency	Hardness<hr>Specific Gravity	Cleavage Fracture & o.<hr>Phys. Props.	Common Form, Aggregates<hr>Crystalline Syst.	Occurrence Assoc. Minerals<hr>Similar Minerals	Name & Chem. Formula<hr>Origin of Specimen
217	violet<hr>white	vitreous, greasy<hr>transpar., transluc.	$\frac{7}{2,6}$	—<hr>brittle, conchoidal	hexagonal, columnar, grown up crystals in druses<hr>trigonal	colour variety of quartz, in druses of volcanic effusive rocks, in ore veins<hr>—<hr>apatite, fluorite	AMETHYST SiO_2 Matto Perro, Uruguay<hr>AMETHYST SiO_2 Banská Štiavnica, Slovakia
218							
219	red, brown, violet to black<hr>white	vitreous, greasy<hr>transpar., opaque	$\frac{7}{4.1-4.3}$	—<hr>brittle, splintery, uneven	rhombododeca-hedral crystals; compact, granular, massive, dissemi-nated<hr>cubic	insets in gneiss & mica schists, in placers<hr>—<hr>cf. No. 526	ALMANDINE $Fe_3Al_2[SiO_4]_3$ (Garnet Family) Bodö, Nordland, Norway
220	violet, red, pink<hr>white	vitreous, greasy<hr>transpar., transluc.	$\frac{7-7.5}{3-3.2}$	—<hr>uneven	columnar to needle-shaped crystals; tubular, radial agg.<hr>trigonal	in pegmatites & granites<hr>—<hr>cf. No. 208	RUBELLITE Na,Li,Mg_3,Al_6 $[(OH)_3 (BO_3)_3$ $Si_6O_{18}]$ (Tourmaline Family) Pala Chief, Calif., USA

No.	Colour<hr>Streak	Lustre<hr>Transparency	Hardness<hr>Specific Gravity	Cleavage Fracture & o.<hr>Phys. Props.	Common Form, Aggregates<hr>Crystalline Syst.	Occurrence Assoc. Minerals<hr>Similar Minerals	Name & Chem. Formula<hr>Origin of Specimen
221	blue, bluish-black<hr>bluish-black	metallic, greasy<hr>opaque	$\frac{1.5-2}{4.6}$	very good soft, flexible	thin-tabular, foliaceous crystals; mostly compact, finely foliaceous, massive, nodular, platy, powdery<hr>hexagonal	weathering product in copper ore veins, as volcanic subli-mation product<hr>chalcopyrite, chalcosine<hr>bornite	COVELLITE CuS (Indigo Copper) Alghero, Sardinia
222	grey, blue & tarnished<hr>brownish-black	metallic<hr>opaque	$\frac{2-3}{3.9-4.3}$	good<hr>brittle	needle-shaped, fibrous, capillary crystals; fibrous, tubular, massive agg.<hr>orthorhombic	in silver ore veins<hr>antimonite, arseno-pyrite, quartz<hr>antimonite	BERTHIE-RITE $FeS . Sb_2S_3$ Herja (Chiuz-baia, Kisbánya), Romania

No.	Colour<hr>Streak	Lustre<hr>Transparency	Hardness<hr>Specific Gravity	Cleavage Fracture & o.<hr>Phys. Props.	Common Form, Aggregates<hr>Crystalline Syst.	Occurrence Assoc. Minerals<hr>Similar Minerals	Name & Chem. Formula<hr>Origin of Specimen
223	sky-blue, azure<hr>blue	silky, velvety<hr>transluc.	$\frac{1}{2.7}$	good<hr>—	fine-fibrous, capillary crystals; bunchy, globular agg.; velvety crusts<hr>orthorhombic	weathering product in ore veins<hr>malachite, azurite, limonite & o.<hr>aurichalcite	CYANO-TRICHITE Cu_4Al_2 $[(OH)_{12}SO_4]$. $2H_2O$ (Lettsomite) Moldova, Banat, Romania
224	colourless, yellow, red, blue, violet<hr>white	vitreous<hr>transpar., transluc.	$\frac{2}{2.1-2.2}$	perfect, cube<hr>soft to brittle, water-soluble	cube-shaped crystals; coarsely to finely granular, compact, spathic, fibrous, massive<hr>cubic	isolated deps.<hr>anhydrite, gypsum & o.<hr>cf. No. 33	ROCK SALT $NaCl$ (Halite) Hallstatt, Salz-kammergut, Austria

No.	Colour / Streak	Lustre / Transparency	Hardness / Specific Gravity	Cleavage Fracture & o. / Phys. Props.	Common Form, Aggregates / Crystalline Syst.	Occurrence Assoc. Minerals / Similar Minerals	Name & Chem. Formula / Origin of Specimen
225	light blue, greenish-blue / bluish, greenish	pearly, silky / transluc.	2 / 3.6	very good / soft	fine needle-shaped, finely foliaceous crystals; fibrous, scaly, granular, compact, massive, as efflorescences / orthorhombic	in oxidation zone of copper-zinc veins / limonite, malachite, smithsonite / chrysocolla, cyanotrichite	**AURI-CHALCITE** $(Zn,Cu)_5$ $[(OH)_3 CO_3]_2$ / Zimapan, Mexico
226	sky-blue / light blue	adamantine, vitreous / transluc.	2.5 / 5.3 – 5.5	very good / brittle to soft	short needle-shaped, tabular, grown up crystals; radial, fibrous, disseminated, crusty, encrustations / monoclinic	in oxidation zone of ore veins / chalcopyrite, galena, malachite, cerussite, barytes, quartz & o. / azurite, lazurite	**LINARITE** PbCu $[(OH)_2 SO_4]$ / Red Gill near Keswick, Cumberland, England
227	blue / white	vitreous / transluc.	2.5 / 2.2 – 2.3	indistinct / brittle, conchoidal, water-soluble	tabular, short-columnar crystals; crusty, reniform, fibrous, granular, scaly, massive, as efflorescences / triclinic	weathering product in oxidation zone of copper ores / — / liroconite, kröhnkite	**CHAL-CANTHITE** $Cu[SO_4] . 5H_2O$ (Copper Vitriol) / Rio Tinto, Spain
228	blue-green, blue-grey / bluish-green	vitreous, greasy / transluc.	2 – 2.5 / 2.9 – 3	indistinct / brittle to soft	flat, lentiform, short-columnar crystals; in druses; compact, disseminated / monoclinic	as weathering product in ore veins / malachite, limonite, quartz & o. / chalcanthite	**LIROCONITE** $Cu_2Al[(OH)_4 AsO_4] . 4H_2O$ / Redruth, Cornwall, England
229	blue, greenish-blue / white	vitreous transpar., transluc.	2.5 – 3 / 2	very good / water-soluble	tabular, long-columnar crystals; granular, fibrous, platy, crusts, fibrous agg. / monoclinic	weathering product in oxidation zone of copper ores / — / chalcanthite	**KRÖHNKITE** $Na_2[CuSO_4]_2 . 2H_2O$ / Chuquicamata, Chile
230	sky-blue, blackish-blue / blue	vitreous to dull / transluc., opaque	3.5 / 3.7 – 3.8	good / brittle, uneven	short-columnar, thick-tabular, needle-shaped crystals; compact, reniform, radial, massive, earthy, botryoidal, encrustations, coatings / monoclinic	in oxidation zone of copper ores, impregnation in sedimentary rocks / malachite, limonite, cuprite, chalcopyrite & o. / linarite, lazurite	**AZURITE** $Cu_3[OH CO_3]_2$ (Blue Carbonate of Copper) / Tsumeb, South-West Africa
231							**AZURITE** $Cu_3[OH CO_3]_2$ (Blue Carbonate of Copper) / Chessy near Lyon, France
232	colourless, white, blue, reddish, yellowish / white	vitreous, pearly / transpar., transluc.	3 – 3.5 / 3.9 – 4	good / brittle, uneven, fibrous	thick-tabular, short-columnar crystals; granular, spathic, massive, tubular, fibrous, nodular, compact / orthorhombic	in fissures, in rock salt deps., in ore veins; as exhalation product, in cracks in limestones & dolomites / aragonite, calcite, sulphur, gypsum / barytes, cryolite, gypsum, calcite	**COELESTINE** $Sr[SO_4]$ / Spania Dolina, Slovakia

No.	Colour / Streak	Lustre / Transparency	Hardness / Specific Gravity	Cleavage Fracture & o. Phys. Props.	Common Form, Aggregates / Crystalline Syst.	Occurrence Assoc. Minerals / Similar Minerals	Name & Chem. Formula / Origin of Specimen
233	colourless, blue, pink, yellow, green, violet / white	vitreous transpar., transluc.	$\frac{4}{3-3.2}$	perfect, octahedron / brittle, conchoidal	cubic, octahedral crystals; granular, spathic, massive, compact / cubic	in ore veins, in rock cracks / — / barytes, apatite, amethyst, cf. No. 73, 212	FLUORITE CaF_2 (Fluor Spar) / Weisseck, Salzburg, Austria
234	colourless, white, yellow, blue, grey, red, brown / white	vitreous, pearly, greasy transluc., transpar.	$\frac{3-3.5}{4.4}$	very good less brittle, conchoidal	thin- to thick-tabular, columnar, lamellar crystals; massive, reniform, granular / orthorhombic	in ore veins, in cracks in sedimentary rocks / — / aragonite, calcite, coelestine, anhydrite, cf. No. 57, 144, 145	BARYTES $Ba[SO_4]$ (Heavy Spar) / Dědova Hora, Czech Republic
235	dark blue to blue-black, yellow, red / white, yellowish	adamantine, greasy, metallic transluc., opaque	$\frac{5.5-6}{3.8-3.9}$	very good brittle	pointed-pyramidal, columnar, thick-tabular, only grown-up crystals / tetragonal	in alpine fissures, in cracks in crystalline schists / rutile, titanite, albite, quartz, chlorite, epidote / —	ANATASE TiO_2 / Sonnblick, Salzburg, Austria
236	colourless, white, blue, grey, greenish-grey, yellowish / white	vitreous, pearly transpar., transluc.	in longitudinal direction 4, diagon. $\frac{6-7}{3.6-3.7}$	very good brittle	wide-tubular, lamellar, flat-tabular crystals; diagonal striation, compact, radiating-lamellar to acicular masses / triclinic	in crystalline schists, granulites, in pegmatites / staurolite, andalusite, almandine, corundum, cf. No. 492	KYANITE $Al_2[O\,SiO_4]$ (Disthene) / Pizzo Forno, Tessin, Switzerland
237	colourless, white, blue, grey, greenish / white	vitreous, greasy transpar., transluc.	$\frac{5-6}{2.3-2.5}$	good conchoidal	rarely isometric crystals; mostly compact, granular / cubic	constituent in igneous rocks / — / leucite, analcime, hauyne, nosean, lazurite, cf. No. 93	SODALITE Na_8 $[Cl_2\,(AlSiO_4)_6]$ / Timmins, Ontario, Canada
238	blue, green-blue, green, red, yellow, grey, white / white, bluish	vitreous, greasy transpar., transluc.	$\frac{5.5-6}{2.4-2.5}$	very good conchoidal	isometric, cubic crystals; compact, granular agg. / cubic	embedded in basaltic rocks; in volcanic ejecta / leucite, nepheline, & o. / sodalite, nosean, lazurite	HAÜYNITE (HAÜYNE) $(Na,Ca)_{8-4}$ $[(SO_4)_2$ $(AlSiO_4)_6]$ / Niedermendig, Eifel, Germany
239	blue, bluish-green, white / white	vitreous transluc., opaque	$\frac{6}{3.1-3.2}$	— splintery, uneven	short-columnar, tabular, pyramidal crystals; mostly compact, massive, granular masses / monoclinic	in carbonate-quartz veins, in argillaceous slates, xenoliths in quartzites, in tin-pegmatite veins / quartz, muscovite & o. / lazurite, turquoise	LAZULITE $(Mg,Fe)Al_2$ $[OH\,PO_4]_2$ (Blue Spar) / Werfen, Salzburg, Austria
240							LAZULITE $(Mg,Fe)Al_2$ $[OH\,PO_4]_2$ (Blue Spar) / Sticklberg, Austria

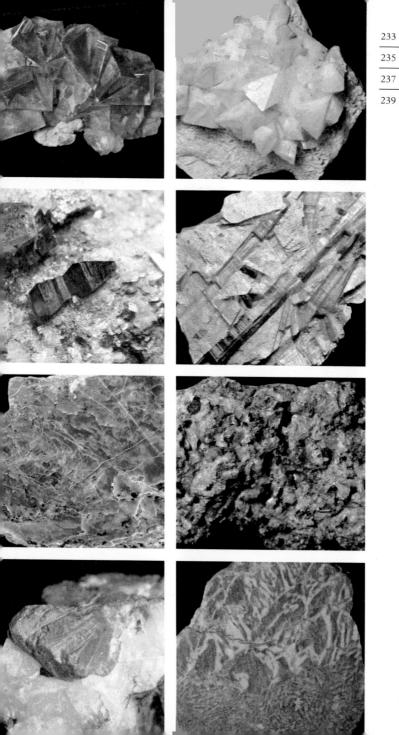

No.	Colour Streak	Lustre Transparency	Hardness Specific Gravity	Cleavage Fracture & o. Phys. Props.	Common Form, Aggregates Crystalline Syst.	Occurrence Assoc. Minerals Similar Minerals	Name & Chem. Formula Origin of Specimen
241	blue, blue-grey / white	vitreous opaque, dull	6.5 / 3.6	— con-choidal	idiomorphic, pyramidal, embedded crystals; no agg. / trigonal	embedded in granular natrolite / neptunite, anatase / —	**BENITOITE** $BaTi[Si_3O_9]$ / San Benito County, California, USA
242	blue / white	vitreous, greasy transluc.	6.5 / 3.2 — 3.4	— splintery, uneven	short-columnar, pseudocubic, di-pyramidal crystals; fine-grained to massive, compact / tetragonal	blue, cupreous vesuvianite, in metamorphic rocks / thulite / —	Vesuvianite variety **CYPRINE** $Ca_{10}(Mg,Fe_2) Al_4 [(OH,F)_4 (SiO_4)_5 (SiO_7)_2] \pm Cu$ / Souland, Norway
243	azure-blue, dark blue / light blue, greenish	pearly transluc.	3.5 / 4.8 — 5.1	very good —	cube-shaped, pseudocubic crystals / tetragonal	as weathering product in copper deps. / malachite, azurite, cuprite, atacamite / —	**BOLEITE** $(26PbCl_2 . 3AgCl) . 24Cu(OH)_2 . 6AgCl . 3H_2O$ / Boleo, Mexico
244	blue, greenish-blue, grey, violet / white	vitreous, greasy transpar., transluc.	7 — 7.5 / 2.6	good con-choidal, strongly pleochroic	short-columnar, platy crystals; mostly compact, granular, embedded / orthorhombic	in pegmatites, in metamorphic rocks / — / nepheline, quartz	**CORDIERITE** $Mg_2[Al_4Si_5O_{18}]$ (Dichroite, Iolite) / Dolní Bory, Czech Republic
245	blue / white	vitreous, greasy, dull opaque, transluc.	7 — 7.5 / 3 — 3.2	— fissile, uneven, splintery	long-columnar to needle-shaped crystals; longi-tudinally striated; tubular to fibrous agg.; massive / trigonal	in pegmatites, in granites / lepidolite, rubellite / —	Tourmaline variety **INDIGOLITE** $(Na,Ca) (Mg,Al,Li)_3 (Al,Fe,Mg)_6 [(OH)_3 (BO_3)_3 Si_6O_{18}]$ / Rožná, Czech Republic
246	blue, red, yellow, brown, black / white	vitreous transpar., transluc.	8 / 3.5 — 4.1	indistinct con-choidal	octahedral, embedded crystals; granular / cubic	in metamorphic limestones & dolo-mites, in basalts / — / corundum, zircon, garnet, cf. No. 360	**SPINEL** Al_2MgO_4 / Åker, Södermanland, Sweden

GREEN MINERALS OF NON-METALLIC LUSTRE   Hardness 1 — 2

No.	Colour Streak	Lustre Transparency	Hardness Specific Gravity	Cleavage Fracture & o. Phys. Props.	Common Form, Aggregates Crystalline Syst.	Occurrence Assoc. Minerals Similar Minerals	Name & Chem. Formula Origin of Specimen
247	green, brownish-green, black-green / green, blue-green	dull opaque	1 — 2 / 2.8 — 2.9	—	massive, compact, earthy, powdery, loose / monoclinic	in vesicles in basaltic tuffs, in sedimentary rocks, in marls, limestone / calcite, zeolite / glauconite	**SELADONITE** $K(Fe,Mg) [(OH)_2AlSi_3O_{10}]$ (Green Earth) / Kadaň, Czech Republic
248	blackish-green, bluish-green / white	vitreous, greasy, pearly transluc., opaque	2 / 2.5 — 2.7	very good soft, inelastic, flexible	thick-tabular, columnar crystals; often distorted; flakes; lamellar agg.; as dusty crusts, earthy, powdery / monoclinic	constituent in crys-talline schists; in alpine cracks, as weathering product / — / green mica	**CLINO-CHLORE** $(Mg,Al)_3 [(OH)_2 AlSi_3O_{10}]Mg_3 (OH)_6$ (Chlorite Family) / Zillertal, Tyrol, Austria

No.	Colour / Streak	Lustre / Transparency	Hardness / Specific Gravity	Cleavage Fracture & o. / Phys. Props.	Common Form, Aggregates / Crystalline Syst.	Occurrence / Assoc. Minerals / Similar Minerals	Name & Chem. Formula / Origin of Specimen
249	green, greenish-white / pale green	dull transluc., opaque	1—2.5 / 3—3.1	good / soft	needle-shaped, capillary, lamellar crystals; mostly earthy, powdery, reniform, scaly, encrustations & coatings, efflorescences / monoclinic	as weathering product in nickel-cobalt ores / erythrite & o. / —	ANNABERGITE $Ni_3(AsO_4)_2 . 8H_2O$ (Nickel Bloom) / Jáchymov, Czech Republic
250	green, light blue / bluish-green	pearly, vitreous transpar., transluc.	1.5—2 / 3.2	very good / soft, elastic, flexible	lamellar crystals; mostly radiating, flabelliform, scaly agg.; compact, reniform, spumous / orthorhombic	weathering product of copper ores / malachite, azurite / —	TYROLITE $Ca_2Cu_9[(OH)_{10}(AsO_4)_4] . 10H_2O$ / Schwaz, Tyrol, Austria
251	green / green-yellow	pearly, dull transluc.	1—2 / 3.5	good / —	needle-shaped, thick-lamellar crystals; radiating agg.; crusty, earthy, powdery, as coatings / monoclinic	decomposition product of uranium ores / other secondary uranium minerals / —	CUPROSKLODOWSKITE $CuH_2[UO_2 SiO_4]_2 . 5H_2O$ (Jachimovite) / Jáchymov, Czech Republic
252	green, yellowish / white	vitreous transpar., transluc.	2 / 1.9	very good / conchoidal, brittle, water-soluble	columnar, tabular, needle-shaped crystals; platy, stalactitic agg.; crusts, efflorescences / monoclinic	decomposition product of pyrites, pyrrhotine, in coal seams, in alum schists, in marls / — / goslarite	MELANTERITE $Fe[SO_4] . 7H_2O$ (Copperas, Green Vitriol) / Kaznějov, Czech Republic
253	emerald-green / light green	pearly, vitreous transpar., transluc.	2 / 2.4—2.6	very good / brittle	thin-tabular crystals; in druses, also lamellar agg.; massive / trigonal	weathering product in ore veins / malachite, azurite, chalcopyrite, cuprite, limonite / —	CHALCOPHYLLITE $(Cu,Al)_3[(OH)_4(AsO_4,SO_4)] . 6H_2O$ / Redruth, Cornwall, England
254	green / pale green	vitreous, pearly, dull transpar., transluc.	1—2 / 2.9—3.1	very good / soft	thin-tabular, platy crystals; mostly fine-grained, compact, as coatings, encrustations, radiating fibrous agg.; disseminated / monoclinic	weathering product in ore veins, in dolomitic limestones / adamite / —	Annabergite variety CABRERITE $(Ni,Mg)_3 [AsO_4]_2 . 8H_2O$ / Laurion, Greece
255	green, brownish, brown-yellow, greenish-white / white	silky transluc.	2 / 2.9—3	good / fibrous structure, soft	short- to long-parallel, fibrous, capillary agg. / monoclinic	filling in cracks & veins in serpentinites, from hydrothermally decomposed olivine, pyroxene, amphibole & o.	Chrysotile variety ASBESTOS $Mg_6[(OH)_8Si_4O_{10}]$ / Alto Adige, Italy
256						chromite, garnierite, pyrope, magnesite, talc, opal / —	Chrysotile variety PICROSMINE $Mg_6[(OH)_8Si_4O_{10}]$ / Alto Adige, Italy

No.	Colour / Streak	Lustre / Transparency	Hardness / Specific Gravity	Cleavage / Fracture & o. Phys. Props.	Common Form, Aggregates / Crystalline Syst.	Occurrence / Assoc. Minerals / Similar Minerals	Name & Chem. Formula / Origin of Specimen
257	dark green / light green	vitreous, pearly / transpar., transluc.	2.5 / 3.1	very good / conchoidal, brittle	thin, lamellar & needle-shaped crystals; flabelliform, rose-shaped agg. / monoclinic	decomposition product of copper ores / gypsum, malachite, azurite / —	**DEVILLINE** $CaCu_4[(OH)_3 (SO_4)]_2 . 3H_2O$ (Herrengrundite) / Špania Dolina, Slovakia
258	emerald-green, grass-green / apple-green	pearly, vitreous / transpar., transluc.	2–2.5 / 3.4–3.6	perfect / soft to brittle	thin-tabular, lamellar micaceous crystals; scaly clusters / tetragonal	weathering product of uranium ores / partly autunite, partly torbernite / —	**CHALCOLITE** $(Cu,Ca) [UO_2 PO_4]_2 . (8-10)H_2O$ (Torbernite, Copper Uranite) / Redruth, Cornwall, England
259	green, yellowish-green / yellowish-green	pearly / transpar., transluc.	2–3 / 3.5	very good / —	thin-tabular, needle-shaped crystals; bunchy, radiate agg.; crusty / tetragonal	in pegmatites, in quartz veins / uranium minerals / other uranites, cf. No. 136	**URANO-CIRCITE** $Ba[UO_2 PO_4]_2 . 10H_2O$ (Uranite, Uran Mica) / Falkenstein, Vogtland, Germany
260	green-yellow, yellowish-green, sulphur-yellow / yellowish, greenish	pearly, vitreous / transluc.	2–2.5 / 3–3.2	very good / soft	thin- to thick-tabular crystals; lamellar agg.; massive / tetragonal	secondary uranium mineral, in pegmatites, in uranium veins / — / other uranium micas, cf. No. 138	**AUTUNITE** $Ca[UO_2 PO_4]_2 . 10H_2O$ (Lime Uranite) / Tinh-Tuc, Tonkin, Vietnam
261	emerald-green, grass-green / apple-green, light green	pearly / transluc.	2–2.5 / 3.4–3.6	very good / brittle	thin-tabular, scaly crystals; flabelliform or rose-shaped bunches; also earthy / tetragonal	in ore veins as secondary uranium mineral, in granitic rocks in cracks & as impregnations / — / autunite, zeunerite	**TORBERNITE** $Cu[UO_2 PO_4]_2 . (8-12)H_2O$ (Copper Uranite) / Smrkovec, Czech Republic
262	deep verdigris green, bluish-green / greenish, white	vitreous, greasy / transpar., transluc.	2.5–3 / 6.4	good / brittle	small, columnar or needle-shaped crystals; bunchy agg. / orthorhombic	weathering product in oxidation zone of copper-lead veins / malachite, anglesite, cerussite / —	**CALEDONITE** $Pb_5Cu_2[(OH)_6 CO_3 (SO_4)_3]$ / Leadhills, Scotland
263	greenish-blue to blue / blue-green	vitreous / transluc.	2.5–3 / 3.5	good / brittle	short-prismatic, tabular crystals; lamellar, fibrous agg.; encrustations / orthorhombic	as weathering product in copper veins / — / —	**LANGITE** $Cu_4[(OH)_6 SO_4] . H_2O$ / Špania Dolina, Slovakia
264	green, blue-green / light green	dull / opaque	2–4 / 2.2–2.7	— / uneven	massive, crypto-crystalline masses, crusts; compact, botryoidal, reniform, earthy, often with agate lamination / monoclinic	as weathering product of olivine rocks, in serpentinites / opal, chrysoprase, magnesite, limonite / pimelite	**GARNIERITE** $(Ni,Mg)_6 [(OH)_6Si_4O_{11}] H_2O$ (Nouméite) / Nouméa, New Caledonia

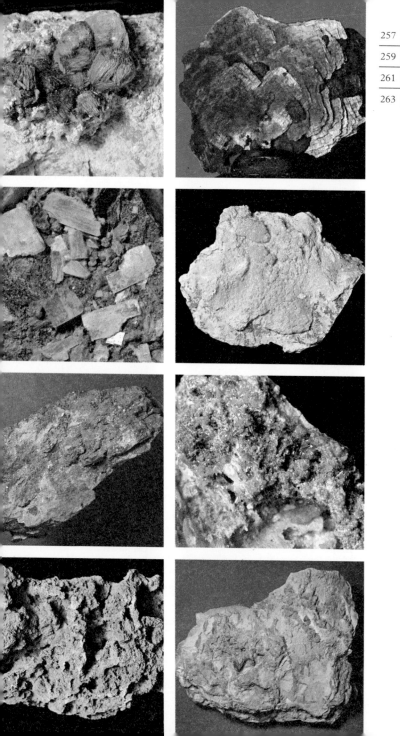

No.	Colour / Streak	Lustre / Transparency	Hardness / Specific Gravity	Cleavage Fracture & o. Phys. Props.	Common Form, Aggregates / Crystalline Syst.	Occurrence Assoc. Minerals / Similar Minerals	Name & Chem. Formula / Origin of Specimen
265	green, greenish-blue, brown / pale green, greenish-blue	dull, greasy / transluc., opaque	$\frac{2-4}{2-2.3}$	— / con-choidal, brittle to soft	cryptocrystalline, compact, reniform, botryoidal, massive, earthy, as crusts or encrustations / monoclinic	in oxidation zone of copper ore deps. / malachite, dioptase, cuprite, cerussite, limonite, azurite / aurichalcite	**CHRYSO-COLLA** Cu_4H_4 $[(OH)_8 Si_4O_{10}]$ / Coquimbo, Chile
266	dark green, emerald-green, blackish-green / apple-green	ada-mantine, vitreous / transpar., transluc.	$\frac{3}{3.7}$	very good / brittle	columnar, needle-shaped, capillary, thick-tabular crystals; compact, massive, earthy, granular, as encrustations / orthorhombic	in oxidation zone of copper ore deps., often in volcanoes / malachite, dioptase, cuprite, haematite, limonite / malachite, olivenite	**ATACAMITE** $Cu(OH)Cl$. $Cu(OH)_2$ (Remolinite) / Bura-Bura, Australia
267	dark green, olive-green, yellow-brown / green-yellow, brown	vitreous, greasy, silky / transluc.	$\frac{3}{4.3}$	poor / con-choidal, brittle	columnar, needle-shaped, tabular crystals in druses; fibrous, reniform, botryoidal, compact, earthy / orthorhombic	in oxidation zone of copper ore deps. / chalcopyrite, arsenopyrite / libethenite	**OLIVENITE** $Cu_2[OH\,As\,O_4]$ / St.Day, Cornwall, England
268	emerald-green / greenish	vitreous, greasy / transpar., transluc.	$\frac{3.5}{2.6}$	— / con-choidal, brittle	small, prismatic crystals; mostly massive, earthy, globular, stalactitic, crusts, encrustations, coatings / cubic	decomposition product of nickel ores, as coatings to chromite / brucite, clino-chlore, chrysolite, serpentine / —	**ZARATITE** $Ni_3[(OH)_4$ $CO_3]$. $4H_2O$ (Emerald Nickel) / Texas, Pennsylvania, USA
269	dark green, brown, black / green-yellow, yellow	ada-mantine, vitreous, greasy / transpar., transluc.	$\frac{3.5-4.5}{4-4.3}$	good / brittle	cube-shaped, pseudocubic, rhombohedral crystals / trigonal	in oxidation zone of iron ore deps. / limonite / —	**BEUDANTITE** $PbFe_3[(OH)_6$ $SO_4,AsO_4]$ / Dernbach, Westerwald, Germany
270	green, yellow, brown, white-grey, yellow-red / white, yellowish, grey	ada-mantine, greasy / transluc.	$\frac{3.5-4}{6.7-7}$	— / uneven, brittle	thick-tabular, columnar, barrel-shaped, ventricular, needle-shaped crystals; compact, massive, reniform, botryoidal, crusts, encrustations, coatings, also fibrous / hexagonal	in weathering zone of lead ore deps. / galena, cerussite, mimetesite, des-cloizite, barytes, limonite, quartz / mimetesite, vana-dinite, campylite, cf. No. 325	**PYRO-MORPHITE** $Pb_5[Cl(PO_4)_3]$ (Green Lead Ore) / Hofsgrund, Black Forest, Germany
271	emerald-green, leek-green / green, bluish-green	vitreous / transluc.	$\frac{3.5}{3.4}$	indistinct / uneven, brittle	short-columnar, thick-tabular, vertically striated crystals; crusts, druses / orthorhombic	in oxidation zone of copper ore deps., in mica schists / olivenite, malachite, azurite / dioptase	**EUCHROITE** $Cu_2[OHAsO_4]$. $3H_2O$ / Ľubietová, Slovakia
272	white, yellow, green, brown, bluish / white	vitreous, silky / transluc.	$\frac{3.5-4}{2.3-2.4}$	good / brittle	fine-fibrous, radiate bunches; hemi-spheric agg. / orthorhombic	in cracks in sand-stone, silica schists, quartzite / — / prehnite, cf. No. 68	**WAVELLITE** $Al_3[(OH)_3$ $(PO_4)_2$. $5H_2O$] / Montgomery Co., Arkansas, USA

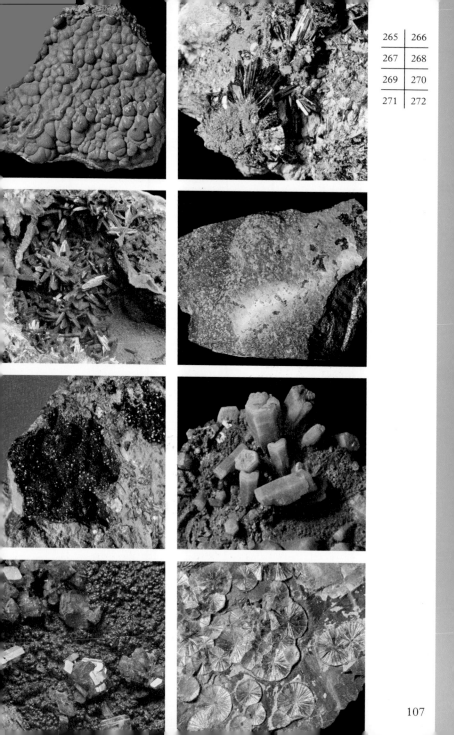

No.	Colour / Streak	Lustre / Transparency	Hardness / Specific Gravity	Cleavage / Fracture & o. Phys. Props.	Common Form, Aggregates / Crystalline Syst.	Occurrence / Assoc. Minerals / Similar Minerals	Name & Chem. Formula / Origin of Specimen
273	emerald-green, dark green,	vitreous, silky, dull	$\dfrac{4}{4.0}$	good fibrous separation brittle	fibrous, needle-shaped, capillary crystals; bunchy agg.; compact, reniform; botryoidal, nodular, stalactitic, subvitreous, agate-like striated, massive, earthy, disseminated, impregnations, encrustations, coatings	in weathering zone of copper deps.; impregnation in sandstone chalcopyrite, bornite, tetrahedrite, chalcosine, cuprite, copper, azurite, haematite, limonite chrysocolla, pseudo-malachite, atacamite	MALACHITE $Cu_2[(OH)_2CO_3]$ Moldova, Banat, Romania
274	greenish-black / light green	transluc., opaque			monoclinic		MALACHITE $Cu_2[(OH)_2CO_3]$ Katanga (now Shaba), Congo
275	dark green, greenish-black / light green	greasy, vitreous transluc.	$\dfrac{4}{3.8}$	— conchoidal, brittle	small, short-columnar, octa-hedral crystals; reniform, globular, radiate, fibrous, bunchy massive orthorhombic	in oxidized zone of copper ores malachite, cuprite, limonite, quartz malachite, pseudomalachite, olivenite, atacamite	LIBETHE-NITE $Cu[OH\,PO_4]$ Ľubietová, Slovakia
276	green, bluish-green, colourless / white	greasy transluc.	$\dfrac{4-5}{2.2-2.5}$	— conchoidal	small, short-columnar, needle-shaped crystals; globular agg.; massive, crusty, reniform orthorhombic	in fissures and seams of silica schists, quartzite — wavellite	VARISCITE $Al[PO_4] . 2H_2O$ Montgomery Co., Arkansas, USA
277	emerald-green, dark green / bluish-green	vitreous, greasy transluc., transpar.	$\dfrac{4-5}{3.8-4.4}$	indistinct conchoidal, brittle	short-columnar, fibrous, grown-up crystals; radiate-fibrous, reniform-botryoidal agg. monoclinic	in oxidized zone of copper deps., in fissures in limestones, dolomites, sandstone malachite, azurite, limonite, chalcedony	PSEUDO-MALACHITE Cu_5 $[(OH)_4 PO_4]_2$ Ľubietová Slovakia
278	dark green, emerald-green / apple-green	dull transluc., opaque	$\dfrac{4.5-5}{4-4.1}$	— conchoidal, brittle	fine needle-shaped spherulites; reniform, shelled agg. monoclinic	in oxidized zone of copper deps. olivinite malachite	CORN-WALLITE Cu_5 $[(OH)_2 As\,O_4]_2$ (Erinite) Carrarach Mine, Cornwall, England
279	dark green, brownish, brown-green / light green, brownish	pearly, greasy transluc., opaque	$\dfrac{4-4.5}{3-3.2}$	very good brittle	tabular, columnar, grown-up crystals; granular agg.; compact hexagonal	metasomatic structure in iron & manganese deps. — —	PYRO-SMALITE $(Mn,Fe)_8$ $[(OH,Cl)_{10}$ $Si_6O_{15}]$ Broddebo, Kalmar, Sweden
280	white, yellow, red, orange-red, green, grey, bluish / white	vitreous, greasy transluc.	$\dfrac{5}{4.3-4.5}$	very good brittle	small rhombo-hedral crystals; often rounded, mostly compact, botryoidal, reni-form, conical, finely granular, massive, earthy, shell-like, striated sinter crusts, chalcedonic trigonal	metasomatic in limestone and dolomite rocks; as isolated masses in fissures and cavities, weathering product of sphalerite galena, hydro-zincite, malachite & o. hemimorphite, prehnite, chal-cedony, cf. No. 411	SMITH-SONITE $ZnCO_3$ (Calamine, Zinc Spar) Tsumeb, South-West Africa

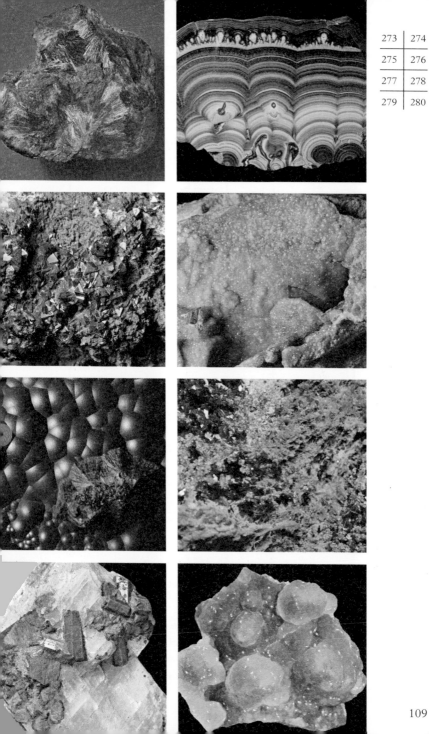

No.	Colour / Streak	Lustre Transparency	Hardness / Specific Gravity	Cleavage Fracture & o. Phys. Props.	Common Form, Aggregates / Crystalline Syst.	Occurrence / Assoc. Minerals / Similar Minerals	Name & Chem. Formula / Origin of Specimen
281	colourless, white, yellow, red, greenish, violet / white	vitreous, greasy / transpar., transluc.	$\frac{5}{3.1}$	clear conchoidal, brittle	hexagonal, short- to long-columnar, tabular crystals; compact, reniform, nodular, massive, granular / hexagonal	as constituent in magmatic rocks, in fissures in crystalline schists, in pegmatites / — / beryl, nepheline, cf. No. 82, 158, 214	**APATITE** $Ca_5[F(PO_4)_3]$ / Horní Slavkov, Czech Republic
282	light green, blue-green / white	greasy to dull opaque	$\frac{5}{2.8}$	— / brittle	compact, concentric spherules, reniform, stalactitic, nodular, disseminated, massive / tetragonal	crusts in cavities in decomposed varicite, in silica schists / — / —	**WARDITE** $NaAl_3[(OH)_4(PO_4)_2] \cdot 2H_2O$ / Lewiston, Utah, USA
283	colourless, greenish, yellowish, grey, brown, bluish-red / white	vitreous, greasy / transpar., transluc.	$\frac{5.5}{4-4.2}$	good conchoidal, splintery	small, needle-shaped, columnar crystals; compact, coarsely to finely granular / trigonal	in manganese & zinc deps. / smithsonite, hemimorphite, zincite, franklinite, rhodonite, limonite, calcite / olivine, epidote	**WILLEMITE** $Zn_2(SiO)_4$ / Franklin, New Jersey, USA
284	emerald-green, dark green / bluish-green	vitreous transpar., transluc.	$\frac{5}{3.3}$	very good conchoidal, brittle	short-columnar, grown-up crystals; in druses; massive agg. / trigonal	in oxidized zone of copper lodes, in fissures in limestone, dolomite, sandstone / chrysocolla, limonite / malachite, atacamite	**DIOPTASE** $Cu_6[Si_6O_{18}] \cdot 6H_2O$ / Renéville, Congo
285	emerald-green / greenish	vitreous transpar., transluc.	$\frac{5-6}{3.2-3.3}$	good conchoidal, brittle	compact, only granular / monoclinic	in crystalline schists & eclogites / garnet, zoisite, cyanite, epidote / fassaite	**OMPHACITE** (Ca,Na) (Mg,Fe,Al) $[Si_2O_6]$ (Pyroxene Family) / Ötztal, Tyrol, Austria
286	colourless, yellowish, green, greenish-black / white	vitreous, greasy / transpar., transluc.	$\frac{5-6}{3.2-3.5}$	clear, good brittle	short-columnar, needle-shaped, grown-up crystals; compact, granular, tubular, shelled, massive / monoclinic	in magnetite lodes, in fissures in metamorphic rocks / chlorite, hessonite, magnetite, apatite, biotite / clinochlore, augite	**DIOPSIDE** $CaMg[Si_2O_6]$ (Pyroxene Family) / Rothenkopf, Zillertal, Tyrol, Austria
287	green, grey-green / white	dull transluc.	$\frac{5.5}{2.9-3}$	— / very massive & tenacious	cryptocrystalline, slaty, only compact, massive / monoclinic	compact actinolite or also anthophyllite, in loose blocks & pebbles of serpentine gabbro / — / jadeite	**NEPHRITE** $(Mg,Fe)_7[OH Si_4O_{11}]_2 Na_2Ca_4 (Mg,Fe)_{10} [(OH)_2O_2Si_{16}O_{44}]$ / Kawa-Kawa, New Zealand
288	grey-green, grey-white, light green, white, brown / white	pearly, silky transluc.	$\frac{5-6}{3.1}$	good fibrous separation, rather brittle	fine, needle-shaped, capillary (up to 15 cm long) crystals; parallely fibrous, felt-like agg. / monoclinic	asbestos variety of cummingtonite / — / chrysotile-asbestos	**AMOSITE** $(Mg,Fe)_7 [OH Si_4O_{11}]_2$ / Lydenburg, Transvaal, South Africa

No.	Colour — Streak	Lustre — Transparency	Hardness — Specific Gravity	Cleavage Fracture & o. Phys. Props.	Common Form, Aggregates — Crystalline Syst.	Occurrence — Assoc. Minerals Similar Minerals	Name & Chem. Formula — Origin of Specimen
289	green, reddish — white	vitreous, metallic glint — transluc.	5.5 – 6 — 2.6	— uneven	compact, finely granular to massive, slaty, — trigonal	— spangles of mica or haematite —	Quartz variety **AVEN-TURINE** SiO_2 — Brazil
290	green, grey — white	vitreous, silky — transpar. transluc.	5.5 – 6 — 2.9 – 3.2	good brittle	long-acicular, capillary crystals; fine-fibrous, felt-like asbestiform agg. — monoclinic	in metamorphic limestones & dolomites, in alpine cracks —	Amphibole variety **BYSSOLITE** $Ca_2Mg_5(OH,F)_2$ $[Si_4O_{11}]_2$ — Knappenwand, Salzburg, Austria
291	colourless, white, yellow, greenish, grey-green, blue-green, brown, red — white	vitreous, greasy — transpar., transluc.	5.5 – 6 — 2.6	indistinct con-choidal to uneven	short-columnar to thick-tabular crystals; mostly massive, compact, granular — hexagonal	rock constituent in volcanic ejecta — apatite, quartz, felspars	**NEPHELINE** $KNa_3[AlSiO_4]_4$ — Vesuvius, Italy
292	grey, yellow, greenish, light rose, red — white	vitreous transluc., opaque	6.5 — 3.2	very good uneven	long-columnar, tabular, thick-tabular crystals; often twinned — monoclinic	in metamorphic rocks & crystalline schists — zoisite, tremolite	**CLINO-ZOISITE** $Ca_2Al_3[O\ OH\ SiO_4\ Si_2O_7]$ — Ampandandrava, Madagascar
293	grey-white, greenish, brownish, pink, red — white	vitreous, pearly opaque	6 – 6.5 — 3.2 – 3.3	very good uneven	columnar to acicular crystals; compact, tubular, radial agg. — orthorhombic	in crystalline schists & metamorphic rocks — amphibole, garnet, vesuvianite, epidote, quartz & o. tremolite	**ZOISITE** $Ca_2Al_3[O\ OH\ SiO_4\ Si_2O_7]$ — Zermatt, Switzerland
294	green, greenish-white, grey — white	vitreous, pearly — transpar., transluc.	6 – 6.5 — 2.8 – 3	clear uneven	tabular, short-columnar crystals; globular, reniform, shelled, flabelli-form agg.; compact, granular, crusts — orthorhombic	in fissures & vesicles of basic igneous rocks & crystalline schists — zeolite, calcite, axinite — hemimorphite, aragonite, staffelite	**PREHNITE** $Ca_2Al[(OH)_2 AlSi_3O_{10}]$ — West Patterson, New Jersey, USA
295	dark green, yellow-green, yellow, brown, red, grey, black — white, grey	vitreous transluc.	6 – 7 — 3.3 – 3.5	very good con-choidal, splintery	columnar, acicular, transversely striated crystals; compact, platy, radial, bunchy agg.; granular to massive — monoclinic	in alpine cracks, in crystalline schists, in metamorphic limestone, in fissures in basalt	**EPIDOTE** $Ca_2(Fe,Al)Al_2$ $[O\ OH\ SiO_4\ Si_2O_7]$ — Knappenwand, Untersulz-bachtal, Salzburg, Austria
296	pistachio-green, yellow-green — white	vitreous transluc.	6 – 7 — 3.3 – 3.5	very good con-choidal, splintery	columnar, acicular crystals; tubular, radial agg.; granular, compact, massive — monoclinic	garnet, vesuvianite, copper — tourmaline, actinolite, vesuvianite	Epidote variety **PISTACITE** $Ca_2(Fe,Al)Al_2$ $[O\ OH\ SiO_4\ Si_2O_7]$ — Erbendorf, Fichtelgebirge, Germany

No.	Colour / Streak	Lustre / Transparency	Hardness / Specific Gravity	Cleavage / Fracture & o. Phys. Props.	Common Form, Aggregates / Crystalline Syst.	Occurrence / Assoc. Minerals / Similar Minerals	Name & Chem. Formula / Origin of Specimen
297	light green, apple-green / white	vitreous, greasy / transluc.	7 / 2.6	— / conchoidal	massive, reniform, shelled, disseminated, crypto-crystalline / trigonal	in nickel ore deps. / — / prehnite	Quartz variety **CHRYSO-PRASE** SiO_2 (coloured green due to presence of nickel compounds) / Szklary, Poland
298	dark green, dirty green, leek-green / whitish	vitreous, greasy / opaque, transluc.	7 / 2.5–2.6	— / conchoidal	irregular nodules, veins, disseminated, cryptocrystalline; massive / trigonal	in igneous rocks, in serpentines / quartz, chalcedony / prase	Quartz variety **PLASMA** SiO_2 / Hrubšice, Czech Republic
299	yellow-green, olive-green, greenish-black, red-brown / white	vitreous, greasy / transpar., transluc.	6.5–7 / 3.3	good / conchoidal	thick-tabular, short-columnar crystals; granular to massive, compact, granular bunches, xenoliths / orthorhombic	constituent in basic igneous rocks in meteorites, in magnetite lodes / chrysoberyl, cf. No. 354	**OLIVINE** $(Mg,Fe)_2[SiO_4]$ (Chrysolite, Peridot) / St. John's Island (Zebirget), Red Sea, Egypt
300	green, yellow-green / white	vitreous, ada-mantine / transpar., transluc.	7 / 3.3–4.1	— / conchoidal, splintery	dodecahedral, mostly grown-up crystals; massive / cubic	in fissures in crystalline schists, in ore deps., in gold placers / — / —	Andradite variety **DEMANTOID** $Ca_3Fe_2[SiO_4]_3$ (Garnet Family) / Frascati, Albanian Mountains, Italy
301	greenish-white, green, grey, yellowish / white	vitreous, greasy / transluc.	6.5–7 / 3.2–3.3	very tenacious, uneven	only compact, massive, granular, fibrous agg.; nodules, pebbles, cryptocrystalline / monoclinic	in crystalline schists / — / nephrite	**JADEITE** $NaAl[Si_2O_6]$ / Mogok, Upper Burma
302	green / white	vitreous / transpar., transluc.	7 / 3–3.2	— / uneven, splintery	columnar to long-columnar crystals; tubular to fibrous agg.; granular, massive / trigonal	in pegmatites, granites & metamorphic rocks / epidote, vesuvianite	Tourmaline variety **VERDELITE** $NaFe_3Al_6[(OH)_4(BO_3)_3 Si_6O_{18}]$ / Dravograd, Slovenia
303	emerald-green, dark green / whitish	vitreous, greasy / transluc., transpar.	7.5–8 / 3.4	— / conchoidal, splintery	dodecahedral crystals; granular to massive, as crusts / cubic	in serpentines rich in chromite, in ore deps. / — / dioptase	**UVAROVITE** $Ca_3Cr_2[SiO_4]_3$ (Garnet Family) / Biser, Central Urals, Russia
304	yellow, light green, emerald-green / white	vitreous, greasy / transpar., transluc.	8.5 / 3.7	clear / conchoidal	tabular, short-columnar, tubular crystals; often twinned, granular / orthorhombic	in granitic pegmatites, granites, syenites, gneiss & mica schists / — / olivine, beryl, apatite, tourmaline, corundum	**CHRYSO-BERYL** Al_2BeO_4 / Haddam, Connecticut, USA

297	298
299	300
301	302
303	304

No.	Colour / Streak	Lustre / Transparency	Hardness / Specific Gravity	Cleavage Fracture & o. Phys. Props.	Common Form, Aggregates / Crystalline Syst.	Occurrence Assoc. Minerals / Similar Minerals	Name & Chem. Formula / Origin of Specimen
305	greenish, yellow-green, blue-green, yellow, red / white	vitreous, dull / transpar., transluc.	7.5 – 8 / 2.6	almost indistinct / conchoidal to uneven	hexagonal, columnar, tabular to acicular crystals; tubular, fibrous agg.; compact / hexagonal	in granitic pegmatites, granites, crystalline schists, in tin deps. / tourmaline, topaz apatite, tourmaline	**BERYL** $Al_2Be_3[Si_6O_{18}]$ / Meclov, Czech Republic
306	dark green, bluish-green / white	vitreous / transpar., transluc.	7.5 – 8 / 2.6	almost indistinct / conchoidal to uneven	hexagonal, columnar crystals / hexagonal	crystals embedded in mica schists, limestone / — cf. No. 516	Beryl variety **EMERALD** $Al_2Be_3[Si_6O_{18}]$ / Muzo, Colombia

No.	Colour / Streak	Lustre / Transparency	Hardness / Specific Gravity	Cleavage Fracture & o. Phys. Props.	Common Form, Aggregates / Crystalline Syst.	Occurrence Assoc. Minerals / Similar Minerals	Name & Chem. Formula / Origin of Specimen
307	brownish, grey, black / brown, grey-black	metallic, dull / opaque	2.5 / 6.2	— / brittle to soft	pseudocubic, small cube-shaped crystals; compact, reniform, botryoidal, mammillary, massive / orthorhombic	in silver veins / pyrargyrite, galena, sphalerite, siderite germanite	**ARGYRODITE** $4Ag_2S . GeS_2$ / Freiberg, Ore Mountains, Germany
308	gold-brown, tombac-brown, dark brown / grey-black	metallic / opaque	4 / 4.6	clear / brittle, uneven	thick-tabular to short-columnar crystals; compact, granular, massive, in masses / hexagonal	in basic igneous rocks, in ore veins / — cf. No. 128	**PYRRHOTITE** FeS (Magnetic Pyrites) / Dell Norte, California, USA

No.	Colour / Streak	Lustre / Transparency	Hardness / Specific Gravity	Cleavage Fracture & o. Phys. Props.	Common Form, Aggregates / Crystalline Syst.	Occurrence Assoc. Minerals / Similar Minerals	Name & Chem. Formula / Origin of Specimen
309	colourless, white, grey, yellow, brown / white	adamantine, greasy / transpar., transluc.	2.5 – 3 / 6 – 6.3	perfect / conchoidal, brittle to soft	short-columnar, tabular, mostly grown-up crystals / tetragonal	in weathering zone of lead veins / anglesite, cerussite	**PHOSGENITE** $Pb_2[Cl_2O_3]$ (Horn Lead) / Monte-Poni, Sardinia, Italy
310	brown, white, grey-white, yellow-brown, black / whitish	greasy to dull / opaque	2 – 5 / 3 – 3.2	— / brittle	radial, fibrous, globular agg.; compact, reniform, nodular, earthy, granular, loose, cryptocrystalline / hexagonal	microcrystalline apatite from sedimentary deps. / — —	Apatite variety **PHOSPHORITE** $[3CaPo_4]_X$ $[(2Ca F_2 CO_3)]_y$ $2H_2O$ / Děražnja, Podolien, Ukraine
311	light brown, silver-grey, dark grey, yellowish, greenish / white	pearly, metallizing / transpar., transluc.	2.5 – 3 / 2.9 – 3.1	perfect / soft to brittle, elastic, flexible, foliaceous	tabular, thin-lamellar, pseudo-hexagonal crystals; loose groups; scaly, lamellar, tubular agg. / monoclinic	in tin ore deps., in granites & gneiss / cassiterite, wolframite, scheelite, fluorite, pycnite, quartz lepidolite	**ZINNWALDITE** $KLiFeAl$ $[(F,OH)_2$ $AlSi_3O_{10}]$ (Lithionite) / Cínovec, Czech Republic
312	colourless, grey, brown, green-yellow, silver-white / white	pearly, vitreous, silky / transpar., transluc.	2 – 2.5 / 2.7 – 2.8	perfect / elastic, flexible, foliaceous	thin- to thick-tabular, short-columnar, pseudo-hexagonal crystals; thin-lamellar, compact, scaly, globular, massive / monoclinic	original constituent of several kinds of rocks, except basic rocks, in tin ore deps. / — other micas	**MUSCOVITE** $KAl_2[(OH,F)_2$ $AlSi_3O_{10}]$ (Mica Family) / Middletown, Connecticut, USA

305	306
307	308
309	310
311	312

No.	Colour / Streak	Lustre / Transparency	Hardness / Specific Gravity	Cleavage / Fracture & o. Phys. Props.	Common Form, Aggregates / Crystalline Syst.	Occurrence / Assoc. Minerals / Similar Minerals	Name & Chem. Formula / Origin of Specimen
313	gold-brown, yellow-green, grey, blackish / greenish	vitreous, pearly, metallic / transpar., transluc.	1—2 / 2.1—2.7	perfect / soft, inflates strongly when heated	pseudohexagonal thin & thick laminae; scaly, massive agg. / — / monoclinic	weathering product of micas / phlogopite, chlorite, magnesite / biotite, phlogopite	**VERMICULITE** Mg_2FeAl $[(OH)_2$ $AlSi_3O_{10}Mg$ $(H_2O)_4]$ / Westchester, Pennsylvania, USA
314	dark brown, deep green, black / dark olive-green	vitreous, metallic / opaque	3.5 / 3.4	very good / elastic	triangular, mostly hexagonal, thin, foliaceous crystals; globular clusters; tubular, radiate-fibrous agg.; reniform / monoclinic	in ore veins / pyrite, siderite, limonite, sphalerite, quartz / —	**STILPNOMELAN** (K,H_2O) $(Fe,Mg,Al)_3$ $[(OH)_2Si_4O_{10}]$ $(H_2O)_2$ / Chabičov, Czech Republic
						Hardness 3 — 4	
315	colourless, yellow, red, brown, green, grey, black / white, yellow, brown	adamantine, greasy / transpar. to opaque	3.5—4 / 3.9—4.2	very good, rhombo-dodecahedral / brittle	tetrahedral, dodecahedral, cube-like crystals; coarse to fine-granular, massive, compact / cubic	in ore veins / galena, chalcopyrite & o. / tetrahedrite, cassiterite, garnet, cf. No. 142, 191, 445	**SPHALERITE** ZnS (Zinc Blende) / Cumberland, England
316	light brown, dark brown / brownish, yellow	adamantine, resinous / transluc., opaque	3—4 / 4	perfect / brittle	columnar, acicular crystals; tubular to fibrous agg.; crusty, shelled, striated, massive / hexagonal	in lead-zinc ore deps. / sphalerite / —	**WURTZITE** ZnS (Radial Blende) / Příbram, Czech Republic
317	brown, yellowish, brown-green, grey, brown-black / white, yellowish	vitreous, pearly, dull / transluc.	3.5—4 / 3.7—3.9	perfect, rhombohedral / brittle	rhombohedral, lenticular, often curved, distorted crystals; saddle-shaped agg.; coarsely to finely granular, spathic, massive / trigonal	in metasomatic ore deps., in ore veins, sedimentary / clay / calcite, dolomite, ankerite, magnesite	**SIDERITE** $FeCO_3$ (Chalybite, Spathose Iron) / Neudorf near Quedlinburg, Harz, Germany
318	light brown, yellowish-white / white	dull / opaque	3.5—4 / 2.8	— / brittle, uneven	globular, reniform, botryoidal, shelled agg.; crypto-crystalline / trigonal	in sedimentary rocks & gypsum / — / —	**MIEMITE** $CaMg[CO_3]_2$ (Dolomite) / Durham, England
319	brown, yellow-brown, whitish-grey / white	dull / opaque	3 / 2.6—2.8	— / uneven	massive, solid masses, banded, cryptocrystalline / trigonal	massive limestones with angular patterns, unevenly coloured by iron hydroxide / — / —	Calcite variety **RUIN MARBLE** $CaCO_3$ / Florence, Italy
320	yellow, white, brown, red-brown / white, yellowish	dull, silky / opaque	3.5—4 / 2.9—3	indistinct, fibrous, jointing / brittle	radiating & parallely fibrous agg.; stalactitic, concentrically shelled, coatings, crusts, sinter formation / orthorhombic	aragonite sinter as deposition of hot springs / — / cf. No. 485	Aragonite variety **SPRUDELSTEIN** $CaCO_3$ / Karlovy Vary, Czech Republic

No.	Colour Streak	Lustre Transparency	Hardness Specific Gravity	Cleavage Fracture & o. Phys. Props.	Common Form, Aggregates Crystalline Syst.	Occurrence Assoc. Minerals Similar Minerals	Name & Chem. Formula Origin of Specimen
321	white, yellowish, brown, grey, black / white	adamantine, greasy transpar., transluc.	3—3.5 / 6.4—6.6	indistinct conchoidal, brittle	columnar, tabular, acicular crystals; often twins, cruciform or radiate arrangements, compact, reniform, massive, tubular, orthorhombic	in weathering zone of lead veins / galena, anglesite, pyromorphite / anglesite, phosgenite, coelestine, barytes, scheelite, cf. No. 401	CERUSSITE $PbCO_3$ (White Lead Ore) Příbram, Czech Republic
322	yellow, brown, blackish-brown / straw-yellow	vitreous, dull opaque	3—4 / 2.9—3.2	clear brittle	very small, rhombohedral, tabular crystals; mostly compact, powdery, reniform, granular, crusty, fibrous trigonal	in weathering zone of ore veins, in clays / limonite, haematite, alunite, quartz / different ochres	JAROSITE $KFe_3[(OH)_6(SO_4)_2]$ Laurión, Greece
323	yellowish, orange, red, grey, brown, green / white	adamantine, greasy transluc., opaque	3 / 7.9—8.3	indistinct brittle to soft	pointed-pyramidal, short-columnar crystals; bundle- & fusiform, grown-up granules tetragonal	in tin ore deps. / scheelite / scheelite, cf. No. 171	STOLZITE $[PbWO_4]$ Cínovec, Czech Republic
324	brown, brown-red, brownish-green, black / yellow, yellow-brown	adamantine, greasy transluc., opaque	3.5 / 5.9—6.2	— conchoidal, brittle	columnar, pyramidal crystals; mostly crusty forms, botryoidal, mammiform, radiate, coatings orthorhombic	in lead-zinc ore deps. / pyromorphite, vanadinite, limonite, cerussite / —	MOTTRAMITE $Pb(Cu,Zn)[OH\,VO_4]$ Friesenberg, South-West Africa
325	brown, green, yellow, yellow-red, / white, yellowish, grey	adamantine, greasy transluc.	3.5—4 / 6.7—7	— uneven, brittle, conchoidal	columnar, barrel-shaped, acicular, ventricular crystals; reniform, botryoidal, compact, massive, crusts, coatings hexagonal	in weathering zone of lead deps. / — / mimetesite, campylite, vanadinite, cf. No. 270	PYROMORPHITE $Pb_5[Cl(PO_4)_3]$ Oloví, Czech Republic
326	yellow, brown, reddish-brown, orange, ruby-red / yellow, brownish	adamantine, greasy transluc., opaque	3 / 6.8—7.1	— conchoidal, brittle	short-columnar, barrel-shaped crystals; reniform, botryoidal, compact, fibrous, thin-tubular agg. hexagonal	in lead deps. / wulfenite, galena, pyromorphite, descloizite & o. / pyromorphite, mimetesite, campylite	VANADINITE $Pb_5[Cl(VO_4)_3]$ Djebel Mahser, Morocco
327	brown, yellow, orange, green / yellow	adamantine, greasy transluc.	3.5 / 7.2	good brittle	barrel-shaped, ventricular, thick-tabular crystals; hemispheric, bundle-shaped agg. hexagonal	in lead deps. / — / —	Mimetesite variety CAMPYLITE $Pb_5[Cl(As,P)O_4]_3$ (Phosphoreous Mimetesite) Příbram, Czech Republic
328	brown, brass-brown, gold-yellow / yellow-brown	adamantine, pearly, metallizing transpar., transluc.	3—4 / 3.3—3.4	perfect brittle	tabular, foliaceous crystals; scaly, rose-shaped, stellate agg. triclinic	embedded in nepheline syenites / amphibole, mica, zircon / —	ASTROPHYLLITE $(K,Na)_3(Fe,Mn)_7(Ti,Zr)_2[Si_8(O,OH)_{31}]$ Los Insel, West Africa

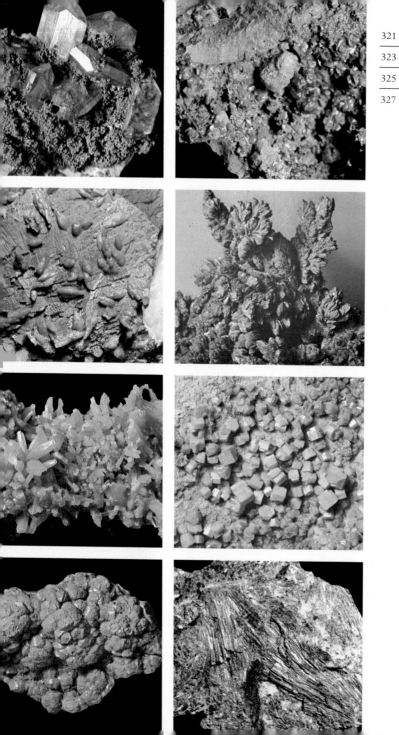

No.	Colour / Streak	Lustre / Transparency	Hardness / Specific Gravity	Cleavage / Fracture & o. / Phys. Props.	Common Form, Aggregates / Crystalline Syst.	Occurrence / Assoc. Minerals / Similar Minerals	Name & Chem. Formula / Origin of Specimen
329	brown-green, black, earthy on surface, yellow / yellowish, white	greasy, waxy, dull on surface / opaque	4 / 3.6 – 3.7	conchoidal, brittle	octahedral, dodecahedral, large crystals; compact, granular, massive / cubic	in granite-pegmatites / euxenite, zircon, biotite & o. / —	**BETAFITE** (Ca,Th,U,Ce) $(Nb,Ta,Ti)_3O_9$ nH_2O / Betafo, Madagascar
330	dark brown, brownish-yellow, grey / whitish	dull / opaque	4 / 3.7 – 3.9	— / brittle	globular, reniform, nodular, concretions; massive, cryptocrystalline / trigonal	argillaceous siderite, in sedimentary rocks, in coal seams / — / —	Siderite variety **PELO-SIDERITE** $FeCO_3$ / Cumberland, England
331	yellowish, brown, grey / white	vitreous, greasy / transluc.	4 – 4.5 / 2.9 – 3.1	very good / brittle	rhombohedral, lentiform crystals; spathic, granular / trigonal	embedded in chlorite schists & talc schists / — / dolomite, ankerite, siderite	**BREUN-NERITE** $(Mg,Fe)CO_3$ (Mesitine Spar, Mesitite) / Greiner Wald, Upper Austria
332	brown-yellow, red-brown, orange, black / brown, orange-yellow	vitreous, greasy / transluc., opaque	4.5 – 5 / 4.4 – 4.8	poor, indistinct conchoidal, brittle	short-columnar, pyramidal, embedded crystals; massive, compact, lamellar, disseminated / tetragonal	in pegmatites / zircon, aegirine, felspars / zircon, xenotime	**THORITE** $Th(SiO_4)$ / Brevik on Langesundsfjord, Norway
333	brown, bronze-brown, grey-green / white, grey	vitreous, pearly, metallic / opaque, transluc.	5 – 6 / 3.2 – 3.5	good striated cleavage planes	tabular, columnar, lamellar crystals; compact, coarsely granular, spathic, bundle-shaped, radial / orthorhombic	in basic rocks / enstatite, olivine, serpentine, chromite, magnetite / enstatite, hypersthene, diallage	**BRONZITE** $(Mg,Fe)_2[Si_2O_6]$ / Gefrees, Fichtelgebirge, Germany
334	brown, blackish-brown / brown, yellowish-brown	greasy / transluc., opaque	5 – 5.5 / 4.3 – 4.5	poor conchoidal, brittle	octahedral, cube-shaped crystals; granular, disseminated / cubic	in granite-pegmatites, in carbonates / zircon, nepheline / —	**PYROCHLORE** $(Ca,Na,Y,Ce,Th,U,Ti)_2$ $Nb_2O_6(F,OH,O)$ / Frederiksvärn near Larvik, Norway
335	brown, ochre-yellow / dark yellow, brown	dull, velvety / opaque	5 – 5.5 / 3.3 – 4.3	good fibrous, brittle	needle-shaped, capillary crystals; fine-fibrous agg.; globular, reniform, mammillary structure / orthorhombic	in oxidation zone of ore veins / — / —	**SAMT-BLENDE** α-FeOOH (Goethite, Lepidocrocite) / Příbram, Czech Republic
336	yellow, yellow-brown, rusty-brown / yellow	silky, dull / opaque	5 – 5.5 also softer 3.7	earthy, fibrous	radial, stalactitic, compact, earthy, cryptocrystalline / orthorhombic	in weathering zone of iron deps. / — / different ochres	**XANTHO-SIDERITE** FeOOH / Lostwithiel, Cornwall, England

No.	Colour / Streak	Lustre / Transparency	Hardness / Specific Gravity	Cleavage / Fracture & o. / Phys. Props.	Common Form, Aggregates / Crystalline Syst.	Occurrence / Assoc. Minerals / Similar Minerals	Name & Chem. Formula / Origin of Specimen
337	brown, red, yellow, orange / grey-white	adamantine, greasy / transluc., opaque	5—5.5 / 4.8—5.5	perfect / conchoidal, brittle	thick-tabular, short-columnar, embedded & grown-up crystals; rolled grains / monoclinic	in pegmatites, granites, syenites, gneiss, in alpine cracks, loose in sands, in placers / zircon, rutile, ilmenite / thorite, orthite	**MONAZITE** $Ce[PO_4]$ / Ambatofotsikely, Madagascar
338	greenish-blue, brownish-green, reddish-brown, blue-green / white	vitreous, greasy / transluc., dull	5 / 3.1—3.2	less distinct / conchoidal, brittle	columnar, hexagonal crystals; granular, compact / hexagonal	in lithium-pegmatites / — / — cf. No. 158	Apatite variety **MOROXITE** $Ca_5[F(PO_4)_3]$ / Renfrew, Quebec, Canada
339	yellow, brown, reddish, greenish, black / white	vitreous, greasy / transpar., transluc.	5—5.5 / 3.4—3.6	indistinct / conchoidal, brittle	columnar, wedge-shaped, tabular, needle-shaped crystals / monoclinic	in alpine cracks, in crystalline schists / — / axinite, cf. No. 162, 463	**TITANITE** $CaTi(O\,SiO_4)$ / Teufelsmühle, Habachtal, Salzburg, Austria
340	brown, black-grey, black / white, grey	vitreous, adamantine / transluc., opaque	6.5 / 3.6	clear / brittle	long-columnar crystals; radial, rose-shaped agg. / monoclinic	in granite-pegmatites / monazite, zircon, beryl, ilmenite, magnetite	**THORTVEITITE** $Sc_2[Si_2O_7]$ / Befanamo, Madagascar
341	brown, brownish-black, yellowish crust / yellow-brown, grey-brown	greasy, sub-metallic / transluc., opaque	5.5—6.5 / 4.6—5.9	— / conchoidal, brittle	tubular, prismatic, tabular crystals; flabelliform agg.; granular / orthorhombic	in granite-pegmatites / zircon, monazite, beryl, ilmenite, magnetite / —	**EUXENITE** $(Y,Ce,U,Pb,Ca)(Nb,Ta,Ti)_2(O,OH)_6$ (Polycrase) / Ampangabe, Madagascar
342	brownish-black, grey-black, blackish, black-green	vitreous, greasy, sub-metallic / opaque	5.5—6 / 4.1	clear / conchoidal, brittle	columnar, longitudinally striated, needle-shaped, capillary crystals; tubular, radial, fibrous agg.; granular, compact / orthorhombic	in contact-metamorphic rocks, in lavas / augite, amphibole / tourmaline, actinolite	**ILVAITE** $CaFe_2 \cdot CaFe_3[OH\,O\,Si_2O_7]$ (Lievrite, Yenite) / Rio Marina, Elba, Italy
343	brown, dark grey, blackish-green, black / white, grey	vitreous / opaque	5—6 / 3.5—3.6	clear / brittle	tubular, needle-shaped crystals; spathic, granular, compact, massive / monoclinic	in metamorphic & metasomatic rocks / magnetite, pyrite & o.	**HEDENBERGITE** $CaFe[Si_2O_6]$ / Nordmark, Värmland, Sweden
344	brownish-green, green, greenish-black / white, grey	vitreous / transpar., transluc.	5—6 / 3.2—3.3	good / brittle	short-, long- & thick-columnar to acicular crystals; compact, disseminated, granular to massive / monoclinic	in cracks of metamorphic rocks, in volcanic ejecta / garnet, spinel, vesuvianite / diopside, amphibole	**FASSAITE** $Ca(Mg,Fe,Al)[(Si,Al)_2O_6]$ / Brosso near Traversella, Piedmont, Italy

337	338
339	340
341	342
343	344

No.	Colour / Streak	Lustre / Transparency	Hardness / Specific Gravity	Cleavage / Fracture & o. / Phys. Props.	Common Form, Aggregates / Crystalline Syst.	Occurrence / Assoc. Minerals / Similar Minerals	Name & Chem. Formula / Origin of Specimen
345	brown, grey / white	vitreous, pearly, metallic, iridescent / transluc.	5 – 6 / 3.1 – 3.2	good soft, elastic	needle-shaped, tabular, fibrous crystals; tubular, fibrous, lamellar agg.; compact, nodules / orthorhombic	orthorhombic amphibole, in metamorphic rocks, in crystalline schists, as radiating-columnar shells, so-called 'Glimmerskugeln' (mica globules) / — / cf. No. 408	**ANTHO-PHYLLITE** $(Mg,Fe)_7$ $[OH\ Si_4O_{11}]_2$ / Heřmanov, Czech Republic
346	brownish, reddish, grey, white, yellowish, colourless / white	vitreous, pearly / transluc., transpar.	6 – 6.5 / 2.5	very good brittle, uneven	short-columnar, thick platy crystals; spathic, granular, massive / monoclinic	main constituent of numerous rocks / — / cf. No. 205	**ORTHO-CLASE** $K(AlSi_3O_8)$ (Felspar Family) / Strzegom, Silesia Poland
347	brown, yellow-brown, red / white	adamantine / transpar., transluc.	6.5 / 4.2 – 4.3	good brittle	acicular to capillary crystals; reticulated agg.; inclusions in rock crystal / tetragonal	as fine needles in alpine cracks, inclusions in quartz / quartz / cf. No. 541	Rutile variety **SAGENITE** TiO_2 / Brazil
348	yellow, red, red-brown, black / yellow, brown	adamantine, metallike / transpar., transluc.	5.5 – 6 / 3.9 – 4.2	poor uneven	thin-tabular, flat crystals / orthorhombic	in alpine cracks / anatase, titanite, adularia, quartz / rutile, cf. No. 198	**BROOKITE** TiO_2 / Riedertobel near Amsteg, Switzerland
349	dark yellow, brown, red, green, yellowish-white / white, grey	vitreous, greasy / transpar., transluc.	6 – 6.5 / 3.1 – 3.3	clear conchoidal	small, short-columnar crystals; disseminated, rounded grains, compact, granular / monoclinic	in metamorphic limestones, in volcanic ejecta, in ore deps. / magnetite, galena & o. / olivine, cancrinite	**CHONDRO-DITE** $Mg_5[(OH),F]_2$ $(SiO_4)_2$ / Franklin, New Jersey, USA
350	brown, blackish-red, red, red-brown / red	vitreous, transluc., opaque	6.5 / 3.4	good uneven, brittle	columnar to tubular crystals; long-radiating agg.; compact, radial, granular to massive / monoclinic	in crystalline schists, in manganese ore deps. / — / —	**PIED-MONTITE** $Ca_2(Mn,Fe)Al_2$ $[O\ OH\ SiO_4$ $Si_2O_7]$ (Manganiferous Epidote) / Aosta, Piedmont, Italy
351	brown, green, blue, yellow, red / white, grey	vitreous, greasy / transluc.	6.5 / 3.2 – 3.4	— uneven & splintery	columnar, needle-shaped, pyramidal, thick-columnar crystals; compact, granular, massive, radial, tubular / tetragonal	in metamorphic rocks, in crystalline schists, in volcanic ejecta / chlorite, diopside, garnet, epidote / grossular, rutile, zircon, epidote	**VESU-VIANITE** $Ca_{10}(Mg,Fe)_2Al_4$ $[(OH)_4(SiO_4)_5$ $(Si_2O_7)_2]$ / Monte Somma, Vesuvius, Italy
352	brown / white, grey	vitreous, transluc., opaque	6.5 / 3.2 – 3.4	— uneven & splintery	long-columnar, striated crystals; radial, tubular agg. / tetragonal	radial vesuvianite	Vesuvianite variety **EGERAN** $Ca_{10}(Mg,Fe)_2Al_4$ $[(OH)_4(SiO_4)_5$ $(Si_2O_7)_2]$ / Hazlov, Czech Republic

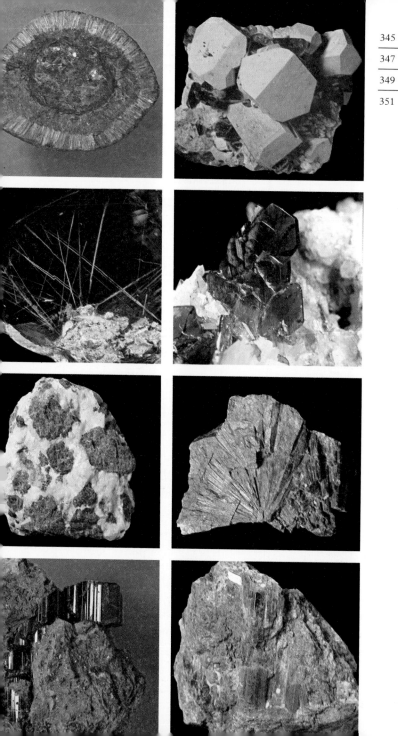

345	346
347	348
349	350
351	352

No.	Colour / Streak	Lustre / Transparency	Hardness / Specific Gravity	Cleavage Fracture & o. Phys. Props.	Common Form, Aggregates Crystalline Syst.	Occurrence Assoc. Minerals Similar Minerals	Name & Chem. Formula Origin of Specimen
353	green-brown, brown, grey-green / white, grey	vitreous, greasy / transluc., opaque	6.5 / 3.4	uneven, splintery	short-columnar, well-formed crystals / tetragonal	in metamorphic tuffaceous rocks, embedded / grossularite / —	Vesuvianite variety WILUITE $Ca_{10}(Mg,Fe)_2$ $Al_4[(OH)_4$ $(SiO_4)_5 (Si_2O_7)_2]$ Vilyui River, Yakutia, Russia
354	yellow-green, red-brown, greenish-black, olive-green / white	vitreous, greasy / transpar., transluc.	6.5 — 7 / 3.3	good con-choidal	tabular, columnar crystals; granular, massive, compact, insets / orthorhombic	constituent in basic igneous rocks, in magnetite deps. / — / cf. No. 299	OLIVINE $(Mg,Fe)_2[SiO_4]$ (Peridote, Chrysolite) Kraslice, Czech Republic
355	colourless, yellow, green, brown, red, blue, orange / white	vitreous, ada-mantine, greasy / transpar., transluc.	6.5 — 7.5 / 3.9 — 4.8	imperfect con-choidal	columnar, pyrami-dal, needle-shaped, embedded crystals; granular, botryoidal / tetragonal	in igneous rocks, in fissures, in crys-talline schists / biotite, amphibole, garnet, quartz & o. / vesuvianite, thorite, titanite, garnet	ZIRCON $Zr[SiO_4]$ Ilmen Mountains, Southern Urals, Russia
356	brown, brown-green, green, black / white, grey	vitreous, greasy / transluc., opaque	7 / 3.3 — 4.1	— con-choidal, brittle	dodecahedral, icosi-tetrahedral crys-tals; compact, granular, massive / cubic	in crystalline schists & meta-morphic rocks, in ore deps. / — / vesuvianite, zircon, ruby	ANDRADITE $Ca_3Fe_2[SiO_4]_3$ (Common Garnet) Ciclova, Romania
357	brown, grey, violet, greenish / white	vitreous / transpar., transluc.	6.5 — 7 / 3.3	good con-choidal, brittle	tabular, wedge-shaped & lentiform crystals; granular, compact, dissemi-nated / triclinic	in granites in fis-sures, in crystalline schists, in meta-morphic limestone, in ore deps. / epidote, chlorite & o. / titanite	AXINITE $Ca_2(Fe,Mn)Al_2$ $[BO_3OH Si_4O_{12}]$ Bourg d'Oisans, Dauphiné, France
358	brown, brownish-black / grey-white	vitreous, dull / transluc., opaque	7 — 7.5 / 3.7 — 3.8	clear con-choidal, splintery	short- & long-columnar crystals; often cruciform twins / orthorhombic	in crystalline schists / kyanite, almandine, muscovite, quartz / garnet	STAUROLITE $Al_4[Fe(OH)_2O_2$ $(SiO_4)_2]$ Quimper, France
359	brown, brown-black / white	vitreous, greasy / transpar., transluc.	7 — 7.5 / 3 — 3.2	— con-choidal, brittle	long-columnar, longitudinally striated, embedded crystals / trigonal	in crystalline schists, in meta-morphic limestone / — / ilvaite	Tourmaline variety DRAVITE $NaMg_3Al_6$ $[(OH)_4 (BO_3)_3$ $Si_6O_{18}]$ (Tourmaline Family) Dobrova, Slovenia
360	brown, red, yellow, black / white	vitreous / transpar., transluc.	8 / 3.5 — 4.1	— con-choidal	octahedral embedded crystals; granular / cubic	in metamorphic limestone & dolo-mite, in basalts, in volcanic ejecta / — / corundum, zircon, garnet, cf. No. 246	SPINEL Al_2MgO_4 Amity, New York, USA

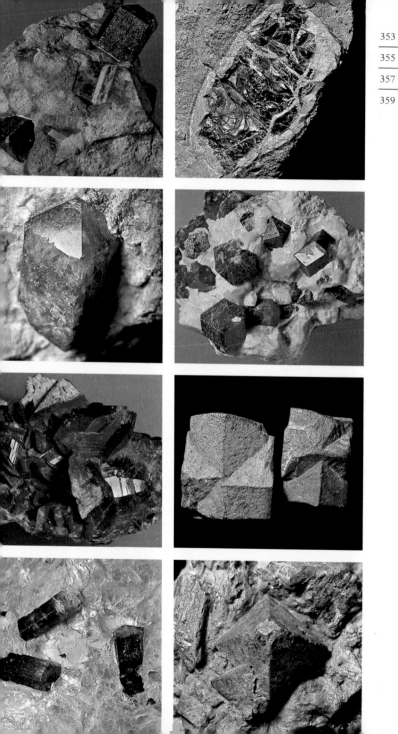

129

No.	Colour / Streak	Lustre / Transparency	Hardness / Specific Gravity	Cleavage / Fracture & o. Phys. Props.	Common Form, Aggregates / Crystalline Syst.	Occurrence / Assoc. Minerals / Similar Minerals	Name & Chem. Formula / Origin of Specimen
361	lead-grey, blackish-grey / grey, black	metallic / opaque	1 — 1.5 / 6.8 — 7.5	very good / flexible, soft, malleable	thin-tabular, lamellar crystals; scaly agg.; compact, granular / orthorhombic	in gold veins / sylvanite, gold, pyrite, tellurium, quartz / —	**NAGYAGITE** $AuTe_2 \cdot 6Pb$ (S,Te) (Black Tellurium) / Săcărâmb, Romania
362	lead-grey to bluish / dark grey, leek-green, shining	metallic / opaque	1 — 1.5 / 4.6 — 4.7	perfect / inelastic, flexible, soft, greasy	flat, tabular crystals; lamellar, fine-scaly, compact to massive, disseminated / hexagonal	in granites, pegmatites, in tin ore deps., in quartz veins / cassiterite, wolframite, fluorite, tourmaline, apatite / graphite	**MOLYB-DENITE** MoS_2 (Molybdic Ochre) / Krupka, Czech Republic

No.	Colour / Streak	Lustre / Transparency	Hardness / Specific Gravity	Cleavage / Fracture & o. Phys. Props.	Common Form, Aggregates / Crystalline Syst.	Occurrence / Assoc. Minerals / Similar Minerals	Name & Chem. Formula / Origin of Specimen
363	silver-white, grey to blackish / silver-white	metallic / opaque	2.5 — 3 / 10.1 to 11.1	hackly / ductile, malleable	filiform, sheet- & curl-shaped, mossy, compact / cubic	in ore veins / argentite, pyrargyrite, galena & o. / — / cf. No. 5, 6	nat. **SILVER** Ag / Wittichen, Black Forest, Germany
364	tin-white, grey / grey	metallic / opaque	2 — 2.5 / 6.1 — 6.3	very good / sectile but brittle	columnar, short-needle-shaped crystals; mostly compact, finely granular, fine-tubular, disseminated / trigonal	associated with nat. gold / sylvanite, pyrite, quartz & o. / —	nat. **TELLURIUM** Te / Fata Bai, Romania
365	dark lead-grey, black / dark grey, shining	metallic, dull / opaque	2 — 2.5 / 6.1 — 6.3	indistinct / hackly, sectile, malleable, flexible	cubic, octahedral, dodecahedral crystals; disseminated, platy, powdery, sooty, reticulated, compact / monoclinic	in pseudomorphs after silver, in silver ore deps. / silver, pyrargyrite, proustite, galena & o. / chalcosine	**ARGENTITE** Ag_2S (Silver Glance) / Freiberg, Ore Mountains, Germany
366	lead-grey / grey-black, dull	metallic, dull / opaque	2.5 / 7.2 — 7.6	perfect, cube spathic, brittle to soft	cubo-octahedral crystals; compact, granular, massive, disseminated, reticulated, platy / cubic	in hydrothermal ore veins, metasomatic in limestone & dolomite, sedimentary / sphalerite, chalcopyrite, tetrahedrite, arsenopyrite, pyrite / antimonite, bournonite	**GALENA** PbS (Lead Glance, Blue Lead) / Joplin, Missouri, USA
367 / 368	lead grey to black / black, dark grey	metallic / opaque	2 — 2.5 / 4.6 — 4.7	perfect / soft, inelastic, flexible, conchoidal	long-columnar, needle-shaped, fragile, capillary, often longitudinally striated crystals; compact, tubular, fibrous, radiate in bunches, capillary entangled, granular, massive / orthorhombic	in ore veins, in quartz veins, metasomatic in limestones / barytes, siderite, pyrite, nat. gold, realgar, orpiment, quartz & o. / bismutite, pyrolusite, galena	**ANTIMONITE** Sb_2S_3 (Antimony Glance, Grey Antimony, Stibnite) / Ichinokawa Mine, Japan / **ANTIMONITE** Sb_2S_3 / Capnic, Romania

No.	Colour / Streak	Lustre / Transparency	Hardness / Specific Gravity	Cleavage Fracture & o. Phys. Props.	Common Form, Aggregates / Crystalline Syst.	Occurrence / Assoc. Minerals / Similar Minerals	Name & Chem. Formula / Origin of Specimen
369	lead-grey, steel-grey, light grey, shining	metallic opaque	2.5 – 3 / 8.1 – 8.8	indistinct / brittle, sectile	distorted, cube-shaped crystals; mostly compact, granular / monoclinic >155° cubic	in hydrothermal ore deps. / nat. gold, tellurium, nagyagite, pyrite, sylvanite & o. / —	**HESSITE** Ag_2Te (Silver Telluride) / Botesti, Romania
370	white-grey, dark grey / dark grey, shining	metallic opaque	2.5 – 3 / 5.5 – 5.8	indistinct / conchoidal, soft	thick-tabular, short-columnar, needle-shaped crystals; compact, massive, finely granular, disseminated, earthy, encrustations / orthorhombic >103° hexagonal	in hydrothermal ore veins, also sedimentary in sandstone & tufa / chalcopyrite, bornite, covellite, pyrite & o. / tetrahedrite, bornite, argentite	**CHALCOCITE** Cu_2S (Copper Glance) / Redruth, Cornwall, England
371	dark reddish-grey, brown-red, violet / black	metallic opaque	2.5 – 3 / 4.5	— / brittle	only compact, finely granular, no crystals / cubic	rare in ore veins / sphalerite, pyrite, tetrahedrite, bornite / bornite, enargite	**GERMANITE** $Cu_3(Fe,Ge)S_4$ / Tsumeb, South-West Africa
372	lead-grey to black / dark grey	metallic opaque	2.5 – 3 / 7.6 – 7.8	very good / soft	no crystals; only compact, finely granular / cubic	in hydrothermal ore deps. / nat. gold, haematite, calcite, dolomite, barytes / galena	**CLAUS-THALITE** $PbSe$ / Falun, Kopparberg, Svealand, Sweden
373	blackish-grey to black / black, shining	metallic opaque	2.5 / 6.2 – 6.3	poor / soft to brittle, conchoidal	thick-tabular, columnar crystals; rose-shaped clusters, compact, disseminated, encrustations / orthorhombic	in silver veins / silver, argentite, baryte, fluorite & o. / argentite, chalcocite	**STEPHANITE** $5Ag_2S . Sb_2S_3$ (Brittle Silver Ore) / Jáchymov, Czech Republic
374	blackish-grey / dark grey, black	metallic opaque	2.5 – 3 / 5.7	clear / soft	pyramidal, needle-shaped crystals; often distorted, needle-shaped, fibrous, satiny agg. / monoclinic	in lead-zinc ore deps. / — / jamesonite, boulangerite	**HETERO-MORPHITE** $11PbS . 6Sb_2S_3$ / Příbram, Czech Republic
375	steel-grey, dark grey / grey-black	metallic opaque	2 – 2.5 / 5.5 – 5.7	clear / soft	long-acicular, fine-capillary, fragile crystals; radial-fibrous, bunchy, entangled agg.; compact, massive, feather-like / monoclinic	in hydrothermal ore veins / galena, bournonite & o. / boulangerite, heteromorphite, antimonite	**JAMESONITE** $4PbS . FeS . 3Sb_2S_3$ (Feather Ore) / Cornwall, England
376	grey-black / black	metallic opaque	2.5 / 5.9 – 6.1	clear / brittle	tabular prismatic crystals; radial-fibrous, globular agg.; crusts / monoclinic	in lead ore deps. / galena, sphalerite & o. / —	**SEMSEYITE** $9PbS . 4Sb_2S_3$ / Herja (Chiuz-baia, Kisbánya), Romania

No.	Colour / Streak	Lustre / Transparency	Hardness / Specific Gravity	Cleavage Fracture & o. Phys. Props.	Common Form, Aggregates / Crystalline Syst.	Occurrence / Assoc. Minerals / Similar Minerals	Name & Chem. Formula / Origin of Specimen
377	blackish-grey / black	metallic / opaque	2.5 / 5.4	— / lamellar, divisible, soft to brittle, malleable	lamellar-cylindrical, shelly agg.; cylindrical bunches, spheroidal / orthorhombic	in hydrothermal silver-tin veins / cassiterite, stannine, sphalerite, pyrite, jamesonite	**CYLINDRITE** $Pb_3Sn_4Sb_2S_{14}$ / Poopó, Bolivia
378	lead-grey, blackish-grey / black	metallic, dull, silky / opaque	2.5 / 5.8 — 6.2	clear / flexible, brittle	long-columnar, needle-shaped, striated crystals; fibrous, radial, feather-like agg.; compact, massive / monoclinic	in hydrothermal ore veins / antimonite, galena, sphalerite, arsenopyrite, pyrite & o. / jamesonite, heteromorphite	**BOULANGERITE** $5PbS . 2Sb_2S_3$ / Příbram, Czech Republic
379	grey, grey-black / black	metallic, sub-metallic, indistinct / opaque	2 — 7 / 5	— / brittle	radial, fibrous, needle-shaped, capillary, compact, in radiate crystal masses; massive, earthy, reniform, cone-shaped, loose / tetragonal	in oxidized zone of manganese ores, hydrothermal in ore veins, sedimentary deps. / psilomelane, manganite, braunite / —	**PYROLUSITE** MnO_2 / Příbram, Czech Republic
380	tin-white, lead-grey, black-tarnished / black	metallic, dull / opaque	3 / 5.7	perfect / brittle, shelly	mostly of crooked shelly form, reniform, compact masses; shelled refraction, mammillated, nodular, platy, compact / trigonal	in ore veins / silver, galena, proustite, sphalerite, chloanthite, niccolite, baryte & o. / —	nat. **ARSENIC** As / St. Andreasberg, Harz, Germany
381	tin-white to lead-grey / lead-grey	metallic / opaque	3.5 / 6.6	perfect / brittle	tabular, cube-like crystals; mostly compact, granular-spathic, lamellar, reniform, disseminated / trigonal	in ore veins / antimonite, allemontite & o. / allemontite, dyscrasite	nat. **ANTIMONY** Sb / Allemont, France
382	lead-grey / grey-black	metallic / opaque	3 — 4 / 4.5 — 5	— / uneven, brittle	tetrahedral, cubic, dodecahedral crystals; compact, granular, disseminated, massive / cubic	in hydrothermal silver veins / galena, chalcopyrite, sphalerite, pyrite, argentite / bournonite, tetrahedrite	**FREIBERGITE** $(Cu,Ag)_3$ $(Sb,As)S_4$ (Silver Fahlerz, Argentiferous Grey Copper Ore) / Freiberg, Germany
383	lead-grey, black / grey	metallic, greasy / opaque	3 / 5.7 — 5.9	indistinct / brittle to soft, conchoidal	tabular, short-columnar, cube-shaped, pyramidal crystals; interpenetrant twins, compact, granular, massive, disseminated, encrustations / orthorhombic	in hydrothermal ore veins / galena, sphalerite, chalcopyrite, tetrahedrite, antimonite / tetrahedrite, boulangerite	**BOURNONITE** $2PbS . Cu_2S . Sb_2S_3$ (Wheel Ore, Endellionite) / Neudorf near Quedlinburg, Harz, Germany
384	grey, yellowish, tarnishing to bronze colour / black	metallic / opaque	4 / 4.3 — 4.5	indistinct / brittle, conchoidal	pseudocubic, tetrahedral crystals; compact, finely granular, disseminated, massive / tetragonal	in ore veins / cassiterite, tetrahedrite, arsenopyrite, pyrite / chalcopyrite, tetrahedrite, arsenopyrite	**STANNINE** Cu_2FeSnS_4 (Tin Pyrites, Bell Metal Ore) / Oruro, Bolivia

377	378
379	380
381	382
383	384

No.	Colour / Streak	Lustre / Transparency	Hardness / Specific Gravity	Cleavage / Fracture & o. / Phys. Props.	Common Form, Aggregates / Crystalline Syst.	Occurrence / Assoc. Minerals / Similar Minerals	Name & Chem. Formula / Origin of Specimen
385	steel-grey / grey, shining	metallic / opaque	4—5 / 7.3—7.8	good / hackly, malleable, ductile	compact, disseminated, in grains, scales, clumps / cubic	in all meteorites, rarely as inclusions in basalt, in ultra-basic rocks / pentlandite / —	nat. **IRON** Fe / Blaafjeld near Ovifak, Greenland
386	copper-red, grey, tarnishing to blue / reddish-brown, black	metallic / opaque	5.5 / 8.2	poor / uneven, brittle	thin-tabular, columnar, needle-shaped crystals; compact, finely granular, lamellar, disseminated / hexagonal	in ore veins / chloanthite, ullmannite, pyrargyrite, galena & o. / niccolite	**BREIT-HAUPTITE** NiSb / Monte Narba, Sardinia, Italy
387	reddish-silver-white, tarnishing to steel-grey / grey-black	metallic / opaque	4.5—5.5 / 4.8	changing / uneven, brittle	octahedral, cubic crystals; compact, granular, disseminated / cubic	in hydrothermal ore veins / galena, tetrahedrite, chalcopyrite / ullmannite, gersdorffite, cobaltite	**LINNAEITE** Co_3S_4 / Schwaben Mine, Müsen, Siegerland, Germany
388	tin-white, grey-white / black, grey	metallic / opaque	4.5—5 / 7.2—7.4	indistinct / conchoidal, brittle	lentiform, disc-shaped crystals; stellate triplets, compact, reniform, botryoidal, finely granular, radiate, fibrous, massive / orthorhombic	in ore veins / niccolite, bismuth, löllingite, siderite, barytes, fluorite / chloanthite, skutterudite, arsenopyrite	**SAFFLORITE** $CoAs_2$ (Smaltite, Tin White Cobalt) / Schneeberg, Germany
389	tin-white, grey / black	metallic / opaque	5.5—6 / 6.2—6.9	clear / brittle	short-columnar, tabular crystals; compact, granular, radial, fibrous / orthorhombic	in ore veins / silver, galena & o. / löllingite, chloanthite, skutterudite, cf. No. 15	**ARSENO-PYRITE** FeAsS (Mispickel, Arsenical Pyrites) / Ciclova, Romania
390	tin-white to dark grey / grey-black	metallic / opaque	5.5 / 6.6	— / jointing due to zoning, brittle, fibrous	cubic, often ventricular, contorted crystals; finely granular, compact, reniform, massive / cubic	in hydrothermal ore veins / arsenic, bismuth, galena, niccolite, ullmannite & o. / safflorite, löllingite, arsenopyrite, rammelsbergite, cf. No. 14	**CHLOAN-THITE** NiAs₃ (White Nickel) / Schneeberg, Germany
391	tin-white, tarnishing dark grey / grey-black	metallic / opaque	5.5 / 6.5	— / uneven, brittle	octahedral crystals; compact, granular, massive, reniform, reticulated / cubic	in silver-cobalt-nickel veins / silver & similar minerals / safflorite, cobaltite, löllingite, arsenopyrite, ullmannite, rammelsbergite, cf. No. 16	**SKUTTE-RUDITE** $CoAs_3$ (Smaltite) / Huelva on Gulf Cadiz, Spain
392	tin-white, tarnishing grey / grey-black	metallic / opaque	5.5—6 / 7.1	clear / brittle	lentiform, prismatic crystals; compact, finely radiate, granular / orthorhombic	in ore veins / smaltite, niccolite / chloanthite, safflorite, arsenopyrite, löllingite, skutterudite	**RAMMELS-BERGITE** $NiAs_2$ / Richelsdorf, Hessen, Germany

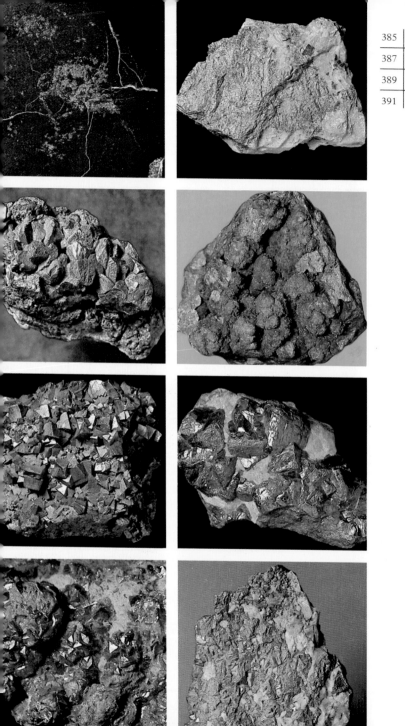

385	386
387	388
389	390
391	392

No.	Colour / Streak	Lustre / Transparency	Hardness / Specific Gravity	Cleavage / Fracture & o. Phys. Props.	Common Form, Aggregates / Crystalline Syst.	Occurrence / Assoc. Minerals / Similar Minerals	Name & Chem. Formula / Origin of Specimen
393	white, grey, yellowish, brown / white, yellowish	ada-mantine / transpar., transluc.	1—2 / 6.4—6.5	good / soft, sectile	tabular, columnar, short-acicular crystals; compact, crusty, earthy, carneous, massive, encrustations / tetragonal	in quicksilver ore deps. / quicksilver, cinnabar, barytes, quartz / —	CALOMEL Hg_2Cl_2 (Horn Quicksilver) / Moschellandsberg, Rhine-Palatinate, Germany
394	yellow-brown, grey, white-grey / white	vitreous, dull / transluc.	2 / 1.6—1.7	good / soft	roof-like, coffin-shaped, tabular, only embedded crystals / orthorhombic	in manure pits & canals, in guano / — / —	STRUVITE $NH_4Mg[PO_4] . 6H_2O$ / Hamburg, Germany
395	white, grey, grey-rose / white	pearly / transluc.	3—3.5 / 3	very good / brittle, friable	thin-tabular, lamellar, pseudo-hexagonal crystals; compact, scaly, granular-lamellar, disseminated / monoclinic	in chlorite schists, in emery deps. / corundum, magnetite, rutile, emerald / —	MARGARITE $CaAl_2[(OH)_2 Al_2Si_2O_{10}]$ / Zillertal, Tyrol, Austria
396	white, grey, yellowish, brownish / white	dull / opaque	1—2 / 2.5—2.6	— / soft, swelling in water	loosely compact, clay-like; massive, earthy, friable masses / monoclinic	clay composed of montmorillonite, sedimentary / — / kaolinite, pyrophyllite	BENTONITE $Al_2Mg(OH)_2 [Si_4O_{10}] (Ca,Na)_x . 4H_2O$ / Rock River, Wyoming, USA
397	white, yellow, grey-white / white	pearly, silver glance / transluc.	1 / 2.5—2.6	very good / soft, flexible, greasy	pseudohexagonal, thin-foliaceous crystals; fine-scaly, compact, massive, earthy, loose / monoclinic	hydrothermal in tin ore deps., in ore veins / — / pyrophyllite, sericite, talc	NACRITE $Al_4[(OH)_8 Si_4O_{10}]$ / Brand-Erbisdorf, Germany
398	yellowish, white, grey, greenish / white	silky, vitreous / transluc.	1—2.5 / 2.6	good / soft to brittle	compact masses, radiate-lamellar, globular, stellate, concentrically shelled agg.; granular / monoclinic	constituents: partly nacrite & kaolinite, partly muscovite, also sericite, pseudomorphoses after topaz, in tin ore deps., in granite / fluorite / —	GILBERTITE $Al_4[(OH)_8 Si_4O_{10}], KAl_2 [(OH,F)_2 AlSi_3O_{10}]$ / St. Just, Cornwall, England
399	grey, white, yellowish, brownish / white	dull / transluc., opaque	1—2 / 2.1—2.3	— / soft, flexible	finely fibrous, felt-like, cryptocrystal-line / monoclinic or orthorhombic	weathering product of serpentine / chalcedony, opal, chlorite, magnesite / —	PALYGOR-SKITE $(Mg,Al)_2 [OH Si_4O_{10}] . 4H_2O$ / Lovinobaňa, Slovakia
400	olive-green, blackish-green, grey-black, greenish-grey	dull, pearly / opaque	2.5 / 3.2	good / soft	compact, finely granular, massive, fine-scaly, oölitic, cryptocrystalline / monoclinic	in sedimentary ore deps., in chlorite schists / limonite, magnetite, garnet / chamosite	THURINGITE $(Fe_2,Fe_3,Al)_3 [(OH)_2Al_2Si_2O_{10} (Mg,Fe_2,Fe_3)_3 (O,OH)_6$ / Šternberk, Czech Republic

393	394
395	396
397	398
399	400

No.	Colour / Streak	Lustre / Transparency	Hardness / Specific Gravity	Cleavage / Fracture & o. Phys. Props.	Common Form, Aggregates / Crystalline Syst.	Occurrence / Assoc. Minerals / Similar Minerals	Name & Chem. Formula / Origin of Specimen
401	white, yellowish, grey, brown, black / white	adamantine, greasy / transpar., transluc.	3—3.5 / 6.4—6.6	indistinct / conchoidal, brittle	columnar, tabular, needle-shaped crystals; twins, triplets, stellate clusters, compact, reniform, massive / orthorhombic	in weathering zone of lead veins / — / anglesite, phosgenite, barytes, scheelite, cf. No. 321	CERUSSITE $PbCO_3$ (Ceruse, White Lead Ore) / Oloví, Czech Republic
402	colourless, white, grey, blackish, greenish / white	adamantine, greasy / transluc., transpar.	3 / 6.1—6.4	good / conchoidal, brittle	tabular, short-prismatic, columnar, needle-shaped crystals; compact, granular, reniform, crusty, earthy / orthorhombic	in oxidation zone of lead ore deps. / limonite, cerussite, galena / cerussite, barytes, scheelite	ANGLESITE $PbSO_4$ (Lead Vitriol) / Monte-Poni, Sardinia, Italy
403	brown, grey, yellowish, greenish / white	pearly, bronze-coloured / transpar., transluc.	2.5—3 / 2.7—2.9	perfect / flexible, foliaceous	pseudohexagonal, thin-tabular, short-prismatic crystals; coarse scales, lamellar agg. / monoclinic	in pegmatites, in metamorphic limestones & dolomites, in serpentine, in apatite veins / — / biotite, muscovite	PHLOGOPITE $KMg_3[(F,OH)_2 AlSi_3O_{10}]$ / Ampandandrava, Madagascar
404	grey, greenish-grey, brownish, greenish-black / grey-green	vitreous, dull / opaque	3 / 3	good / uneven	massive, granular, compact, oölitic, concentrically shelled / monoclinic	sedimentary ore deps. / limonite, magnetite, siderite, calcite & o. / thuringite	CHAMOSITE $(Fe_2Fe_3)_3[(OH)_2 AlSi_3O_{10}](Fe,Mg)_3(O,OH)_6$ / Nučice, Czech Republic
405	colourless, white, grey, yellowish, blackish / white	vitreous, dull / transluc., transpar.	3.5—4 / 3	perfect / conchoidal, brittle	rhombohedral crystals; compact, reniform, nodular, coarsely granular, spathic, massive / trigonal	metasomatic deps. replacing limestone & dolomite, in serpentine, in talc schists / — / ankerite, calcite, dolomite	MAGNESITE $MgCO_3$ (Bitter Spar) / Trieben, Styria, Austria
406	brown-red, grey to black, brownish-green / yellow-brown, orange-yellow	adamantine, vitreous, greasy, dull / opaque	3.5 / 5.7—6.2	— / conchoidal, brittle	columnar, pyramidal, tabular crystals; radiate agg.; crusty, botryoidal, mammillary, coatings / orthorhombic	in oxidation zone of ore veins / pyromorphite, vanadinite, cerussite, mimetesite, limonite / —	DESCLOIZITE $Pb(Zn,Cu)[OH VO_4]$ / Total Wreck Mine, Arizona, USA
407	leek-green, grey, blackish / light grey	vitreous, greasy, dull / transpar., transluc.	3.5—4 / 3.1—3.8	good / splintery, brittle	short-columnar, pyramidal, tabular, needle-shaped crystals; globular agg.; reniform, finely granular, massive / orthorhombic	weathering product of iron-arsenic minerals, in cavities in limonite / arsenopyrite / pharmacosiderite	SCORODITE $Fe[AsO_4] \cdot 2H_2O$ / Graul Mine near Schwarzenberg, Germany
408	whitish-grey, yellowish-grey, brown / white	vitreous, pearly, silky / transluc.	5—5.5 / 2.8—3.5	very good / brittle	finely fibrous, fine needle-shaped, capillary, compact, nodular / orthorhombic	in metamorphic rocks, in mica schists / — / chrysotile, cf. No. 345	ANTHOPHYLLITE $(Mg,Fe)_7[OH Si_4O_{11}]_2$ (Anthophyllite Asbestos) / Massachusetts, USA

No.	Colour / Streak	Lustre / Transparency	Hardness / Specific Gravity	Cleavage Fracture & o. Phys. Props.	Common Form, Aggregates / Crystalline Syst.	Occurrence Assoc. Minerals / Similar Minerals	Name & Chem. Formula / Origin of Specimen
409 / 410	yellow-brown, grey, black, irised tarnish / rusty brown, yellow	sub-vitreous, silky, greasy, dull / opaque	5—5.5 also softer / 3.6—3.7	— / con-choidal, fibrous	cryptocrystalline, fibrous, tubular, reniform, cone-shaped, globular, shelled, stalactitic, oölitic, botryoidal, compact, earthy, loose, in pseudomorphs after pyrite, siderite & o. ferruginous minerals / orthorhombic	as weathering product in all iron deps., sedimentary deps., in hydrothermal veins / pyrolusite, haematite, chalcedony & o. / haematite, cf. No. 482	**LIMONITE** Predominantly cryptocrystalline mixture of goethite (α-FeOOH), less often of lepidocrocite (γ-FeOOH) (Brown Iron Ore, Brown Haematite, Brown Ironstone) / Herdorf, Siegerland, Germany / **LIMONITE** / Elba, Italy
411	white, yellow, red, green, grey, bluish / white	vitreous, greasy / transluc.	5 / 4.3—4.5	very good / brittle	small rhombohedral crystals; compact, botryoidal, reniform, finely granular, massive, sinter crusts / trigonal	metasomatic in limestone & dolomite, in zinc deps. / — / hemimorphite, cf. No. 280	**SMITHSONITE** $ZnCO_3$ (Galmei) / Laurion, Greece
412	grey, greenish, brownish / white	vitreous, pearly / transluc., opaque	5.5 / 3.1—3.3	clear / uneven	columnar, thick-tabular, needle-shaped crystals; compact, granular, spathic / orthorhombic	rock constituent in serpentine, in pegmatic apatite veins / apatite, phlogopite, olivine, bronzite / apatite, hypersthene	**ENSTATITE** $Mg_2[Si_2O_6]$ (Pyroxene Family) / Bamle near Oedergården, Norway
413	brown, grey, green, black / white	vitreous, pearly, silky, metallic / opaque	5—6 / 3.5—3.7	good / striated cleavage planes	columnar, tabular, lamellar, granular, compact / orthorhombic	rock constituent in basic rocks, in crystalline schists, in volcanic ejecta / olivine, enstatite / enstatite, diallage	**HYPERSTHENE** $(Fe,Mg)_2[Si_2O_6]$ / St.Paul Island, Labrador
414	white, light grey, greenish / white	vitreous, silky / transluc.	5—6 / 2.9—3	very good / brittle	needle-shaped, fibrous, capillary, radial, compact, asbestos-like / monoclinic	in metamorphic limestone & dolomite, in talc schists / — / chrysotile, pectolite, wollastonite	**TREMOLITE** $Ca_2Mg_5(OH,F)_2[Si_4O_{11}]_2$ (Amphibole Family) / Aosta, Piedmont, Italy
415	grey, brown, yellowish, green, rose-red / white	vitreous, pearly, silky / transluc., opaque	5.5—6 / 3.2—3.4	very good / uneven	long-columnar, needle-shaped, tubular, fibrous, lamellar, radial / orthorhombic	in metamorphic rocks, in crystalline schists, in granites, in ore veins / — / bronzite	**GEDRITE** $(Mg,Fe)_6Al_2[OH(AlSi)Si_3O_{11}]_2$ (Amphibole Family) / Gèdres, Pyrenees, France
416	grey, brown, white, blue, blackish / white	vitreous, greasy / transpar., transluc.	5.5—6 / 2.2—2.4	very good / con-choidal	columnar, dodecahedral crystals; compact, granular / cubic	in eruptive rocks; phonolites, basalts, in volcanic ejecta / leucite, nepheline, sodalite, hauyne	**NOSEAN** $Na_8[SO_4(AlSiO_4)_6]$ / Laacher See, Eifel, Germany

413 | 414

415 | 416

143

No.	Colour / Streak	Lustre / Transparency	Hardness / Specific Gravity	Cleavage Fracture & o. Phys. Props.	Common Form, Aggregates / Crystalline Syst.	Occurrence / Assoc. Minerals / Similar Minerals	Name & Chem. Formula / Origin of Specimen
417	grey, yellowish, reddish / white	vitreous, greasy transluc.	6 / 3.8 — 4.3	good con-choidal, splintery	columnar, needle-shaped crystals; compact, finely to coarsely granular / hexagonal	manganiferous willemite variety, in zinc deps. / zincite, franklinite / —	TROOSTITE $(Zn,Mn)_2[SiO_4]$ / Sterling Hill near Ogdensburg, New Jersey, USA
418	yellow, green, brown-red, grey to black / white	vitreous, metallic, brilliant transluc.. opaque	6.5 / 4.2	compara-tively good con-choidal	thick-tabular, short-columnar crystals; granular, massive / orthorhombic	in pegmatites, in tin ore veins, in obsidians / — / —	FAYALITE $Fe_2[SiO_4]$ (Olivine Family) / Fayal Island, Azores
419	colourless, white, greyish / white	vitreous transpar., dull	6.5 / 2.9	— con-choidal	rarely cube-shaped crystals; mostly compact, coarsely granular, irregular grains / cubic	in granite pegma-tites / beryl, petalite / hyalite, quartz	POLLUCITE (Cs,Na) $[AlSi_2O_6] H_2O$ / San Piero in Campo, Elba, Italy
420	grey, brownish, reddish, yellowish / white	vitreous, pearly transluc., opaque	6 — 6.5 / 2.5	very good uneven, brittle	tabular, bench-shaped crystals; only embedded / monoclinic	constituent in eruptive rocks / quartz, biotite, amphibole, nepheline / orthoclase, plagio-clase	SANIDINE $K[AlSi_3O_8]$ (Felspar Family) / Drachenfels, Pfälzer Wald, Germany
421	colourless, white, green-grey, grey, blue / white	vitreous, pearly transpar., transluc.	5 — 6 / 2.7	clear —	short-prismatic, thick-columnar, tubular crystals; granular, fibrous, radial, massive / tetragonal	in metamorphic rocks, as volcanic ejecta / — / felspars, spodumene, cf. No. 87	MEIONITE Ca_8 $[(Cl_2,SO_4,CO_3)_2$ $(Al_2Si_2O_8)_6]$ (Scapolite Family) / Vesuvius, Italy
422	grey, grey-bluish, grey-yellowish / white	vitreous, silky, dull transluc.	6 — 7 / 2.5 — 2.6	— con-choidal	fibrous to crypto-crystalline, reni-form, globular, bo-tryoidal, shelled, stalactitic, mammil-lary, crusts, nodules, concretions, amy-gdaloidal filling, fine-fibrous, finely radial / trigonal	micro- to crypto-crystalline quartz of gelatigenous origin, in fissures & cavi-ties in basaltic rocks, in ore veins / quartz, zeolite, calcite / prehnite, cf. No. 501	CHALCE-DONY SiO_2 / Tri Vody, Slovakia
423							CHALCE-DONY SiO_2 / Grákollur, Reydarfjördur, Iceland
424	grey, grey-brown to black / white	greasy, dull transluc., opaque	7 / 2.5 — 2.6	— con-choidal, splintery	nodular, platy con-cretions, often with white weathering crust, massive / amorphous	in sedimentary rocks, in chalk / — / —	Opal variety FIRESTONE $SiO_2 . nH_2O$ (Flint) / Rügen Island, Germany

No.	Colour Streak	Lustre Transparency	Hardness Specific Gravity	Cleavage Fracture & o. Phys. Props.	Common Form, Aggregates Crystalline Syst.	Occurrence Assoc. Minerals Similar Minerals	Name & Chem. Formula Origin of Specimen
425	steel-grey, black / black	sub-metallic, shining, dull / opaque	7 / $\overline{4.8-5}$	clear / uneven, brittle	rhombohedral, small crystals; compact, finely crystalline, fibrous, granular, massive / tetragonal	idiomorphic pyrolusite, in manganese deps. / — / — / cf. No. 379	**POLIANITE** MnO_2 / Schneeberg, Germany
426	grey, reddish-grey, brownish / white	vitreous, greasy, dull / transluc., opaque	7 / $\overline{3.1-3.2}$	good to indistinct / uneven, brittle	thick-columnar to acicular crystals; granular, compact, tubular, radial, fibrous / orthorhombic	in metamorphic rocks, in mica schists & gneiss in pegmatites / garnet, tourmaline, rutile, quartz / tourmaline	**ANDALUSITE** $Al_2[O\ SiO_4]$ / Lisenz-Alpe, Sellrain, Tyrol, Austria
427	colourless, yellowish, dark brown, grey / white	vitreous, greasy / transpar., transluc.	7—7.5 / $\overline{2.9-3}$	indistinct / conchoidal	columnar crystals; granular, compact / orthorhombic	pneumatolytic in dolomite, in gneiss, in alpine cracks, in volcanic ejecta / — / topaz, datolite	**DANBURITE** $Ca[B_2Si_2O_8]$ / Russel, St.Lawrence Co., New York, USA
428	grey-brown, yellowish, reddish, bluish / white	vitreous, greasy, dull / transpar., transluc.	9 / $\overline{3.9-4.1}$	fissile (jointing) / conchoidal, splintery	columnar, barrel-shaped, thick-tabular crystals; granular, compact, massive / trigonal	in pegmatites, in crystalline schists, in metamorphic limestone, dolomite, syenite & basalt / — / zircon, spinel, apatite, topaz, cf. No. 512	**CORUNDUM** Al_2O_3 / Ambositra, Madagascar

No.	Colour Streak	Lustre Transparency	Hardness Specific Gravity	Cleavage Fracture & o. Phys. Props.	Common Form, Aggregates Crystalline Syst.	Occurrence Assoc. Minerals Similar Minerals	Name & Chem. Formula Origin of Specimen
429	tombac-brown, red to black, iridescent tarnish / black	metallic / opaque	3 / $\overline{4.9-5.3}$	— / conchoidal, brittle to soft	cube-shaped, cubic octahedral, dodecahedral crystals; compact, platy masses, granular, massive, coatings / cubic	in copper veins / chalcopyrite, pyrite, chalcocite / pyrrhotine, niccolite (fresh), chalcocite, chalcopyrite, covellite	**BORNITE** Cu_5FeS_4 / Messina, Transvaal, South Africa
430	black / black	metallic / opaque	3 / $\overline{7.7-7.8}$	— / brittle	small, tetrahedral, dodecahedral crystals; powdery, coatings / cubic	in quicksilver deps. / cinnabar / —	**METACINNABARITE** HgS / Idrija, Slovenia
431	grey to black / black	metallic / opaque	3—4 / $\overline{4.5-5}$	— / conchoidal, brittle	tetrahedral, dodecahedral, grown-up crystals; compact, granular to massive / cubic	in hydrothermal ore veins / galena, pyrite, bornite, chalcopyrite, sphalerite, siderite, quartz / chalcocite, bournonite, tennantite, cf. No. 483	**TETRAHEDRITE** $(Cu,Zn,Ag,Fe)_3$ $(Sb,As)S_{3-4}$ (Grey Copper, Fahlerz) / Capnic, Romania
432	dark grey, black, iridescent tarnish / black	metallic / opaque	3 / $\overline{6.4}$	very good / conchoidal	thin- to thick-tabular crystals; twin striation; globular, reniform masses / monoclinic	in ore veins, in dolomites / realgar, sphalerite, galena, pyrite & o.	**JORDANITE** $5\ PbS\ .\ As_2S_3$ / Binnental, Wallis, Switzerland

425	426
427	428
429	430
431	432

147

No.	Colour / Streak	Lustre / Transparency	Hardness / Specific Gravity	Cleavage Fracture & o. Phys. Props.	Common Form, Aggregates / Crystalline Syst.	Occurrence Assoc. Minerals / Similar Minerals	Name & Chem. Formula / Origin of Specimen
433	black / black	metallic, greasy, dull / opaque	5.5 / 5.2	imperfect conchoidal, brittle, magnetic	octahedral, dodecahedral crystals; compact, massive, coarsely & finely granular, disseminated / cubic	isolated deps., in crystalline schists, in basalts, in alpine cracks / — / ilmenite, chromite, haematite	**MAGNETITE** Fe_3O_4 / Alto Adige, Italy
434	black / reddish-brown, brown	metallic, sub-metallic / opaque, transluc.	5.5 / 4.8 − 4.9	very good uneven, brittle	pointed-pyramidal, pseudooctahedral crystals; compact, granular, spathic / tetragonal	in metasomatic & hydrothermal ore veins, in limestone & dolomite / pyrolusite, psilomelane, braunite / magnetite, braunite, pyrolusite	**HAUSMANNITE** Mn_3O_4 / Ilmenau, Thuringia, Germany
435	black, steel-grey, reddish-brown, red, iridescent tarnish / cherry-red, reddish-brown	metallic to dull / opaque	5.5 − 6.5 / 5.2 − 5.3	— / uneven, brittle, shelled separation	rhombohedral, tabular, lentiform crystals; lamellar, scaly agg.; rose-shaped clusters, compact, granular, radial, columnar, massive, earthy, mammillary / trigonal	in isolated deps., hydrothermal in ore veins, in metamorphic rocks, metasomatic, sedimentary in alpine cracks, in craters of volcanoes & in lavas, as colouring / — / ilmenite, magnetite, chromite, franklinite, cf. No. 201	**HAEMATITE** Fe_2O_3 (Iron Glance, Specularite) / Rio Marina, Elba, Italy
436							**HAEMATITE** Fe_2O_3 / Gotthard area, Switzerland
437							**HAEMATITE** Fe_2O_3 (Iron Mica) / Donovaly, Slovakia
438	brown, black, grey, yellow / white, yellow, light brown	adamantine, metallic / transluc., opaque	6 − 7 / 6.8 − 7.1	indistinct conchoidal, brittle	short-columnar, pointed-pyramidal, needle-shaped crystals; knee-shaped twins; compact, reniform, shelled, granular, fibrous, massive, mammillated masses / tetragonal	in pegmatites, in granites (gneiss) wolframite, fluorite, topaz, zinnwaldite, scheelite, molybdenite, apatite, quartz / tourmaline, sphalerite, ilmenite, wolframite, magnetite, rutile, garnet	**CASSITERITE** SnO_2 (Tinstone) / Horní Slavkov, Czech Republic
439							**CASSITERITE** SnO_2 (Tinstone) / Horní Slavkov, Czech Republic
440	black / brownish-black	metallic, greasy / opaque	6 − 6.5 / 4.7 − 4.8	clear brittle	octahedral crystals; compact, massive, granular, crusty / tetragonal	in hydrothermal, metasomatic veins, in limestone & dolomite, in ore deps. / hausmannite, pyrolusite, barytes, calcite, quartz / magnetite, hausmannite, franklinite	**BRAUNITE** $MnMn_6[O_8SiO_4]$ / Oehrenstock, Thuringia, Germany

No.	Colour Streak	Lustre Transparency	Hardness Specific Gravity	Cleavage Fracture & o. Phys. Props.	Common Form, Aggregates Crystalline Syst.	Occurrence Assoc. Minerals Similar Minerals	Name & Chem. Formula Origin of Specimen
441	black, steel-grey / black, grey, shining	sub-metallic, dull / opaque	1−2 / 2−2.2	perfect / flexible, greasy	thin-tabular crystals; lamellar, scaly, compact, massive, earthy, disseminated, dendritic / hexagonal	in metamorphic rocks, crystalline schists, limestone, in pegmatites / pyrite, garnet / molybdenite	**GRAPHITE** C / Sri Lanka
442	black, dark brown / black, dark brown	dull / opaque	1−2 / 2.3−3.7	— / —	cryptocrystalline, compact, spumous, nodular, earthy, sooty, scaly, reniform, botryoidal, dendritic, coatings / amorphous	in oxidized zone of manganese ore deps. / psilomelane, pyrolusite, limonite, asbolan	**WAD** $MnO_2 \cdot nH_2O$ / Solnhofen, Fränkische Alb, Germany
443	black, grey, greenish / brownish-black, dark green	greasy, dull, sub-metallic / opaque	4−6 / 9−10.9	— / conchoidal, brittle, radio-active	rarely cube-shaped, octahedral crystals; compact, reniform, globular, scaly, mammilliform, massive / cubic	in granite- & syenite-pegmatites, in hydrothermal ore veins, sedimentary / mica, galena, molybdenite, dolomite, fluorite / thorianite, psilomelane	**URANINITE** UO_2 with (UO_3,Th,Pb) (Pitch Blende, Pitch Ore) / Příbram, Czech Republic
444	black, dark brown, greenish / white, grey	vitreous, pearly, sub-metallic / transpar., transluc.	2.5−3 / 2.8−3.2	perfect / elastic, flexible, soft to brittle	tabular, columnar, pseudohexagonal crystals; compact, lamellar, scaly / monoclinic	rock constituent in granites, pegmatites, basic rocks, basalts, metamorphic rocks, in volcanic ejecta / — / vermiculite, phlogopite	**BIOTITE** $K(Mg,Fe,Mn)_3$ $[(OH,F)_2$ $AlSi_3O_{10}]$ (Iron Mica, Micaceous Iron Ore) / Krupka, Czech Republic
445	red-yellow, grey, brown, green, black / white, yellow, brown	adamantine, greasy, sub-metallic / transpar., opaque	3.5−4 / 3.9−4.2	very good / brittle	tetrahedral, dodecahedral, cube-shaped crystals; coarsely to finely granular, massive, compact, fibrous / cubic	in ore veins / galena, chalcopyrite & o. / — / cf. No. 142, 191, 315	**SPHALERITE** ZnS (Zinc Blende, Mock Ore, Mock Lead, Black Jack) / Cumberland, England
446	grey to black / grey-black, black	sub-metallic, dull / opaque	3−4 / 5.1	— / conchoidal, brittle	tetrahedral, dodecahedral, cube-shaped crystals; twins, compact, granular, disseminated, massive / cubic	in hydrothermal ore veins / cinnabar, quicksilver, chalcopyrite, barytes / bournonite	**SCHWAZITE** $(CuHg)_3SbS_4$ (Mercury Fahlore) / Kogel near Brixlegg, Tyrol, Austria
447	dark brown, black / whitish, grey	vitreous, pearly, sub-metallic / transluc.	3−4 / 3.3	very good / uneven, brittle	small, prismatic crystals; granular / orthorhombic	in metamorphic limestones / spinel, magnetite, serpentine	**WAR-WICKITE** $(Mg,Fe)_3Ti$ $[O BO_3]_2$ / Ilfeld, Harz, Germany
448	black, greenish-black / dark green	vitreous, transluc., opaque	3.5−4 / 3.4	good / brittle	hexagonal & sometimes triangular, pyramidal, tetrahedron-shaped crystals; globular clusters / monoclinic, sometimes trigonal	in ore veins / pyrite, siderite, calcite, sphalerite, limonite / —	**CRON-STEDTITE** $Fe_4Fe_2[(OH)_x$ $Fe_2Si_2O_{10}]$ / Příbram, Czech Republic

No.	Colour / Streak	Lustre / Transparency	Hardness / Specific Gravity	Cleavage / Fracture & o. Phys. Props.	Common Form, Aggregates / Crystalline Syst.	Occurrence / Assoc. Minerals / Similar Minerals	Name & Chem. Formula / Origin of Specimen
449	black, dark brown blackish-green	sub-metallic opaque	3.5−4 / 3.9−4	very good / brittle	small, octahedral or cube-shaped crystals; compact, granular, lamellar, disseminated / cubic	in ore veins / galena, sphalerite, pyrite, rhodonite, rhodochrosite / —	ALABAN-DITE MnS (Mangan-Blende) / Săcărâmb, Romania
450	black brown-black	sub-metallic, dull opaque	4.5−5 / 5.4	— / brittle	mammilliform, reniform, botry-oidal masses; concentrically shelled agg. / tetragonal	in weathering zone of manganese ore deps. / — / pyrolusite	CORONA-DITE Pb₂Mn₈O₁₆ / Imini, Antiatlas Morocco
451	black, grey, brown-black dark brown	sub-metallic, silky opaque	4 / 4.3−4.4	perfect uneven, brittle	columnar crystals; strongly striated, compact, granular, radial, needle-shaped / orthorhombic	in hydrothermal ore veins, sedimentary / pyrolusite, barytes, calcite & o. / pyrolusite, anti-monite	MANGANITE MnOOH (Brown Manganese Ore) / Ilfeld, Harz, Germany
452	green-grey, brownish-green, black white, grey	vitreous, pearly, sub-metallic transluc.	4 / 3.2−3.3	very good / —	compact, granular, spathic, shelled, embedded / monoclinic	constituent in basic rocks; chemically diopside & augite with specially good cleavage / — / bronzite, hyper-sthene	DIALLAGE Ca(Mg,Fe) [Si₂O₆] (Al,Fe,Ca)₂ [(Si,Al)₂O₆] (Pyroxene Family) / Diethendorf, Ore Mountains, Germany
453	black, grey-black dark brown, black	sub-metallic, dull opaque	4.5−5 / 6.8−7.5	good uneven, brittle	thick-tabular, short-prismatic crystals; compact, granular / monoclinic	in hydrothermal ore veins, in tin deps. / wolframite, cassi-terite & o. / —	FERBERITE FeWO₄ / Ehren-friedersdorf near Annaberg, Ore Mountains, Germany
454	brownish-black, yellowish-brown yellowish-brown, red-brown, greenish-grey	sub-metallic, greasy transluc., opaque	4−4.5 / 6.4−7.1	very good uneven, brittle	tabular, needle-shaped crystals; lamellar, tubular agg. / monoclinic	in tin deps. / wolframite, cassi-terite, topaz, quartz & o. / —	HÜBNERITE MnWO₄ / Horní Slavkov, Czech Republic
455	black, dark brown black, brown-black	greasy, metallic opaque	5−5.5 / 7.1−7.5	very good uneven, brittle	thick-tabular, short-columnar, pris-matic, needle-shaped crystals; compact, radial, tubular, thin-tabular, dissemi-nated / monoclinic	in tin or deps., in hydrothermal ore veins / cassiterite, schee-lite, molybdenite, zinnwaldite, fluorite, topaz, tourmaline	WOLFRA-MITE (Mn,Fe)WO₄ / Cínovec, Czech Republic
456	black black-green	vitreous, silky, dull opaque	5 / 3.6−4	— / brittle	compact, fine-fibrous, radial, tubular, entangled fibres, massive; palmaceous agg. / orthorhombic	metasomatic in limestone & dolo-mite, in magnetite deps. / — / —	LUDWIGITE (Mg,Fe)₂Fe [O₂BO₃] / Moravica, Banat, Romania

449	450
451	452
453	454
455	456

No.	Colour / Streak	Lustre / Transparency	Hardness / Specific Gravity	Cleavage Fracture & o. Phys. Props.	Common Form, Aggregates / Crystalline Syst.	Occurrence Assoc. Minerals / Similar Minerals	Name & Chem. Formula / Origin of Specimen
457	black, brownish-black / brown	vitreous, greasy, sub-metallic / opaque	5.5 / 4.5 — 4.8	— / uneven, brittle	rarely octahedral crystals; massive, granular, compact, disseminated / cubic	in ultrabasic rocks, in serpentines / olivine, bronzite & o. / magnetite, franklinite, hercynite	CHROMITE Cr_2FeO_4 (Chromic Iron, Chrome Iron Ore) / Gulsen near Kraubath, Styria, Austria
458	black / black-brown	sub-metallic, greasy, dull / opaque	5 — 6 / 4.7	ex-foliation (scaling) / con-choidal, brittle	thick-tabular, platy crystals; massive, granular, compact, rose-shaped clusters / trigonal	in basic igneous rocks, in alpine cracks, in placers / rutile, haematite, magnetite, titanite, apatite / chromite, magnetite, haematite	ILMENITE $FeTiO_3$ (Titanoferrite) / Fleschhorn, Switzerland
459	black, red-brown, yellowish / white, grey	ada-mantine, sub-metallic, greasy / opaque	5.5 / 4	good / con-choidal	cube- & octa-hedron-shaped crystals; compact, granular, reniform, pseudocubic / monoclinic	in pegmatites, basalts, crystalline schists, in metamorphic limestones / —	PEROVSKITE $CaTiO_3$ / Akhmatov Mine near Zlatoust, Urals, Russia
460	black / black, brown	sub-metallic, greasy, dull / opaque	4 — 6 / 4.4 — 4.7	— / uneven, brittle	cryptocrystalline, botryoidal, reniform, mammilliform, compact, stalactitic, massive, fibrous / monoclinic	in oxidized zone of manganese ore deps., hydrothermal, sedimentary / pyrolusite, limonite, siderite, pyrite / pyrolusite, hausmannite	PSILO-MELANE $(Ba,Mn)_3$ $(O,OH)_6$ Mn_8O_{16} / Příbram, Czech Republic
461	brown-black / whitish-brown	vitreous, sub-metallic / opaque	5.5 — 6.5 / 5.1 — 6.3	— / uneven, brittle, con-choidal	columnar, bi-pyramidal crystals; granular, compact / tetragonal	in granite-pegmatites, in placers / — / columbite, tantalite, gadolinite	FERGUSO-NITE $YNbO_4$ / Ytterby near Waxholm, Sweden
462	brown, black / dark yellow, brown-yellow	ada-mantine, sub-metallic, silky / transluc., opaque	5 — 5.5 / 3.3 — 4.3	good / brittle	thin-lamellar, needle-shaped crystals; compact, granular, folia-ceous, radiating, fibrous, mammilliform, earthy / orthorhombic	in oxidized zone of ore veins, sedimentary / haematite, pyrite, siderite, galena, quartz / manganite, haematite, lepidocrocite	GOETHITE α-FeOOH (Needle Iron-stone, Acicular Iron Ore) / Příbram, Czech Republic
463	yellow, brown, reddish, greenish, black / white, grey	vitreous, greasy / transpar., transluc.	5 — 5.5 / 3.4 — 3.6	indistinct / con-choidal, brittle	columnar, wedge-shaped, tabular, needle-shaped crystals; compact, granular / monoclinic	in alpine cracks, in crystalline schists, in magnetite deps. / — / axinite, cf. No. 162, 339	TITANITE $CaTi[O SiO_4]$ (Sphene) / Arendal, Aust-Agder, Norway
464	brown, black / greenish-grey, brown	vitreous, greasy / transluc., opaque	6 / 4.1	indistinct / con-choidal	thick-tabular, columnar, needle-shaped crystals; granular, compact, disseminated / monoclinic	in granites, syenites, pegmatites, in volcanic ejecta / felspars, quartz & o. / gadolinite, fergusonite, samarskite	ALLANITE $(Ca,Ce,La,Na)_2$ (Al,Fe,Be,Mg, Mn_3) $[OH(SiO_4)_3]$ (Orthite) / Březová, Czech Republic

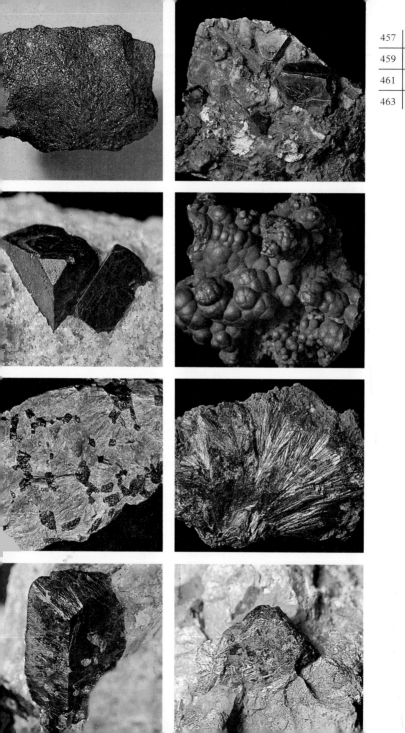

No.	Colour / Streak	Lustre / Transparency	Hardness / Specific Gravity	Cleavage Fracture & o. Phys. Props.	Common Form, Aggregates / Crystalline Syst.	Occurrence Assoc. Minerals / Similar Minerals	Name & Chem. Formula / Origin of Specimen
465	black, brown-black / brown	vitreous transluc.	5—6 / 3.2	good conchoidal	short- to long-columnar crystals; no agg. / monoclinic	in syenites benitoite, natrolite / —	NEPTUNITE $Na_2FeTi[Si_4O_{12}]$ / San Benito County, California, USA
466	brown, dark grey, blackish-green, black / white, grey	vitreous opaque	5—6 / 3.5—3.6	clear brittle	tubular, needle-shaped crystals; granular, spathic, compact, massive / monoclinic	in metamorphic & metasomatic rocks magnetite, pyrite & o. / cf. No. 343	HEDEN-BERGITE $CaFe[Si_2O_6]$ (Pyroxene Family) / Långban, Sweden
467	black, brownish-black, dark green / greyish-green	vitreous transluc., opaque	5—6 / 3.3—3.5	good conchoidal	short-columnar, thick-tabular, needle-shaped crystals; compact, granular, massive, needle-shaped, disseminated / monoclinic	rock constituent in basic rocks, in tuffs, lavas & volcanic ejecta / amphibole	AUGITE $(Ca,Mg,Fe_2,Fe_3,Ti,Al)_2[(Si,Al)_2O_6]$ (Pyroxene Family) / Lukov, Czech Republic
468	black, greenish-black / grey-white, brown	vitreous, greasy transluc., opaque	5—6 / 2.9—3.3	very good conchoidal	pseudohexagonal, short-columnar to acicular crystals; compact, tubular, fibrous, radiating, granular, massive / monoclinic	rock constituent of many igneous rocks, in crystalline schists biotite, garnet, epidote, magnetite & o. / augite, tourmaline	AMPHIBOLE $(Ca,Na,K)_{2-3}(Mg,Fe_2,Fe_3,Al)_5[(OH,F)_2(Si,Al)_2Si_6O_{22}]$ (Common & Basaltic Hornblende) / Lukov, Czech Republic
469	black, brownish-black / brownish, black, brown	ada-mantine, greasy, dull transluc., opaque	6 / 5.2—6	clear uneven, brittle	thick-tabular, short-columnar crystals; compact, embedded / orthorhombic	mixed crystals of niobite & tantalite, in granite-pegmatites / beryl, cryolite / —	COLUMBITE $(Fe,Ti)(Nb,Ta)_2O_6$ (Niobite) / Moss, Norway
470	black, deep blue / grey-green, blue-grey, whitish	vitreous transpar., transluc.	5.5—6 / 3.4—3.5	very good uneven, brittle	thick- & long-columnar crystals; compact, tubular, granular / monoclinic	in nepheline-pegmatites, syenites nepheline, zircon, sodalite & o. / aegirite, acmite	ARFVED-SONITE $Na_2Fe_2(SiO_3)_4$ (Amphibole Family) / Kangerdlugsuak Greenland
471	black / grey-black	vitreous, metallic, dull opaque	6—6.5 / 5.2—5.5	— brittle, uneven	pyramidal, prismatic, thick-tabular crystals; compact / tetragonal	mixed crystals of tapiolite & rutile, in pegmatites / — / —	STRÜVERITE $(Fe,Ti)(Nb,Ta)_2O_6$ / Ampangabe, Madagascar
472	black / brown	greasy, sub-metallic opaque	6—6.5 / 7.9—8	good brittle	columnar, short-acicular crystals; compact / orthorhombic	in granite-pegmatites / — / —	TANTALITE $(Fe,Mn)(Ta,Nb)_2O_6$ / Bodenmais, Bavarian Forest, Germany

No.	Colour / Streak	Lustre / Transparency	Hardness / Specific Gravity	Cleavage Fracture & o. Phys. Props.	Common Form, Aggregates / Crystalline Syst.	Occurrence Assoc. Minerals / Similar Minerals	Name & Chem. Formula / Origin of Specimen
473	black, dark grey, brown / grey, brownish	vitreous, greasy / opaque	6−7 / 5.5−6	− / brittle	fine-crystalline, mammilliform, radiating-fibrous, crusty, massive / monoclinic	mixture of baddeleyite & decomposed zircon / − / −	Baddeleyite variety **ZIRCONIA** ZrO_2 (Zircon-favas) / Minas Gerais, Brazil
474	black, brownish-black / greenish-grey	vitreous, greasy / opaque	6.5−7 / 4−4.7	good / conchoidal, splintery	thick-tabular, short-columnar crystals; compact, massive, embedded / monoclinic	in granite-pegmatites, in alpine cracks / − / fergusonite, samarskite	**GADOLINITE** $Y_2FeBe_2[O\,SiO_4]_2$ / Ytterby near Waxholm, Sweden
475	black, blackish-green / greyish-green	vitreous, sub-metallic, dull / opaque	7.5−8 / 3.8	− / conchoidal	octahedral crystals; rounded grains, compact, granular / cubic	in basic igneous rocks, in metamorphic limestone / pyroxene, biotite, vesuvianite, corundum, graphite picotite, garnet	**PLEONAST** $(Al,Fe)_2(Mg,Mn)O_4$ (Spinel Family Ceylonite) / Monzoni in Fassatal, South Tyrol, Italy
476	black / reddish-brown, dark brown	sub-metallic, metallic / opaque	6−7 / 4.6−5	poor / conchoidal, brittle	octahedral crystals; compact, granular, massive / cubic	in manganese-zinc ore deps., in metamorphic limestone / zincite, willemite, rhodonite, garnet chromite, magnetite	**FRANK-LINITE** Fe_2ZnO_4 / Franklin, New Jersey, USA
477	deep brown, black / white	vitreous transpar., transluc.	7 / 2.6	− / conchoidal	short-columnar, pointed, hexagonal crystals; horizontally striated / trigonal	in alpine cracks, in pegmatites, in ore deps. / − / −	Quartz variety **MORION** SiO_2 / Příbram, Czechoslovakia
478	black / white, greenish	vitreous, greasy, dull / opaque	6.5−7 / 3.6−4.1	− / conchoidal, splintery, brittle	dodecahedral, icositetrahedral crystals; compact, granular, massive / cubic	in basic eruptive rocks (basalt, phonolite, nepheline-syenite) / − / pleonaste	**MELANITE** $Ca_3Fe_2[SiO_4]_3 + (Na,Ti)$ (Garnet Family) / Franklin, New Jersey, USA
479	black / white	vitreous, greasy / opaque	7−7.5 / 3−3.1	− / conchoidal to uneven, splintery	triangular, short- to long-columnar, acicular crystals; longitudinally striated; tubular, to fibrous, radiating agg.; massive, compact / trigonal	in granites, pegmatites, in crystalline schists, in metamorphic limestone & dolomite, in ore veins / muscovite, topaz, quartz, beryl, fluorite, apatite amphibole, ilvaite	Tourmaline variety **SCHORL** $NaMg_3Al_6[(OH)_{1+3}(BO_3)_3\,Si_6O_{18}]$ (Iron Tourmaline) / Siberia, Russia
480							**TOURMA-LINE** / Montana, USA

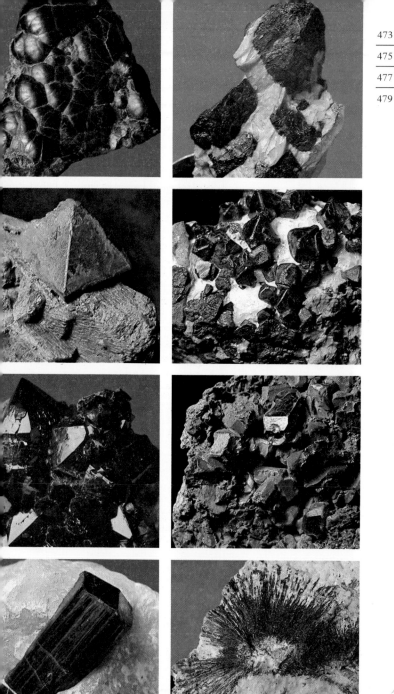

No.	Colour / Streak	Lustre / Transparency	Hardness / Specific Gravity	Cleavage Fracture & o. Phys. Props.	Common Form, Aggregates / Crystalline Syst.	Occurrence Assoc. Minerals / Similar Minerals	Name & Chem. Formula / Origin of Specimen
481	grey, yellow, brown, black / white, grey, yellowish	dull / opaque	3.5−4 / 3.9−4.2	good con-choidal, brittle	fine-fibrous, shelled, reniform masses; crusty, striated / cubic, hexagonal	in lead-zinc ore deps., partly sphalerite, partly wurtzite / − / −	ZINC BLENDE ZnS / Stolberg near Aachen, Germany
482	yellow-brown, grey, yellow, black, iridescent tarnish / rusty brown, yellow	sub-vitreous, silky, dull opaque	5−5.5 / 3.6−3.7	− con-choidal, fibrous	cryptocrystalline, fibrous, tubular, cone-shaped, shelled, stalactitic, earthy, loose / orthorhombic	weathering product in iron ore deps. / − / − cf. No. 409, 410	LIMONITE FeOOH . nH$_2$O (Brown Haematite, Brown Ironstone, Brown Iron Ore) / Železník, Slovakia
483	grey to black, iridescent tarnish / black	metallic to dull / opaque	3−4 / 4.5−5	− con-choidal, brittle	tetrahedral, dode-cahedral crystals; compact, granular, massive, coated with chalcopyrite / cubic	in hydrothermal veins galena, pyrite, bornite, chalco-pyrite, siderite, quartz cf. No. 431	TETRA-HEDRITE (Cu,Zn,Ag,Fe)$_{12}$ (Sb,As)$_4$S$_{3-4}$ (Fahl Ore) / Lizard, Corn-wall, England
484	red, blue, yellow, green / white	pearly, iri-descent / transluc.	3 / 2.6−2.8	− con-choidal, brittle	massive limestone containing fossil mollusc shells / −	in sedimentary limestones / − / −	LUMACHEL CaCO$_3$ (Shell Marble) / Bleiberg, Carinthia, Austria
485	yellow, white, red-brown, violet, grey, brown / white, yellowish	dull, silky opaque	3.5−4 / 2.9−3	− fibrous separa-tion, brittle	fibrous agg.; con-centrically shelled, stalactitic, crusts, sinter formations / orthorhombic	aragonite sinter, deposited at hot springs / − / − cf. No. 320	SPRUDEL-STEIN CaCO$_3$ (Aragonite) / Karlovy Vary, Czech Republic
486	white, yellow, grey, brown, red / white	dull transluc., opaque	5.5−6 / 2.1−2.2	− porous, rough	crusty, botryoidal, pea-shaped, earthy, loose, coatings / amorphous	opal sinter, de-posited at geysers & hot springs / − / −	GEYSERITE SiO$_2$. nH$_2$O (Siliceous Sinter, Opal) / Stóra Geysir, Iceland
487	white, yellow, brown, grey / white	greasy transluc., opaque	3.5−4 / 5.8−6.4	− con-choidal	radiating, needle-shaped, globular agg.; cryptocrystal-line / hexagonal	calcareous pyro-morphite, in lead-zinc ore deps. galena, sphalerite, pyrite, barytes / −	POLY-SPHAERITE (Pb,Ca)$_5$ [Cl(PO$_4$)$_3$] (Miesite) / Stříbro, Czech Republic
488	blue-green, yellowish, brownish, greenish, gold-brown / blue-grey, gold-brown, yellow	silky, dull transluc., opaque	5.5−6 / 3.2−3.3	very good fibrous	parallely fine-fibrous agg.; zonally contorted, cracked, platy / monoclinic	fibrous riebeckite asbestos, as crack filling in fine-grained quartz rocks, in crystalline schists, partly silicified grey-blue falcon eye, partly decomposed & yellow tiger eye / − cf. No. 543	CROCI-DOLITE Na$_2$Fe$_4$Fe$_2$ [(OH,F) Si$_4$O$_{11}$]$_2$ (Amphibole Family, Rie-beckite Asbestos, Tiger's Eye, Cat's Eye) / Griquatown, South Africa

No.	Colour / Streak	Lustre / Transparency	Hardness / Specific Gravity	Cleavage / Fracture & o. Phys. Props.	Common Form, Aggregates / Crystalline Syst.	Occurrence / Assoc. Minerals / Similar Minerals	Name & Chem. Formula / Origin of Specimen
489	green, yellow, black, red, brown, spotted / white, grey	greasy, dull / transluc., opaque	3—4 / 2.5—2.6	— / conchoidal, soft to splintery	microcrystalline, foliaceous, scaly, massive, compact, disseminated / monoclinic	fillings in veins & cracks in peridotites & grained limestone; in pseudomorphs after olivine / chromite, magnetite, opal, talc & o. / —	**SERPENTINE** $Mg_6(OH)_8$ $[Si_4O_{10}]$ (Antigorite) / Lizard, Cornwall, England
490	grey-blue, grey-yellow, violet, bluish, greenish / white, grey	silky / transluc., opaque	3—4 / 2.3—2.5	good / flexible to brittle	fine-fibrous, capillary crystals; felt-like, parallelly fibrous agg. / monoclinic	filling in veins & cracks in serpentines / olivine, tremolite & o. / — / cf. No. 255	**ASBESTOS** Mg_6 $[(OH)_6Si_4O_{10}]$ (Chrysotile) / Nevyansk near Yekaterinburg, Urals, Russia
491	yellow, brown, black, grey / white, grey	vitreous, dull / opaque	7 / 3.1—3.2	— / uneven, splintery, brittle	long-columnar, rounded crystals; with cruciform dark core (pigmented by some carbonaceous substance) / orthorhombic	in metamorphic rocks, in clay schists / staurolite, cordierite, tourmaline / —	Andalusite variety **CHIASTOLITE** $Al_2[O\ SiO_4]$ (Macle) / Lancaster, Lancashire, England
492	colourless, blue, yellow, greenish, grey / white	vitreous, pearly / transpar., transluc.	4 along cleavage planes, 6 across cleavage planes / 3.6—3.7	very good / brittle	wide-tubular, lamellar crystals; fibrous, radiating, foliaceous / triclinic	in crystalline schists, pegmatites, granulites / staurolite, andalusite, corundum / sillimanite, cf. No. 236	**CYANITE** $Al_2[O\ SiO_4]$ (Disthene) / Pizzo Forno, Tessin, Switzerland
493	colourless, green, red, brown, yellow, black / white	vitreous / transpar., transluc.	7—7.5 / 2.9—3.2	— / uneven, splintery	triangular, columnar crystals; longitudinally striated, zonal colouring / trigonal	in pegmatites, in granites & metamorphic rocks / — / cf. No. 208, 302, 479, 480	**TOURMALINE** $NaFe_3Al_6[(OH)_4(BO_3)_3]Si_6O_{18}]$ / Minas Gerais, Brazil
494							**TOURMALINE** $NaFe_3Al_6[(OH)_4(BO_3)_3Si_6O_{18}]$ / Grotta d'Oggi, Elba
495	white, grey, green, blue, red, yellow, iridescent / white	pearly, greasy, opalescent / transluc.	5.5—6.5 / 1.9—2.5	— / conchoidal to uneven, brittle, strong internal reflections	belts & veins, irregular nodules, compact, disseminated, concretions / amorphous	in cavities in young volcanic igneous rocks, in sandstones, conglomerates, clays; due to decomposition of siliceous rocks / — / — / cf. No. 535	Opal variety **PRECIOUS OPAL** $SiO_2 \cdot n\ H_2O$ / Cooper Creek, Queensland, Australia
496							Opal variety **PRECIOUS OPAL** $SiO_2 \cdot n\ H_2O$ / Bulls Creek, Queensland, Australia

163

No.	Colour Streak	Lustre Transparency	Hardness Specific Gravity	Cleavage Fracture & o. Phys. Props.	Common Form, Aggregates Crystalline Syst.	Occurrence Assoc. Minerals Similar Minerals	Name & Chem. Formula Origin of Specimen
497	white, grey, green, blue, red, yellow, iridescent / white	pearly, greasy, opalescent / transluc.	5.9 − 6.5 / 1.9 − 2.5	— / conchoidal to uneven, brittle	bands & veins, irregular nodules, compact, disseminated, concretions / amorphous	— / — / — / cf. No. 495, 535	Opal variety **PRECIOUS OPAL** $SiO_2 . n\,H_2O$ / Bulls Creek, Queensland, Australia
498	white, grey, black / white	vitreous, greasy / transluc.	6 − 7 / 1.9 − 2.5	— / conchoidal, brittle	irregular nodules, bands, veins, massive / amorphous	milk opal with embedded black, mossy, arborescent structures composed of foreign substances / — / —	**MOSSY OPAL** $SiO_2 . nH_2O$ / Kansas near Collyer, Trego Co.; USA
499	red, yellow, red-brown, brown / yellowish	vitreous, dull / opaque	7 / 2.5 − 2.6	— / conchoidal, brittle, splintery	nodules, grains, concretions, massive, crusty / trigonal	quartz containing iron oxides & iron hydroxides, in iron ore deps. / — / —	Quartz variety **EISEN-KIESEL** $SiO_2 + (Fe_2O_3)$ / Zaječov, Czech Republic
500	yellow-brown, red, white, yellowish / white	vitreous with metallic lustre / opaque	6 − 6.5 / 2.6 − 2.7	very good / uneven, brittle	thick-tabular, massive, granular, spathic / triclinic	plagioclase containing mica or haematite scales, constituent in granites, syenites / granites, syenites / —	**SUNSTONE** $Ca[Al_2Si_2O_8]$ $Na[AlSi_3O_8]$ (Plagioclase Family, Aventurine Felspar) / Frederiksvärn, Norway
501	grey, white, yellow, brown, bluish / white	vitreous, dull / transluc.	7 / 2.6	— / conchoidal	fine-fibrous, reniform, botryoidal, mammilliform, crusts, nodules, concretions / trigonal	micro-crypto-crystalline quartz, in cracks & cavities of basaltic rocks / — / cf. No. 422	**CHALCE-DONY** SiO_2 / Tampa Bay, Florida, USA
502	red, white / white	vitreous transluc., opaque	7 / 2.5 − 2.6	— / conchoidal, brittle	massive, compact, nodules, pebbles, stratified, crypto-crystalline / trigonal	white-red stratified chalcedony / — / —	Chalcedony variety **CORNELIAN ONYX** SiO_2 / Brazil
503	yellow-green, brown, grey, variously coloured / white	greasy, dull / opaque	7 / 2.5 − 2.6	— / uneven, splintery	finely granular, massive, compact, nodules, pebbles, irregular masses / trigonal, amorphous	chalcedony with admixtures, in cracks, fissures & cavities in different rocks / —	**JASPER** SiO_2 / Cairo, Egypt
504	multi-coloured / white	vitreous, greasy, dull / transluc., opaque	7 / 2.5 − 2.6	— / conchoidal	finely granular, massive, compact, stratified, nodules, pebbles, irregular masses / trigonal, amorphous	variegated chalcedony composed of different coloured bands, in vesicles & cavities, in amygdaloidal volcanic rocks / — / —	**AGATE** SiO_2 / India

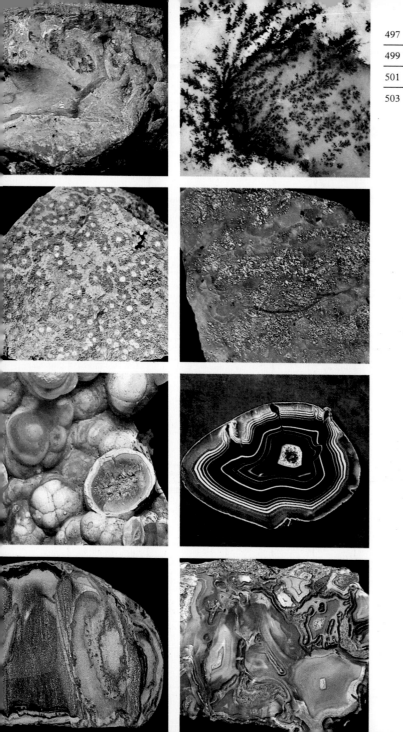

No.	Colour / Streak	Lustre / Transparency	Hardness / Specific Gravity	Cleavage / Fracture & o. Phys. Props.	Common Form, Aggregates / Crystalline Syst.	Occurrence / Assoc. Minerals / Similar Minerals	Name & Chem. Formula / Origin of Specimen
505	red, yellow, greenish, variegated / white	vitreous, greasy, dull / transluc., opaque	7 / 2.5 – 2.6	— / conchoidal	most finely granular, massive, nodules, pebbles, compact, striated / trigonal	stratified, in cross fracture of banded chalcedony, partly with parallel bands, as filling in amygdaloidal volcanic rocks / — / —	**AGATE** SiO_2 / St. Wendel, Saar, Germany
506	black, white / white	vitreous / transluc., opaque	7 / 2.5 – 2.6	— / conchoidal	massive, nodules, amygdale filling, pebbles, irregular masses, cryptocrystalline / trigonal	white-black-banded chalcedony / — / —	Chalcedony variety **ONYX** SiO_2 / Minas Gerais, Brazil
507	grey, white, red, brown, variegated / white	vitreous, greasy, dull / transluc., opaque	7 / 2.5 – 2.6	— / conchoidal	most finely granular, massive, nodules, irregular masses, pebbles, finely shelled structure / trigonal, amorphous	filling in cavities & amygdales in basalts / — / —	**AGATE** SiO_2 / Levín u Nové Paky, Czech Republic
508	grey to black, white / white	vitreous / transluc., opaque	7 / 2.5 – 2.6	— / conchoidal	massive, compact, pebbles, amygdaloidal, cryptocrystalline / trigonal	white-grey-banded chalcedony, filling in amygdaloidal volcanic rocks / — / —	Chalcedony variety **ONYX** SiO_2 / Uruguay
509							**AGATE** SiO_2 / India
510	variegated / white	vitreous, greasy, dull / transluc., opaque	7 / 2.5 – 2.6	— / conchoidal	most finely granular, massive, irregular masses, rounded debris, nodules, layered structure, stratified / trigonal	filling in cavities, cracks & vesicles in extruded rocks, especially basalts / — / —	**AGATE** SiO_2 / Měděnec, Czech Republic
511							**AGATE** SiO_2 / Ratnapura, Sri Lanka
512	blue, yellow, colourless, red, brown, grey / white	vitreous, greasy / transpar., transluc.	9 / 3.9 4.1	separation planes / conchoidal, splintery	short-columnar, fusiform, thick-tabular crystals; granular, compact, massive / trigonal	in pegmatites, crystalline schists, in metamorphic limestones & dolomites, in granite, syenite & basalt, in placers / — / zircon, spinel, garnet, cordierite, apatite, topaz, tourmaline, cf. No. 428, 514, 515	**CORUNDUM** Al_2O_3 / Sri Lanka

505	506
507	508
509	510
511	512

Precious Stones

The large family of precious stones includes all minerals of beautiful appearance which catch our eye with their sparkling colours, transparency and lustre. A precious stone must be to a certain extent indestructible and possess the capacity of resisting wear. Only the harder minerals (7—10) possess such properties, preserving their beautiful appearance even when subjected to being worn as jewellery. The most valuable precious stones are those which are rarely found naturally. Fashion — unpredictable as it is — sometimes plays an important part in determining the popularity of the various kinds.

Precious stones do not form any natural group of minerals, their number varying with the whim of fashion. The most enduring favourites — unaffected by fashion — are the diamond, the ruby, the sapphire and the emerald. These four stones occupy a special position, and are considered the 'true precious stones', others of lesser value being called 'semi-precious'. As it is not easy to draw a definite boundary between precious and semi-precious stones, it is preferable to use the term 'gemstones' for the latter.

Since the primeval age of history precious stones have always been associated with man. Primitive people appreciated their value as jewellery, and knew perfectly well how to make full use of their special qualities. Precious stones were believed to possess some mysterious, magical properties, and a special healing power. Stones were thought to be connected with the stars and were believed to be able to influence human fate. Therefore everybody should carry his so-called 'birth-stone' with him (the stone for the month in which he was born), as this was supposed to safeguard his health, happiness and property. Independent of the stars, however, every stone worn as an amulet was thought to possess a special power, as Goethe wrote in his charming verses:

> 'If carnelian your mascot be
> brings happiness and welfare thee;
> It drives away all wrong apace
> protecting you and all your place.'

As with many other superstitions, this one has survived until the present day, and every modern jeweller will recommend the right 'birth-stone' for you. In the present technical world the importance of precious stones — which are used in a number of different industries — has been growing continuously. Last but not least let us mention space research which would be impossible without precious stones.

Treatment of Precious Stones — Cutting Form

At first precious stones were used in their natural form. Only later people began to polish them to stress their colour and lustre. The art of treating precious stones was best understood by the Indians and Egyptians. The optical properties of transparent stones enhanced by a symmetrical cut of small, smooth surfaces called facets.

 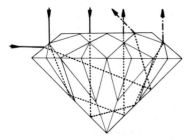

Brilliant Cut and Light Refraction in a Cut Stone

When cutting precious stones several different cuts may be applied, from the simplest step cut to the most complicated cuts with many facets. The so-called brilliant cut has been popular since the 17th century. It is used for diamonds as well as for other transparent precious stones. In this cut a special arrangement of facets causes a repeated reflection within the mineral and intensifies the rays of light emerging from it. In this way the lustre and colour of the mineral are enhanced and a special brilliance is achieved. Light refraction causes the splitting-up of each ray of white light into its coloured constituents. The result is a 'play of colours' better known as a 'play of fire'.

Opaque, coloured minerals are often cut into facetless domed forms. This treatment is called the Cabochon Cut. The special art and science of gem-engraving is called glyptography, at which the ancient Greeks and Romans excelled.

When treating a precious stone the expert must be perfectly acquainted with his material. Moreover he must know how to make full use of its physical properties, i.e. the cleavage, hardness and pleochroism of the individual mineral types. When mounting a stone in a jewel the jeweller must also take into account its power of resisting high temperature, pressure, and acids as well as its shock resistance.

The unit of weight for gemstones is a carat which equals 0.2 gm; 1 gm = 5 carats.

Imitations and Synthetic Precious Stones

Because of their rarity and consequent high value precious stones have always tempted people to try to imitate them. As early as in the Middle Ages imitation precious stones were being made of glass, others were artificially coloured or lined underneath with silver foil to achieve a brighter lustre. A special sort of imitation is the so-called doublet. It consists of two stones cemented together. Sometimes genuine stones are cemented together with glass, or two smaller genuine pieces may be cemented to each other. All imitations and counterfeits merely have the appearance of genuine stones but not their physical properties.

As with gold, alchemists tried in vain to find some nostrum that would help them to change inferior stones into gemstones. The artificial production of precious stones is the achievement of modern 'alchemists'. Stones produced in laboratories are equal to natural stones, i.e. they have the same chemical as well as physical properties. Consequently, synthetic gems are genuine stones but not natural products. One of the oldest and most successful techniques for artificial production of gems is the Verneuil process. In this process gems are made by remelting fine powdery raw material in an oxy-hydrogen flame. Large numbers of rubies, sapphires, spinels, rutiles and others that do not occur naturally, are still obtained in this way. Stones (called boules) made by the Verneuil process are of cylindrical form bounded by no straight plane.

Synthetic quartz (rock crystal, smoky quartz and citrine), is produced under high pressure and temperature in steel bombs by so-called hydrothermal synthesis. Synthetic emeralds can be produced from meltings under high temperatures in the form of perfect crystals.

The diamond — the king of precious stones — is now produced artificially under high pressure and temperature in special furnaces. The crystals obtained are too small to be used for jewellery and like most of the synthetic precious stones, they are used extensively in industry.

Identification of Precious Stones

Even the most experienced specialist cannot positively identify a precious stone at first sight, especially since there are so many perfect imitations. It is usually not difficult to tell a genuine precious stone from a glass imitation. One can thus distinguish an aquamarine from its synthetic imitation, the spinel, since both these stones differ in their chemical and optical properties.

A number of precious stones can be identified by means of the enclosed tables. Others cannot be identified so easily and require accurate measurements of the important optical properties such as the refraction index, double refraction, pleochroism and so on, which require special apparatus.

How can one distinguish synthetic from genuine precious stones? This question is often difficult to answer since they differ practically only in the manner of their growth. A powerful microscope, however, reveals different inclusions in the stones, minute bubbles and other characteristic internal markings. In genuine stones such impurities are usually spaced along the crystal planes whereas in stones produced by the Verneuil process curved growth lines may be observed, and the inclusions are lenticular forming flat-topped shells. In some synthetic stones, such as emerald, obtained by certain techniques, even the microscopic examination does not provide a reliable proof.

In this book precious stones are arranged according to their value and according to natural groups commonly used in the study of gemstones. The enclosed tables provide examples of synthetic stones completed with refractive index and references to the relevant numbers of the same minerals in the preceding mineral tables.

Apart from the popular minerals already mentioned, moldavite is quoted amongst the precious stones. It belongs to the so-called tektites. It is a refractory glass with a schlieric (streaked) texture. The moldavites have a rather irregular form, are dark-green or bottle-green, and their surfaces have a pitted or grooved appearance.

Tektites are found in only a few places in the world. Apart from meteorites they have been considered, and are still sometimes believed, to be of extraterrestrial origin. According to recent theory they are more likely to originate from terrestrial sediments which were remelted when large meteorites crashed to the earth's surface some time ago. Their origin, however, has not yet been satisfactorily explained.

In the past moldavites were cut as jewels, and imitations were often made from green bottle glass. At the moment it is fashionable to use moldavites as jewels in their original rough form.

Rocks

Rocks were mentioned only briefly in the introductory chapter. Individual rocks are composed of minerals each of a certain definite composition. This composition depends upon the kind of material and on the conditions prevailing at the time of their origin. According to their structure rocks may be divided into the following three large classes:
1. magmatic rocks (igneous or eruptive rocks)
2. sedimentary rocks (deposited rocks)
3. metamorphic rocks (alteration rocks, crystalline schists)

Classification of Rocks

Magmatic rocks may be divided according to the position in which the hot molten magma had solidified.

Intrusive, or plutonic rocks (called after Pluto, the God of the Underworld). The magma crystallized below the surface of the earth.

Extrusive, or volcanic rocks (after Vulcan, the God of Fire). In a volcanic eruption some of the liquid magma poured out upon the earth's surface and solidified there.

Veinstones. The magma invaded and penetrated fissures and cracks in the adjacent rocks and crystallized there.

According to their composition, acidic rocks (rich in silicates, SiO_2) are distinguished from basic, or alkaline rocks (low in SiO_2). Acidic rocks are mostly light in colour, and are mainly composed of quartz, felspars (orthoclase, plagioclase, microcline), felspar derivatives (nepheline, leucite, sodalite), and muscovite. Alkaline rocks, on the other hand, are composed of dark minerals, such as amphibole, pyroxene, biotite and olivine.

The most important magmatic rocks can be divided according to their diminishing content of silica. The main constituents are indicated in brackets.

Intrusive rocks: granite (quartz, felspar, mica, amphibole, pyroxene), syenite (felspar, mica, amphibole, pyroxene), diorite (felspar, amphibole, pyroxene, biotite), gabbro (felspar, amphibole, augite, biotite, olivine), peridotite (olivine, pyroxene, amphibole).

Extrusive rocks: quartz porphyry and liparite (quartz, felspar, biotite, pyroxene, amphibole), porphyry and trachyte (felspar, biotite, amphibole, pyroxene), phonolite (felspar, pyroxene, nepheline or leucite), andesite (felspar, biotite, amphibole, pyroxene), basalt and melaphyre (felspar or nepheline, leucite, pyroxene, olivine, glass), dolerite (felspar, pyroxene, partly olivine), glass.

Veinstones: aplites and pegmatites (their composition resembles that of intrusive rocks). Aplites are finely granular, pegmatites in extreme cases are coarsely granular.

Sedimentary rocks or deposited rocks are secondary rocks which are derived from decomposed and weathered older rocks. Therefore they are the products of decomposition which have been transported by water, ice or wind to some other place and deposited there. According to the way in which they were formed we distinguish the following kinds of sediments:

1. clastic sediments
2. chemical sediments
3. organic (biogenic) sediments.

Clastic sediments (weathered particles separated according to their specific weight and grain size) can be loose, as in gravel (broken stone), loess, and sand. In conglomerates or breccias, sandstones and claystones, the loose particles are cemented by clay, lime or quartz.

Chemical sediments originate from substances dissolved in water which have precipitated, either due to evaporation or to the change in the chemical composition of the solution. They include rock salt, gypsum, limestone, limonite, and bauxite.

Organic sediments, such as chalk, some calcareous rocks and coal, originated as a result of accumulations of the remains of dead animals and plants.

In sedimentary rocks, apart from the manner of their origin and their composition, the size of their grains is also important. Coarse and angular pieces cemented by a binding agent are called breccias. Coarsely cemented rounded pebbles are called conglomerates. In sandstones the grains are much smaller and sometimes cannot be distinguished by the naked eye. Similar to sandstones are the greywackes (quartz, felspar, and other igneous fragments) and the arkoses (quartz and felspar). Grains smaller than 0.02 mm are found in clays (kaolinite and montmorillonite) and limestones such as marl, chalk, calcite and dolomite, and also in quartz.

The *metamorphic rocks* originated from sedimentary or magmatic rocks under the influence of high pressures and temperatures deep within the earth. The original constituents of these rocks were remelted, mixed, compressed or folded, and crystallized to form new minerals. Metamorphic rocks are similar in composition to magmatic rocks, but their constituents are usually arranged in stratified layers similar to those of sedimentary rocks.

The alteration of acidic magmatic rocks results in the formation of gneiss schist and granulite; greenstone, amphibole and serpentinite come from alkaline rocks. Through recrystallization marble originates from limestones, and quartzite from sandstones. A slaty mixture of quartz and mica produces mica schist, claystone or marl produces phyllite.

Apart from the rock forming minerals already mentioned under magmatic rocks, the following minerals are especially characteristic of the alteration rocks: kyanite, sillimanite, zoisite, straurolite, garnet, talc, etc.

Structure and Texture of Rocks

The structure of rocks, i.e. the spatial distribution of minerals in rocks is an important external characteristic feature enabling them to be classified. There is a difference between the structure (manner in which rocks are formed) and the texture (arrangement of constituent parts). Structure means the mutual relationship of individual constituents which is derived from the manner of origin of the rock. According to the size of the constituents a coarse or fine-crystalline to glassy structure will result. If larger crystals are disseminated in the uniform rock matrix, the structure is called porphyritic.

Texture means the spatial distribution of individual constituents. In magmatic rocks the texture can be banded, uniform, massive, porous, or amygdaloidal. Altered (metamorphic) and sedimentary rocks have a coarse- to fine-layered, foliaceous, fibrous, or striated texture.

Identification of Rocks

With our simple techniques only an approximate identification of rocks can be made. More exact identification being possible only with the aid of a polarising microscope.

Texture, structure and jointing are important and characteristic properties of rocks. They often enable a determination of the rock's origin to be made. By means of a pocket lens individual mineral constituents may be identified. Note carefully the proportion of the main constituents, such as quartz, felspars, mica, amphibole, pyroxene, olivine, and carbonates. The identification is made easier when the minerals forming the rocks are large.

Precious Stones and Rocks

Identification Tables and Plates

PRECIOUS STONES AND GEMSTONES

No.	Colour / Streak	Lustre / Transparency / Refractive Index	Hardness / Specific Gravity	Cleavage / Fracture & o. / Phys. Props.	Common Form, Aggregates / Crystalline Syst.	Occurrence / Assoc. Minerals / Similar Minerals	Name & Chem. Formula / Origin of Specimen
513	colourless, yellow, blue, red, green, grey / white	adamantine transpar. 2.42	10 / 3.5	perfect / conchoidal, brittle	octahedral, cube-shaped, dodecahedral crystals; often bulbous & striated faces / cubic	embedded in ultrabasic rocks, in conglomerates, in sands, in placers / — / cf. No. 118	DIAMOND C / Kimberley, South Africa
514	blue, greyish, white / white	vitreous transluc. 1.76	9 / 3.9—4	separation planes / conchoidal, splintery	rounded crystals & grains / trigonal	corundum with stellate inclusions, sapphire with stellate opalescence; in placers of precious stones, in channel beds / — / cf. No. 428, 512	Corundum variety ASTERIATED SAPPHIRE Al_2O_3 / Sabaragamuwa, Sri Lanka
515	colourless, red, blue, violet, yellow, orange / white	vitreous transpar. 1.76	9 / 3.9—4	— / conchoidal, splintery	cylindrical, rounded 'grains' / trigonal	synthetic corundum produced by Verneuil process / — / cf. No. 428, 512	CORUNDUM Al_2O_3 / — / synthetic
516	green / white	vitreous transpar., transluc. 1.57	7.5—8 / 2.6—2.8	— / conchoidal, brittle	hexagonal, short-columnar, thick-tabular crystals / hexagonal	produced synthetically / — / cf. No. 306	EMERALD $Al_2Be_3[Si_6O_{18}]$ (Beryl) / synthetic
517	pale green, pale blue / white	vitreous transpar. 1.57	7.5—8 / 2.6—2.8	— / conchoidal, brittle	short- to long-columnar crystals; tubular agg.; loose grains, pebbles / hexagonal	cf. No. 305	Beryl variety AQUAMARINE $Al_2Be_3[Si_6O_{18}]$ / Itambacuri, Brazil
518	yellow, yellowish-green / white	vitreous transpar., opalescent 1.57	7.5—8 / 2.6—2.8	— / conchoidal, brittle	short- to long-columnar crystals; tubular agg.; loose grains, pebbles / hexagonal	cf. No. 305	HELIODOR $Al_2Be_3[Si_6O_{18}]$ (Beryl) / Nerchinsk, Transbaikal, Russia
519	rose / white	vitreous transpar., transluc. 1.58	7.5—8 / 2.6—2.8	— / conchoidal, brittle	short-columnar, thick-tabular crystals / hexagonal	cf. No. 305	MORGANITE $Al_2Be_3[Si_6O_{18}]$ (Rose Beryl) / Pala Chief, California, USA
520	green, red, blue, brown, black, multi-coloured / white	vitreous transpar., transluc. 1.62 to 1.64	7—7.5 / 3—3.1	— / uneven, brittle, splintery	triangular, short- to long-columnar crystals / trigonal	in pegmatites, granites, metamorphic rocks / — / cf. No. 302, 479, 493, 494	TOURMALINE $NaFe_3Al_6[(OH)_4(BO_3)_3Si_6O$ / Grotta d'Oggi, Elba, Italy

513	514
515	516
517	518
519	520

No.	Colour / Streak	Lustre / Transparency / Refractive Index	Hardness / Specific Gravity	Cleavage / Fracture & o. Phys. Props.	Common Form, Aggregates / Crystalline Syst.	Occurrence / Assoc. Minerals / Similar Minerals	Name & Chem. Formula / Origin of Specimen
521	colourless, blue, red, orange, yellow, green, brown / white	vitreous / transpar., transluc. / 1.92 to 1.98	7 − 7.5 / 4.2 − 4.7	— / conchoidal, brittle	short-columnar to acicular crystals; rounded, loose grains / tetragonal	in volcanic rocks, in crystalline schists, in placers of precious stones / garnet, rutile, vesuvianite, sapphire, spinel, cf. No. 355	**ZIRCON** $Zr[SiO_4]$ / Ceylon
522	blue & in all colours / white	vitreous / transpar. / 1.72	8 / 3.5 − 3.7	poor / conchoidal, brittle	cylindrical, rounded 'grains' / cubic	produced synthetically by Verneuil process / cf. No. 246, 360	**SPINEL** Al_2MgO_4 / synthetic
523	colourless, yellow, blue, red, rose, brown / white	vitreous / transpar. / 1.61	8 / 3.5 − 3.6	perfect / uneven	short- to long-columnar crystals; with orthorhombic outline, compact, granular, massive / orthorhombic	in granite-pegmatites, in tin ore veins, in placers of precious stones / quartz, corundum, phenakite, beryl, aragonite, cf. No. 117	**TOPAZ** $Al_2[F_2SiO_4]$ / Schneckenstein near Falkenstein, Ore Mountains, Germany
524	green in daylight, red in artificial light / white	vitreous / transpar., transluc. / 1.75	8.5 / 3.6 − 3.7	good / conchoidal	tabular, pseudo-hexagonal triplets, striated / orthorhombic	in granite-pegmatites, in granites, gneiss, mica schists / olivine, beryl, apatite, tourmaline, corundum, cf. No. 304	**ALEXANDRITE** Al_2BeO_4 (Chrysoberyl) / Takovaya River, Russia
525	green, greenish-yellow / white	vitreous, greasy / transpar. / 1.8 to 1.9	6.5 − 7.5 / 3.8 − 3.9	poor / conchoidal, splintery	dodecahedral, grown-up crystals / cubic	in cracks & crystalline schists, in gold placers / cf. No. 300	Andradite variety **DEMANTOID** $Ca_3Fe_2[SiO_4]_3$ (Garnet Family) / Ala, Piedmont, Italy
526	red, violet / white	vitreous, greasy / transpar. / 1.7 to 1.8	7 / 4.1 − 4.3	uneven, brittle, splintery	rhombdodecahedral crystals; rounded grains / cubic	in gneiss & mica schists, in placers of precious stones / cf. No. 219	**ALMANDINE** $Fe_3Al_2[SiO_4]_3$ (Garnet Family) / India
527	blood-red / white	vitreous / transpar. / 1.7 to 1.8	7 − 7.5 / 3.7 − 3.8	— / conchoidal, splintery	rounded grains without crystalline boundary, embedded or weathered or loose grains / cubic	in serpentine, peridotite, kimberlite, secondary in sands, conglomerates, in placers / —	**PYROPE** $Mg_3Al_2[SiO_4]_3$ (Garnet Family, Bohemian Garnet) / Podsedice, Czech Republic
528	yellow-green / white	vitreous / transpar. / 1.6 to 1.7	6.5 − 7 / 3.3 − 3.5	good / conchoidal	thick-tabular, short-columnar crystals; granular to massive, granular nodules, insets / orthorhombic	in basic volcanic rocks, in magnetite deps. / chrysoberyl, cf. No. 299	**OLIVINE** $(Mg,Fe)_2[SiO_4]$ (Chrysolite, Peridot) / Podmoklice, Czech Republic

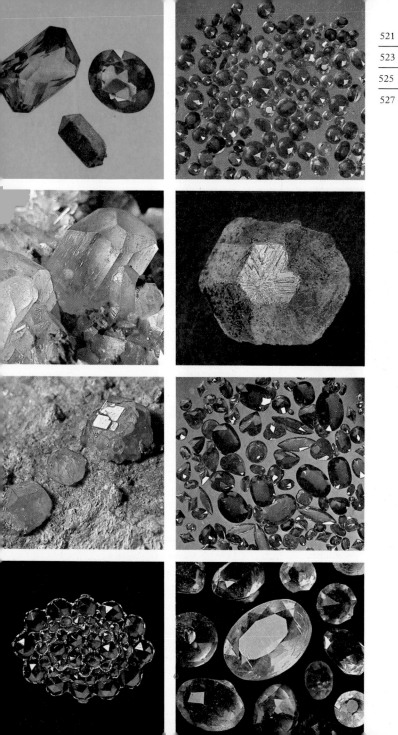

PRECIOUS STONES AND GEMSTONES

No.	Colour Streak	Lustre Transparency Refractive Index	Hardness Specific Gravity	Cleavage Fracture & o. Phys. Props.	Common Form, Aggregates Crystalline Syst.	Occurrence Assoc. Minerals Similar Minerals	Name & Chem. Formula Origin of Specimen
529	pale green, yellow white	vitreous transpar. 1.67	6.5–7 3.1–3.2	good conchoidal	columnar, thick-tabular crystals; compact, wide-tubular, spathic monoclinic	in granite-pegmatites & crystalline schists — scapolite, cf. No. 108	Spodumene variety HIDDENITE LiAl$[Si_2O_6]$ Figueira, Brazil
530	violet, rose white	vitreous transpar. 1.67	6.5–7 3.1–3.2	good conchoidal	columnar, thick-tabular, longi-tudinally striated crystals; spathic, compact, wide-tubular monoclinic	in granite-pegma-tites lepidolite, rubellite amblygonite, scapolite, amethyst, cf. No. 108	Spodumene variety KUNZITE LiAl$[Si_2O_6]$ Pala Chief, California, USA
531	colour-less white	vitreous transpar. 1.55	7 2.65	— conchoidal	columnar to acicular crystals in druses trigonal	hydrothermal formation, in cracks & fissures, in magmatic rocks, crystalline schists, in ore veins — phenakite, topaz, beryl, cf. No. 109	QUARTZ SiO_2 (Rock Crystal) Hot Springs, Arkansas, USA
532	light yellow, gold-yellow white	vitreous transpar. 1.55	7 2.65	— conchoidal	columnar crystals; in druses, loose rounded grains in placers trigonal	cf. No. 167	Quartz variety CITRINE SiO_2 Rio Grande do Sul, Brazil
533	violet white	vitreous transpar. 1.55	7 2.65	— conchoidal	columnar crystals in druses trigonal	in druses, in volcanic extruded rocks — apatite, cf. No. 217	Quartz colour variety AMETHYST SiO_2 Capnic, Romania
534	clove-brown, smoky grey white	vitreous transpar. 1.55	7 2.65	— conchoidal	columnar crystals in druses trigonal	in pegmatites, in alpine cracks, in ore deps. — brown topaz	Quartz colour variety SMOKY QUARTZ SiO_2 Gotthard area, Switzerland
535	white, grey, green, blue, red, yellow, brilliant play of colours white	pearly, greasy transluc. 1.45	5.5–6.5 1.9–2.5	— uneven, brittle, strong internal reflexion	bands & veins, irregular nodules, compact, dissemi-nated, concretions amorphous	in cavities in young volcanic rocks — — cf. No. 495	PRECIOUS OPAL $SiO_2 . n\,H_2O$ Dubník, Slovakia
536	light rose, rose-red white	greasy transluc. 1.55	7 2.65	— conchoidal, brittle, striated	only compact, dis-seminated, massive, large-granular trigonal	in pegmatites & granites beryl, tourmaline, lepidolite & o. —	ROSE QUARTZ SiO_2 San Miguel on Rio Jequetinonha, Brazil

No.	Colour Streak	Lustre Transparency Refractive Index	Hardness Specific Gravity	Cleavage Fracture & o. Phys. Props.	Common Form, Aggregates Crystalline Syst.	Occurrence Assoc. Minerals Similar Minerals	Name & Chem. Formula Origin of Specimen
537	yellow-green, differently coloured — white	greasy, dull opaque —	7 $\overline{2.5-2.6}$	— uneven, splintery	most finely granular, massive, concentrically arranged layers, nodules, pebbles, irregular masses (trigonal) amorphous	chalcedony with extraneous admixtures — — cf. No. 503	**JASPER** SiO_2 Kabamby, Madagascar
538	varie-gated — white	vitreous, greasy transluc., opaque 1.55	7 $\overline{2.5-2.6}$	— con-choidal	most finely granular, massive, compact, stratified, nodules, pebbles, irregular masses (trigonal) amorphous	chalcedony of layered structure, fine-shelled; filling in amygdaloidal volcanic rocks — — cf. No. 504	**AGATE** SiO_2 Levin, Czech Republic
539	blood-red, yellow-red — white, reddish	greasy transluc 1.55	7 $\overline{2.5-2.6}$	— con-choidal	massive, compact, reniform, botry-oidal, nodules, pebbles, irregular masses trigonal	cf. No. 422	Chalcedony variety **CORNELIAN** SiO_2 Brazil
540	apple-green — white	vitreous, greasy transluc. 1.55	7 $\overline{2.6}$	— con-choidal	massive, reniform, shelled, dissemi-nated, crypto-crystalline trigonal	in nickel ore deps. — prehnite, cf. No. 297	Chalcedony variety **CHRYSOPRASE** SiO_2 Szklary, Poland
541	yellow, red, brown — white	ada-mantine transpar., transluc. 2.6 to 2.9	6.5 $\overline{4.2-4.3}$	good brittle	finest, needle-shaped, capillary crystals; as in-clusions in rock crystal & smoky quartz tetragonal	as inclusions in quartz, in alpine cracks — — cf. No. 347	**SAGENITE** TiO_2 (Rutile) Modriach, Styria, Austria
542	red-brown, metallic iri-descence — white	vitreous transluc. 1.54	5.5—6 $\overline{2.6}$	— uneven	compact, finely granular, massive, slaty trigonal	quartz with em-bedded lamellae of mica or haematite — — cf. No. 289	Quartz variety **AVENTURINE** SiO_2 (Aventurine Quartz) Mariazell, Styria, Austria
543	gold-brown, blue-green, yellow-ish — white	silky, dull transluc., opaque —	5.5—6 $\overline{3.2-3.3}$	very good fibrous	agg. of parallel fine fibres, zonally curved, platy monoclinic	fibrous riebeckite asbestos, partly silicified & decom-posed — — cf. No. 488	**CROCIDOLITE** $Na_2Fe_3Fe_2$ $[(OH,F)Si_4O_{11}]_2$ (Riebeckite Asbestos, Tiger's Eye, Cat's Eye) South Africa
544	grey, brown, blue, violet, shining, grey with a rich play of colour — white	pearly, vitreous transluc. 1.54	6—6.5 $\overline{2.7}$	very good uneven, brittle	thick-tabular, compact, spathic, granular, massive triclinic	constituent in basic igneous rocks & in crystalline schists — —	**LABRADORITE** isomorphous mix-ture of $Na[AlSi_3O_8]$ & $Ca[Al_2Si_2O_8]$ (Felspar Family) Kangek, Greenland

PRECIOUS STONES AND GEMSTONES

No.	Colour Streak	Lustre Transparency Refractive Index	Hardness Specific Gravity	Cleavage Fracture & o. Phys. Props.	Common Form, Aggregates Crystalline Syst.	Occurrence Assoc. Minerals Similar Minerals	Name & Chem. Formula Origin of Specimen
545	green, bluish-green / white	vitreous, pearly transluc. / 1.53	6 / 2.5	very good / uneven, brittle	short-columnar, tabular crystals; compact, granular, spathic / triclinic	constituent in igneous rocks, in pegmatites / — / —	Microcline variety **AMAZONITE** $K[AlSi_3O_8]$ (Amazonstone) / Pikes Peak, Colorado, USA
546	sky-blue, green-ish-blue / white	greasy opaque / 1.61	5—6 / 2.6—2.9	— / con-choidal, brittle	cryptocrystalline, compact, reniform, massive, con-choidal, botryoidal, crusts, veins, coatings / triclinic	as filling of cracks in siliceous schists & sandstone / chalcedony / lazurite	**TURQUOISE** $CuAl_6$ $[(OH)_2PO_4]_4 \cdot 4H_2O$ (Callaite) / Anatoly, Turkey
547	sky-blue, green-ish-blue light blue	greasy, dull opaque / 1.56	5.5 / 2.3—2.4	— / con-choidal, brittle	mostly compact, massive, finely granular / cubic	in metamorphic limestones, with disseminated pyrite, in volcanic ejecta / — / sodalite, nosean, hauyne, lazulite	**LAZURITE** $(Na,Ca)_8$ $[(SO_4,S,Cl)_2$ $(AlSiO_4)_6]$ (Lapis Lazuli) / Baikal on Lake Baikal, Russia
548	green, striated light green	vitreous, silky opaque / 1.7 to 1.9	3.5—4 / 4	— / jointing, fibrous, brittle	compact, reniform, botryoidal, mammilliform, agate-like, striated / monoclinic	in weathering zone of copper deps. / — / chrysocolla, pseudomalachite, cf. No. 273	**MALACHITE** Cu_2 $[(OH)_2CO_3]$ / Katanga (now Shaba), Congo
549	green, grey-green / white	greasy, dull transluc. / 1.62	5.5 / 2.9—3	— / very massive & tenacious (tough)	cryptocrystalline, slaty, compact, massive / monoclinic	massive actinolite or anthophyllite; in loose blocks & pebbles of serpen-tinized gabbro / jadeite, cf. No. 287	**NEPHRITE** $(Mg,Fe)_7$ $[OHSi_4O_{11}]_2Na_2Ca$ $(Mg,Fe)_{10}$ $[(OH)_2O_2Si_{16}O_{44}]$ (Amphibole Family) / New Zealand
550	greenish-white, green, grey, yellow-ish white	vitreous, greasy transluc. / 1.65	6.5—7 / 3.2—3.3	— / uneven, very tenacious (tough)	compact, massive, granular, fibrous, nodules, pebbles, cryptocrystalline / monoclinic	inserts in crystal-line schists / nephrite, cf. No. 301	**JADEITE** $NaAl[Si_2O_6]$ (Pyroxene Family) / China
551	dark green / white	vitreous, dull transpar. / 1.48 to 1.5	5.5 / 2.3—2.4	— / con-choidal, sharp-edged	irregular pieces, nodular, grooved chippings with sculptured surface / amorphous	tektite glass with schlieric (streaked) texture, in sands / — / —	**MOLDAVITE** / Besednice, Czech Republic
552	honey-yellow, orange, brown-ish, whitish white	greasy transpar., transluc. / 1.54	2—2.5 / 1—1.1	— / con-choidal, brittle, com-bustible	pebbles, rounded grains, plates, stratified, drop-shaped, disseminated / amorphous	fossil resin, in sedimentary rocks / — / cf. No. 140	**AMBER** $C_{12}H_{20}O$ (Succinite) / Warnemünde, Mecklenburg, Germany

ROCKS a) IGNEOUS ROCKS

No.	Mode of Formation	Structure	Main Constituents	Accessory Minerals	Colours	Specific Gravity / Remarks	Name / Origin of Specimen
553	magmatic plutonic rock (acidic)	coarse- to fine-grained	quartz, orthoclase, microcline, plagioclase, muscovite, biotite, amphibole, augite	apatite, zircon, topaz, tourmaline, beryl, titanite, rutile, magnetite, ilmenite, haematite, pyrite, monazite, fluorite, cordierite, garnet & o.	white-grey, dark grey, white-reddish, greenish, yellowish, bluish, red, black-white	2.6−2.7 — slab structure, very hard, solid	**GRANITE** — Giant Mountains, Czech Republic
554	magmatic plutonic rock	fine- to coarse-grained, sometimes porphyritic	orthoclase, plagioclase, biotite, amphibole, augite; contains none or very little quartz	apatite, zircon, titanite, manganite, olivine, garnet	grey, dark grey, reddish	2.7−2.9 — very hard, solid	**SYENITE** — Plauenscher Grund, Germany
555	magmatic plutonic rock	medium- to fine-grained	amphibole, pyroxene, biotite, some quartz, diallage	apatite, titanite, zircon, rutile, magnetite, ilmenite, pyrrhotite, pyrite	black-white, grey-green, regularly speckled	2.8−3 — very hard, tenacious	**DIORITE** — Göda near Bautzen, Germany
556	magmatic plutonic rock (basic)	coarse- to fine-grained	plagioclase, pyroxene, amphibole, biotite, some olivine, enstatite, hypersthene	quartz, apatite, ilmenite, spinel, corundum, magnetite, titanite, pyrrhotite, chromite, pyrite, rutile, garnet	grey-black, white-grey, brownish, greenish, grey-green, reddish, speckled	2.8−3.1 — solid, tenacious	**GABBRO** — Hof, Bavaria, Germany
557	magmatic extruded rock (basic)	fine-grained, massive, vitreous, with insets, porphyritic, also porous	orthoclase, plagioclase, biotite, amphibole, pyroxene, some quartz	apatite, zircon, titanite, magnetite	grey, yellowish, brown, brown-green, reddish, light speckles	2.5−2.8 — not too solid	**PORPHYRY** — Tatobity, Czech Republic
558	magmatic extruded rock (basic)	fine-grained, very massive, porphyritic	plagioclase, nepheline, leucite, augite, amphibole, melilite, olivine, glass	magnetite, ilmenite, biotite, apatite, hauyne, perovskite, zeolite, aragonite, calcite	black, greenish, dark green, grey	2.8−3.3 — very hard, solid, tenacious, columnar jointing	**BASALT** — Spechtshausen near Freital, Germany
559	magmatic extruded rock (basic)	fine- to coarse-grained, massive, compact, porphyritic, porous, amygdaloidal	plagioclase, augite, hypersthene, olivine, some glass, ore minerals	chlorite, magnetite, ilmenite, agate, quartz, calcite, zeolite	black, dark grey, brown, reddish, red-brown, grey-green	2.8−3.3 — fresh hard & tenacious	Basalt variety **MELA-PHYRE** (Amygdaloid, Mandelstone) — Kozákov, Czech Republic
560	magmatic extruded rock (acidic)	vitreous, fine-crystalline (lava solidified due to quick cooling)	glass	(only in microscopic quantities) quartz, biotite, oligoclase	black, dark grey, brown	2.3−2.6 — brittle, conchoidal fracture, used also as gemstone	**OBSIDIAN** — Lipari, Italy

ROCKS b) SEDIMENTARY ROCKS

No.	Mode of Formation	Structure	Main Constituents	Accessory Minerals	Colours	Specific Gravity / Remarks	Name / Origin of Specimen
561	clastic sedimentary rock	coarse-grained, angular pieces cemented by some binding agent	varying, e.g. quartz, calcite, dolomite, ore minerals & o.	varying	different	strongly varying / grains larger than 2 mm	BRECCIA / Tinos, Greece
562	clastic sedimentary rock	unequal grains, pebbles cemented by binding agent	quartz, quartzite, siliceous schist	clay minerals, limonite, haematite, calcite & o.	varying due to colour of mineral constituents & binding agent	varies strongly / grains larger than 2 mm	CONGLO-MERATE / Bělá, Czech Republic
563	clastic sedimentary rock	clastic, medium- to fine-grained, porous, stratified	quartz, some opal	chalcedony, muscovite, felspar, haematite, limonite, zircon, rutile, glauconite & o.	light grey, yellowish, reddish, brown, multi-coloured	2 – 2.65 / grain size 0.05 to 2 mm	SAND-STONE / Vrchlabí, Czech Republic
564	clastic sedimentary rock	fine-grained to massive, clastic, stratified.	kaolinite, or o. clay minerals, quartz	muscovite, zircon, rutile, calcite, bituminous substances	grey, blue-grey, white-grey, yellowish, yellow-brown, reddish to black	2.8 / grain size less than 0.02 mm	CLAY-STONE / Kopanina, Czech Republic
565	clastic, partly biogenetic rock	massive, porous, layered	calcite, dolomite, quartz, clay minerals	clay minerals, bituminous substances	light to dark grey, yellowish, reddish	2.6 – 2.8 / grain size less than 0.02 mm	MARL / Jáchymov, Czech Republic
566	biogenetic, partly clastic sedimentary rock	fine-grained to massive, clastic, layered,	kaolinite & o. clay minerals, quartz	muscovite, calcite, zircon, rutile, bituminous substances	grey, blue-grey, reddish to black	2.8 / grain size less than 0.02 mm, easily cleaved	FIRE CLAY / Handlová, Slovakia
567	chemical partly biogenetic sedimentary rock	porous, layered	calcite, aragonite	clay minerals, quartz, haematite, limonite, bituminous substances	white, yellow, brown, reddish, grey-white, marbled	2.6 – 2.8 / —	TRAVER-TINE / Sliač, Slovakia
568	chemical sedimentary rock	oölithic, massive, porous, earthy	alunogel, diaspore, böhmite, hydrargillite, kaolinite	haematite, goethite, lepidocrocite, chlorite, calcite, phosphorite, opal	white, yellow, brown, red-brown, violet, green, grey, speckled	2.4 – 2.5 / —	BAUXITE / Gánt, Hungary

Table 7

ROCKS c) METAMORPHIC OR ALTERATION ROCKS

No.	Mode of Formation	Structure	Main Constituents	Accessory Minerals	Colours	Specific Gravity / Remarks	Name / Origin of Specimen
569	alteration rock	medium- to small-grained, veinous	quartz, orthoclase, plagioclase, biotite, muscovite, amphibole, pyroxene	apatite, zircon, rutile, garnet, cordierite, silimanite, epidote, pyrite, graphite	grey, grey-white, brown, red-brown, grey-black	2.6–2.8 slab jointing	**GNEISS** Kunštát, Czech Republic
570	alteration rock	small- to medium-grained, schistose, veinous	quartz, muscovite, biotite, paragonite	albite, garnet, rutile, staurolite, epidote, tourmaline, kyanite, andalusite, graphite	yellowish, brown, brown-red, grey	2.6–3.2 slab jointing	**MICA SCHIST** Vrchlabí, Czech Republic
571	alteration rock	fine-grained, massive, schistose, veinous	quartz, orthoclase, plagioclase, garnet, diopside, hypersthene	apatite, zircon, rutile, kyanite, hercynite, biotite	white, grey, grey-white, dark grey	2.6–2.9	**GRANULITE** Gersdorf near Chemnitz, Stadt, Germany
572	alteration rock	fine-grained, schistose, veinous, massive	quartz, chlorite, sericite, partly albite	rutile, albite, tourmaline, magnetite	greenish, grey-green, grey, grey-white to black	2.7–2.8 often with micaceous to silky lustre	**PHYLLITE** Ankogel, Salzburg, Carinthia, Austria
573	alteration rock	small- to coarse-grained, massive, veinous	calcite, dolomite	quartz, mica, talc, epidote, serpentine, tremolite, forsterite & o.	white, yellowish, bluish, green, grey, red, black, multicoloured	2.6–2.8	**MARBLE** Schwarzenberg, Ore Mountains, Germany
574	alteration rock	fine-grained to massive, schistose, veinous, compact	chlorite, sericite, amphibole, actinolite, epidote, albite	quartz, calcite	green, grey-green	2.7–2.8	**GREEN-SCHIST** (Greenstone) Kraslice, Czech Republic
575	alteration rock (basic)	small- to coarse-grained, schistose, veinous, massive	amphibole, plagioclase	albite, quartz, garnet, apatite, titanite, rutile, epidote, zoisite, biotite, chlorite, diopside	black, grey-black, greenish-black	2.7–2.8 tenacious	**AMPHIBOLITE** Stupava, Czech Republic
576	alteration rock (basic)	schistose, veinous, massive, compact	olivine, serpentine	garnet, bronzite, chromite, amphibole, magnetite, talc, chrysotile (asbestos)	grey-green, green, black-green, grey to black, speckled red	2.6–2.7	**SERPENTINE** Dobšiná, Slovakia

No. 569–576

Table 7

IDENTIFICATION TABLE ACCORDING TO COLOUR AND HARDNESS

Hardness	Colour					
	colourless	white-whitish	yellow-yellowish	orange	red-reddish-pink	violet
1 – 2	17, 25, 29 – 31, 33, 35 – 39	(1), 2, 17 – 31, 33, 35, 36 – 38, 255, 256, 393, 396, 397 – 399	17, 18 – 25, 27, 28, 31, 33, 35, 36, 38, 39, 129, 131 – 133, 252, 313, 396 – 399	33, 129, 133, 181	19, 21, 22, 28, 31, 33, 36, 39, 181 – 183, 210	33, 209, 210
2 – 3	40, 42 – 46, 48, 50, 139, 309, 312, 402	3 – 7, 40 – 50, 139, 140, 211, 309, 310, 312, 364, 380, 402	7, 41 – 48, 119, 121, 122, 133 – 136, 138 – 141, 171, 172, 259, 260, 309 – 312, 326, 403	133, 135, 140, 141, 169 – 172, 188, 326	40, 44 – 49, 135, 171, 172, 177, 184 – 189, 210, 211, 326, 371, 429	46, 210, 211, 371
3 – 4	51, 55, 57 – 59, 61, 66, 67, 69, 71, 142, 151, 232, 321, 401, 405	8, 51, 55 – 61, 63 – 72, 146, 151 – 153, 174, 193, 211, 232, 310, 318, 320, 321, 381, 395, 401, 405, 487	51, 55 – 57, 59 – 61, 64, 67 – 70, 72, 123, 124, 128, 142, 143, 146 – 153, 174, 175, 193, 232, 270, 310, 317, 318, 320 – 322, 327, 328, 384, 401, 405, 481, 487, 489	143, 146, 147, 148, 174, 175, 327	51, 57 – 59, 61, 64, 67, 70 – 72, 142, 151, 192 – 196, 211, 232, 270, 320, 324, 406, 489	58, 61, 211, 212
4 – 5	73, 75 – 80, 158, 213, 214, 236, 276	9, 12, 73 – 80, 157, 160, 164, 280, 310, 387, 388, 411	73 – 80, 156 – 160, 164, 197, 214, 236, 280, 310, 322, 329, 331, 411	73, 156, 280, 332	73, 75 – 78, 80, 157, 158, 179, 197, 213, 214, 280, 411	73, 158, 213, 214
5 – 6	81, 84 – 89, 91 – 95, 98, 99, 101 – 104, 112, 158, 161, 204, 283, 286, 291, 421	10 – 16, 81, 104, 112, 154, 158, 161, 162, 204, 238, 239, 288, 291, 389 – 392, 414, 416, 421, 486, 495	81, 84 – 86, 88 – 91, 94, 97, 98, 100, 103, 112, 154, 155, 158, 161 – 163, 198, 235, 238, 283, 286, 291, 336, 337, 341, 415, 417, 459, 486, 488, 495	155, 337	81, 85, 88 – 90, 100, 102, 103, 112, 158, 162, 180, 198 – 202, 204, 235, 238, 283, 289, 291, 337, 386, 415, 417, 435, 486, 495	158, 215
6 – 7	105, 107 – 109, 112, 161, 205, 236, 355, 419, 531	105 – 109, 112, 161, 164, 165, 205, 206, 236, 293, 294, 301, 349, 419, 491, 498, 500, 502, 506	106 – 109, 112, 125, 127, 161, 164 – 166, 203, 205, 236, 292, 295, 301, 349, 351, 355, 418, 420, 422, 438, 500, 529, 532, 541, 544	355	107, 109, 112, 200, 201, 203, 205 – 207, 292, 293, 295, 299, 347, 349 – 351, 355, 418, 420, 500, 502, 526, 536, 539, 541, 544	107, 109, 216, 217, 357, 526, 530, 533, 544
7 – 8	113 – 117, 427, 521, 522	113, 115, 116	113 – 117, 167, 168, 176, 244, 246, 305, 427, 518, 521, 522	117, 176, 521, 522	116, 117, 176, 208, 219, 220, 246, 305, 360, 519 – 522, 527	208, 219, 220, 244
8 – 9	428, 512, 515	514	304, 428, 512, 515	515	428, 512, 515, 524	515, 524
10	118, 513		118, 513		118, 513	

		Colour		
blue-bluish	**green-greenish**	**brown-brownish**	**grey**	**black-blackish**
1, 33, 209, 21, 223−225, 50	19−21, 23, 24, 28, 36, 209, 210, 247−256, 313, 398	19, 20, 25, 31, 36, 39, 129, 132, 255, 256, 313, 393, 394, 396, 399, 442	2, 20, 22−24, 31, 35, 36, 39, 210, 255, 256, 313, 361, 362, 393, 394, 396−399, 441	39, 209, 221, 247, 248, 313, 441, 442
22, 226−229, 263, 265	136−139, 171, 172, 210, 211, 228, 229, 259−267, 311, 400, 402, 403, 444	40, 47, 49, 119, 135, 139−141, 169−171, 177, 189, 265, 267, 307, 309−312, 326, 400, 403, 404, 429, 444	3, 5, 6, 41−44, 47, 49, 171, 172, 184−186, 210, 211, 222, 228, 307, 309−312, 364−367, 369−380, 400, 402−404, 432	5, 6, 169, 177, 184, 186, 307, 310, 365, 367, 372, 373, 379, 380, 400, 402, 404, 429, 430, 432, 444
57, 58, 61, 68, 69, 230, 232−234, 243, 265	61, 64, 68, 142, 146, 149, 150, 153, 174, 175, 211, 264, 265, 268−273, 275, 314, 317, 324, 327, 407, 452, 489	51, 57, 59−61, 68, 69, 71, 72, 123, 128, 142, 143, 146−148, 150−152, 174, 175, 192, 195, 265, 269, 270, 308, 310, 314−322, 324, 325, 327, 328, 401, 406, 447, 449, 481, 487, 489	8, 56−61, 64, 66, 67, 69−71, 142, 146, 153, 174, 192, 195, 211, 270, 310, 317, 321 381−384, 395, 401, 405−407, 431, 446, 451, 452, 481, 487, 489	142, 269, 275, 310, 314, 317, 321, 324, 383, 401, 405− 407, 431, 445− 449, 451, 452, 481, 489
73, 79, 236, 276, 280, 282, 338, 411	73, 78, 79, 157−160, 213, 214, 269, 276− 282, 284, 329, 333, 338, 411	79, 156, 157, 197, 269, 310, 329−333, 338, 454	9, 12, 74, 76, 79, 80, 160, 164, 179, 236, 280, 310, 330, 331, 333, 385, 387, 388, 411, 443, 453	269, 310, 329, 332, 443, 450, 453, 454, 456, 460
7, 93, 112, 15, 235, 237− 239, 283, 386, 416, 421, 470, 488, 495, 546, 547	87, 90, 93, 94, 98, 101, 103, 104, 112, 158, 162, 163, 238, 239, 283, 285−291, 343, 344, 412−415, 467, 488, 495, 545, 546, 551	81, 90, 91, 112, 154, 161−163, 180, 198, 200, 201, 283, 288, 291, 334−337, 339, 341−345, 348, 408, 409, 412, 413, 415, 416, 435, 455, 457, 459, 462, 464, 486, 488, 542	12−16, 82−87, 89, 92− 94, 102, 112, 162, 180, 201, 204, 238, 283, 287, 288, 290, 291, 342, 343, 345, 386, 389−392, 408, 409, 412−417, 421, 435, 443, 486, 495	112, 162, 198, 201, 235, 286, 334, 341−344, 409, 413, 416, 433−435, 443, 455, 457−470
105, 107, 112, 116, 236, 241, 242, 351, 355, 522, 544	108, 112, 165, 166, 216, 292−302, 349, 351, 353−357, 418, 529, 540	106, 109, 112, 161, 166, 200, 201, 203, 205−207, 293, 295, 299, 340, 347, 349−357, 420, 426, 438, 473, 477, 491, 500, 503, 534, 541, 544	108, 109, 112, 164, 165, 201, 205, 206, 236, 241, 292, 294, 295, 301, 340, 357, 418−420, 422, 425, 426, 438, 473, 491, 498, 503, 504, 544	112, 201, 203, 295, 299, 340, 354, 356, 418, 425, 438, 440, 471−474, 476− 478, 491, 498, 506
114, 117, 244− 246, 305, 517, 520−522	114, 117, 168, 303, 305, 306, 475, 516−518, 520−522, 528	116, 176, 219, 246, 358−360, 427, 520−522	113−115, 244, 427	219, 246, 358− 360, 475, 479
428, 512, 514, 515	304, 524	428, 512	428, 512	
118, 513	118, 513	118, 513	118, 513	118

IDENTIFICATION TABLE ACCORDING TO COLOUR AND LUSTRE

Lustre	Colour					
	colourless	white–whitish	yellow–yellowish	orange	red–reddish–pink	violet
metallic		1–5, 7–16, 179, 364, 380, 381, 387, 388, 392	119, 123–125, 127, 128, 198, 235, 384		4, 177, 179, 180, 198, 201, 235, 371, 386, 429, 435	209, 371
adamantine	39, 142, 309, 355, 402	49, 146, 157, 162, 309, 321, 393, 402	39, 129, 131, 142, 143, 146, 147, 156, 157, 162, 171, 172, 175, 188, 197, 198, 203, 235, 270, 309, 321, 326, 327, 337, 355, 393, 438, 459	143, 146, 147, 156, 171, 172, 175, 181, 188, 326, 327, 337, 355	39, 49, 142, 157, 162, 171, 172, 181, 182, 184, 185, 186, 188, 195–198, 203, 210, 235, 270, 324, 326, 337, 347, 355, 406	210
vitreous	25, 29–31, 33, 35–37, 40, 42–46, 48, 50, 51, 55, 57–59, 61, 66, 67, 71, 73, 75–81, 84–89, 91–95, 98, 99, 101–105, 107–109, 113, 115–117, 158, 161, 205, 213, 232, 236, 237, 283, 286, 291, 312, 355, 405, 419, 427	25, 27, 29–31, 33, 35–37, 40, 42–48, 51, 55, 56–61, 64, 66–68, 70–72, 74–81, 83–95, 99–108, 110, 111, 113, 115, 116, 152, 153, 158, 161, 162, 164, 165, 193, 205, 206, 213, 232, 236–239, 280, 291, 293, 294, 301, 312, 349, 398, 405, 414, 416, 419, 498, 500, 501	25, 27, 31, 33, 35, 36, 42–48, 51, 55–57, 59–61, 64, 67, 68, 70, 72–81, 84–86, 88–91, 94, 98, 100, 103, 106, 107, 111, 113, 115–117, 131, 137, 138, 150, 152, 153, 158, 161, 162, 164–168, 176, 193, 205, 232, 236, 238, 246, 252, 280, 283, 286, 291, 292, 295, 301, 304, 305, 312, 317, 322, 328, 331, 332, 349, 351, 355, 398, 405, 417, 418, 420, 422, 427, 428, 529	33, 176, 280, 332, 355	31, 33, 36, 40, 44–48, 51, 57–59, 61, 64, 67, 70–73, 75–78, 80, 81, 85, 88–90, 100, 102, 103, 107, 111, 116, 117, 158, 162, 176, 183, 189, 192–194, 199, 200, 202, 205, 206–208, 213, 219, 232, 238, 246, 280, 283, 289, 291–293, 295, 305, 349–351, 415, 417, 355, 406, 418, 420, 428, 519, 527, 530	33, 46, 58, 61, 73, 158, 208, 209, 213, 214, 215, 217, 219, 244, 357, 544
greasy	17, 35, 36, 39, 40, 43, 44, 57, 61, 69, 81, 85, 86, 93, 109, 142, 146, 158, 237, 276, 286, 291, 427	17, 20, 22, 35, 36, 40, 47, 49, 51, 55, 57, 61, 62, 64, 69, 74, 81, 82, 85, 86, 93, 110, 112, 140, 157, 158, 159, 162, 165, 237, 291, 301, 310, 349, 416, 487, 495, 498	17, 20, 22, 35, 36, 39, 43, 44, 57, 61, 62, 64, 69, 74, 81, 85, 86, 112, 129, 131, 140–142, 146–148, 155, 157–159, 162, 165–167, 171, 172, 175, 176, 203, 235, 286, 291, 301, 327, 331, 349, 427	140, 141, 146, 147, 169, 171, 172, 175, 176, 181, 327	22, 36, 39, 40, 44, 57, 61, 64, 81, 85, 112, 142, 157, 158, 162, 171, 172, 176, 181, 187, 203, 208, 235, 291, 349, 536	61, 158, 208, 214, 217, 244
pearly	31, 40, 50, 51, 55, 57–59, 69, 71, 79, 87, 99, 101–105, 107, 113, 205, 213, 232, 236, 312	20, 21, 23, 27, 31, 40, 47, 49, 51, 55, 57–60, 69–72, 79, 83, 87, 99–105, 107, 113, 152, 164, 193, 205, 211, 213, 232, 236, 288, 293, 294, 312, 395, 397, 495	20, 21, 23, 27, 31, 47, 51, 55, 57, 59, 60, 69, 70, 72, 79, 100, 103, 107, 113, 131, 132, 136–138, 150, 152, 164, 193, 205, 232, 236, 311, 312, 317, 328, 397, 403, 420, 495		21, 31, 40, 47, 49, 51, 57–59, 70–72, 100, 102, 103, 107, 189, 193, 194, 200, 205, 210, 211, 213, 232, 293, 395, 415, 420, 495	58, 209, 210, 211, 213, 544
silky	31, 45, 48, 79, 80, 84, 88, 139, 312	27, 28, 31, 41, 45, 48, 68, 72, 79, 80, 83, 84, 88, 134, 139, 206, 255, 312, 398, 414	27, 28, 31, 41, 45, 48, 68, 72, 79, 80, 84, 88, 132–134, 139, 148, 163, 255, 312, 336, 398, 415	133	28, 31, 45, 48, 72, 80, 88, 206, 415	216
dull	25, 30, 37, 38, 42, 43, 48, 69, 92, 113, 405	18–21, 23–26, 30, 37, 38, 41–43, 48, 56, 63, 65, 69, 70, 82, 92, 96, 97, 113, 134, 154, 160, 249, 310, 380, 396, 399, 405, 486, 501	18–21, 23–25, 38, 41–43, 48, 56, 69, 70, 97, 113, 131–135, 143, 149, 150, 154, 156, 160, 305, 317, 329, 335, 396, 399, 405, 422, 428	133, 135, 143, 156, 170	19, 21, 48, 70, 135, 154, 184, 186, 187, 194, 201, 305, 428, 435, 486, 489, 499	209

Colour				
blue-bluish	**green-greenish**	**brown-brownish**	**grey-greish**	**black-blackish**
209, 221, 222, 235	209	119, 123, 128, 180, 198, 201, 307, 429, 435, 449, 454, 455	5, 8, 9, 12−16, 179, 180, 201, 222, 307, 361, 362, 364, 365−367, 369−388, 392, 425, 431, 432, 435, 441, 446, 451	5, 198, 201, 209, 221, 235, 307, 365, 367, 372, 373, 376, 379, 380, 383, 425, 429−435, 440, 441, 446, 449−451, 453−455, 458, 460, 476
226, 235, 355	142, 146, 157, 162, 171, 172, 175, 266, 269, 270, 324, 327, 355, 402, 406	39, 49, 129, 142, 143, 146, 147, 157, 162, 171, 175, 198, 203, 269, 270, 309, 316, 321, 324, 326, 327, 337, 340, 347, 355, 393, 438, 459, 462	39, 49, 142, 146, 171, 172, 184−186, 195, 210, 270, 309, 321, 340, 393, 402, 406, 438	39, 142, 162, 184, 186, 198, 203, 235, 269, 321, 324, 340, 402, 406, 438, 459, 462, 469
33, 57, 58, 61, 68, 73, 79, 87, 93, 105, 107, 117, 209, 226−230, 232, 236−239, 241, 242, 244−246, 250, 263, 280, 305, 351, 355, 416, 422, 428, 544	36, 61, 64, 68, 73, 78, 79, 90, 93, 94, 98, 101, 103, 104, 108, 117, 138, 153, 158, 162, 165, 166, 168, 206, 209, 213, 228, 236−239, 248, 250, 252, 253, 254, 257, 258, 262, 263, 266−269, 271−273, 275, 277, 280, 283−286, 289−306, 313, 314, 317, 333, 343, 344, 349, 351, 353, 355, 356, 357, 398, 406, 407, 412−415, 418, 452, 529, 545, 551	25, 31, 36, 40, 47, 51, 57, 59−61, 68, 71, 72, 79, 81, 90, 91, 106, 111, 116, 150, 152, 161, 162, 166, 171, 188, 192, 200, 205−207, 219, 246, 267, 269, 283, 291, 293, 295, 299, 312−314, 317, 322, 328, 331−333, 340, 342, 343−345, 349−353, 355−359, 394, 404, 408, 409, 412, 413, 415, 416, 420, 426−428, 444, 447, 464, 473, 477, 534, 544	31, 35, 36, 42−44, 56−61, 64, 66, 67, 70, 71, 76, 79, 80, 83−87, 89, 92−94, 102, 107, 108, 111, 113, 153, 164, 165, 192, 205, 206, 228, 236−238, 241, 244, 280, 283, 292, 294, 295, 301, 312, 313, 317, 331, 340, 343, 345, 357, 394, 398, 404−409, 412−420, 422, 426−428, 452, 473, 491, 498, 501, 534, 544	162, 209, 219, 246, 269, 273, 275, 286, 295, 299, 313, 314, 317, 332, 340, 342−344, 356, 358, 359, 404−407, 409, 413, 416, 418, 444, 447, 448, 452, 456, 457, 461, 464, 465, 467, 468, 470, 471, 473−475, 477−479, 491, 498
57, 61, 69, 93, 235, 237, 242, 244, 245, 265, 416, 546, 547	20, 22, 36, 61, 64, 93, 112, 142, 146, 157, 158, 159, 162, 165, 166, 171, 172, 175, 237, 248, 262, 265, 267, 268, 275, 276, 279, 282, 286, 291, 297, 301, 303, 327, 329, 338, 349, 443, 489, 495	20, 36, 39, 40, 57, 61, 69, 81, 112, 129, 140−142, 146−148, 157, 162, 166, 169, 171, 175, 176, 203, 265, 267, 291, 310, 327, 331, 334, 341, 342, 345, 349, 359, 416, 424, 427, 454, 455, 464, 473, 487	20, 35, 36, 39, 43, 44, 57, 61, 64, 82, 85, 86, 93, 112, 142, 146, 165, 171, 172, 237, 244, 301, 331, 416, 424, 427, 443, 473, 487, 495, 498	39, 112, 142, 162, 169, 203, 235, 275, 286, 310, 329, 341, 342, 359, 416, 424, 443, 454, 455, 457, 460, 464, 468, 469, 472−474, 478, 479, 489, 498
21, 57, 58, 69, 79, 87, 105, 107, 209, 225, 232, 236, 243, 250, 544	20, 21, 23, 79, 101, 103, 104, 136, 138, 209, 211, 213, 236, 248, 250, 251, 253, 254, 257, 258, 261, 279, 288, 293, 294, 311, 313, 317, 333, 400, 403, 412, 413, 415, 452, 495, 545	20, 31, 40, 47, 49, 51, 57, 59, 60, 69, 71, 72, 79, 132, 150, 152, 189, 200, 205, 288, 293, 311, 312, 313, 317, 328, 333, 403, 408, 412, 413, 415, 420, 444, 447, 544	20, 23, 31, 40, 57−60, 70, 71, 79, 83, 87, 102, 107, 113, 164, 205, 210, 211, 236, 294, 311, 312, 313, 317, 345, 395, 397, 400, 403, 408, 412, 413, 415, 420, 452, 495, 544	209, 313, 317, 400, 413, 444, 447, 452
8, 79, 216, 223, 225, 272	28, 68, 79, 139, 163, 206, 216, 255, 273, 290, 398, 413−415, 488	31, 68, 72, 79, 132, 139, 148, 163, 206, 255, 312, 336, 408, 413, 415, 462, 488	31, 41, 79, 80, 83, 84, 206, 312, 398, 408, 413−415, 451	273, 413, 451, 456, 462
1, 69, 209, 30, 265, 305, 22, 428, 501, 47	19−21, 23, 24, 160, 209, 247, 249, 251, 254, 264, 265, 273, 278, 282, 287, 305, 317, 400, 406, 407, 443, 475, 488, 489	19, 20, 25, 69, 135, 143, 150, 154, 170, 201, 265, 307, 310, 317, 330, 335, 336, 358, 394, 396, 399, 404, 409, 424, 426	19, 20, 23, 24, 41−43, 56, 70, 82, 92, 113, 160, 184, 186, 201, 307, 317, 365, 366, 378, 380, 394, 396, 399, 400, 409, 422	184, 186, 201, 209, 273, 307, 310, 317, 358, 365, 380, 400, 409, 424, 425, 433, 441−443, 446, 450, 453, 456, 458, 460

Cleav-age	Colour					
	colourless	white-whitish	yellow-yellowish	orange	red-reddish-pink	violet
very good	25, 31, 33, 35, 42, 44 − 46, 48, 49, 51, 55, 57 − 59, 66, 71, 73, 79, 80, 88, 91, 94, 99, 101 − 105, 107, 108, 115, 117, 118, 142, 205, 213, 236, 309, 312, 405	2, 4, 7, 13, 20, 21, 23, 25, 27, 31, 33, 35, 41, 42 ,44 − 48, 35, 41, 42, 44 − 48, 51, 55, 57 − 60, 66, 70 − 72, 79, 80, 83, 88, 91, 94, 99 − 105, 107, 108, 115, 153, 164, 205, 206, 211, 213, 236, 238, 280, 293, 309, 312, 364, 380, 381, 395, 397, 405, 414, 416, 500	20, 21, 23, 25, 27, 31, 33, 35, 41, 42, 44 − 48, 51, 55, 57, 59, 60, 70, 72, 73, 79, 80, 88, 91, 94, 100, 103, 107, 115, 117, 118, 123, 131, 132, 136 − 138, 142, 149, 150, 153, 164, 168, 197, 205, 235, 236, 238, 252, 260, 280, 292, 295, 309, 311, 312, 317, 328, 331, 337, 397, 403, 405, 415, 420, 488, 500	33, 280, 337	21, 31, 33, 44 − 49, 51, 57 − 59, 70 − 73, 80, 88, 100, 102, 103, 107, 117, 118, 142, 182, 183, 186, 189, 192, 194, 197, 199, 205, 206, 210, 211, 213, 235, 238, 280, 292, 293, 295, 337, 395, 415, 420, 500	33, 46, 58, 73, 107, 209, 210, 211, 213, 544
good	30, 40, 50, 67, 75, 76, 84, 87, 93, 116, 232, 283, 286, 402	8, 10 − 12, 15, 28, 30, 40, 56, 67, 68, 74 − 76, 84, 87, 90, 93, 116, 146, 152, 165, 193, 232, 249, 255, 286, 288, 393, 398, 402	28, 56, 67, 68, 74 − 76, 84, 90, 116, 133, 143, 146, 152, 156, 163, 165, 175, 188, 193, 203, 232, 255, 283, 335, 393, 398, 417, 418, 459, 481, 529	133, 143, 146, 156, 170, 175, 181, 188	28, 40, 67, 75, 76, 90, 116, 181, 184, 185, 188, 193, 196, 200, 203, 232, 283, 347, 350, 417, 418, 530	215, 244, 357, 530
clear	37, 38, 43, 116, 158, 286, 421	10, 15, 16, 37, 38, 43, 64, 116, 134, 157, 158, 162, 165, 286, 294, 349, 392, 421	38, 43, 64, 116, 128, 134, 157, 158, 162, 163, 165, 172, 304, 322, 349	172	64, 116, 157, 158, 162, 172, 195, 349	158, 216
poor	17, 61, 77, 78, 81, 86, 291, 355, 427	17, 61, 77, 78, 81, 82, 86, 106, 291, 320, 321, 387, 388	17, 61, 77, 78, 81, 86, 106, 124 − 127, 166, 171, 198, 246, 291, 305, 320, 321, 332, 355, 384, 427, 438	171, 332, 355	61, 77, 78, 81, 171, 198, 246, 291, 305, 355, 386	61
none	29, 36, 39, 69, 85, 89, 92, 95, 98, 109, 113, 114, 139, 161, 239, 276, 419	1, 3, 5, 9, 14, 18, 19, 22, 24, 26, 29, 36, 62, 63, 65, 69, 85, 89, 92, 95 − 97, 110 − 113, 139, 140, 154, 159 − 161, 179, 301, 310, 318, 390, 391, 396, 399, 419, 486, 487, 495, 498, 501	18, 19, 22, 24, 36, 39, 62, 69, 85, 89, 97, 98, 111 − 114, 119 − 122, 124, 125, 127, 129, 135, 139 − 141, 147, 148, 154, 155, 159 − 161, 167, 176, 270, 301, 326, 330, 336, 341, 351, 396, 399, 422, 428, 438, 486, 487, 489, 491, 495, 499, 501, 518	129, 135, 140, 141, 147, 169, 176, 326	19, 22, 36, 39, 85, 89, 111, 112, 135, 154, 176, 177, 179, 180, 187, 201, 202, 207, 208, 219, 270, 289, 324, 326, 351, 371, 406, 428, 429, 486, 489, 495, 499, 519, 527, 536	208, 217, 219, 371

		Colour		
blue-bluish	**green-greenish**	**brown-brownish**	**grey**	**black-blackish**
1, 33, 57, 58, 3, 79, 105, 07, 117, 118, 09, 221, 224 —, 26, 229, 233 —, 36, 238, 243, 50, 280, 416, 70	20, 21, 23, 73, 79, 94, 101, 103, 108, 117, 118, 136, 138, 142, 146, 149, 150, 153, 168, 206, 209, 211, 213, 225, 238, 248, 250, 252 — 254, 257 — 261, 266, 279, 280, 284, 292, 293, 295, 296, 311, 313, 314, 317, 403, 414, 415, 444, 452, 467, 488, 545	25, 31, 47, 49, 51, 57, 59, 60, 71, 72, 79, 91, 123, 132, 142, 146, 150, 189, 192, 205, 206, 279, 293, 295, 309, 311 — 317, 328, 331, 337, 346, 403, 408, 415, 416, 420, 444, 447, 449, 454, 455, 488, 500, 544	13, 20, 23, 31, 35, 41, 42, 44, 49, 57 — 60, 66, 70, 71, 79, 80, 83, 94, 102, 107, 108, 118, 142, 146, 153, 164, 186, 192, 205, 206, 210, 211, 236, 238, 280, 292, 295, 309, 311 — 313, 317, 331, 361, 362, 364 — 366, 367, 372, 380, 381, 395, 397, 403, 405, 408, 411, 414 — 416, 420, 432, 441, 446, 451, 452, 544	118, 142, 186, 209, 221, 235, 295, 313, 314, 317, 367, 372, 380, 405, 416, 432, 434, 441, 444 — 447, 449, 451, 452, 454, 455, 468, 470
8, 87, 93, 215, 8, 87, 93, 215, 22, 223, 230, 32, 237, 244, 63	28, 68, 87, 90, 93, 104, 163, 165, 175, 249, 251, 255, 262, 263, 269, 272, 273, 283, 285, 286, 288, 290, 299, 333, 344, 357, 398, 400, 402, 407, 413, 418, 529	40, 68, 90, 116, 143, 152, 156, 163, 170, 175, 200, 203, 255, 269, 283, 288, 299, 327, 333, 335, 344, 345, 347, 350, 354, 357, 393, 394, 404, 413, 459, 462, 481	8, 12, 15, 56, 67, 74, 76, 84, 87, 93, 165, 184, 185, 222, 244, 283, 288, 290, 345, 357, 385, 393, 394, 398, 400, 402, 404, 407, 413, 417, 418, 481	184, 203, 269, 273, 286, 299, 344, 400, 402, 404, 407, 413, 418, 448, 453, 459, 462, 465, 467, 472, 474, 481
16, 421	64, 157, 158, 162, 163, 165, 172, 216, 281, 286, 294, 304, 343, 349, 412, 466	116, 128, 157, 162, 163, 308, 322, 340, 342, 343, 349, 358, 412, 426, 466, 467	15, 16, 43, 64, 165, 172, 195, 294, 340, 342, 343, 374 — 378, 389, 392, 412, 421, 425, 426, 466	162, 286, 340, 342, 343, 358, 376, 425, 440, 466, 469
1, 227, 228, 46, 338, 355, 86	61, 78, 166, 171, 267, 271, 277, 291, 305, 306, 338, 355	61, 81, 106, 166, 171, 198, 246, 267, 291, 320, 321, 323, 332, 334, 338, 339, 348, 355, 427, 438, 464	61, 82, 86, 171, 321, 365, 369, 370, 373, 383, 384, 386 — 388, 401, 427, 438	198, 246, 321, 332, 365, 373, 384, 433, 438, 464, 476
9, 114, 239, 41, 242, 245, 65, 351, 422, 28, 495, 501, 17, 546, 547	19, 22, 24, 36, 98, 112, 114, 139, 159, 160, 239, 247, 264, 265, 268, 270, 275, 276, 278, 282, 287, 289, 297, 298, 300 — 303, 324, 329, 351, 353, 356, 406, 443, 475, 489, 495, 517, 518, 551	19, 36, 39, 69, 111, 112, 119, 129, 135, 139 — 141, 147, 148, 154, 161, 169, 176, 180, 201, 207, 219, 265, 270, 307, 310, 318, 319, 324 — 326, 329, 330, 336, 341, 351, 352, 353, 356, 359, 360, 396, 399, 409, 424, 428, 429, 438, 442, 473, 477, 486, 487, 489, 491, 499, 501, 534	5, 9, 14, 19, 22, 24, 36, 59, 85, 89, 92, 111 — 114, 160, 179, 180, 201, 241, 270, 301, 307, 330, 363, 371, 377, 379, 382, 390, 391, 396, 399, 406, 409, 419, 422, 424, 428, 431, 438, 443, 473, 483, 486, 487, 491, 495, 498, 501, 534	5, 39, 112, 169, 201, 219, 275, 307, 310, 324, 329, 341, 356, 359, 379, 406, 409, 424, 429 — 431, 433, 435, 438, 442, 443, 450, 456 — 458, 460, 461, 471, 473, 475, 477 — 479, 483, 489, 491, 498

IDENTIFICATION TABLE ACCORDING TO STREAK AND HARDNESS

Hard-ness	Streak					
	white-whitish	silver-white	yellow-yellowish	orange	pink	red-reddish
1−2	17−39, 132, 224, 248, 252, 255, 256, 393, 394, 396−399		129, 131, 133, 134, 183, 251, 393 129, 131, 133, 134, 183, 251, 393	181, 183	210	182, 210
2−3	39−55, 139−141, 170−172, 189, 211, 227, 229, 262, 309, 310, 311, 312, 319, 323, 398, 402, 403, 444, 484	4, 5, 363	7, 119, 129, 133, 135−138, 169, 188, 259, 260, 267, 326	187, 188	210, 211	177, 184−186, 210
3−4	56−73, 142, 145−147, 151−153, 174, 190−194, 211, 212, 232−234, 236, 270, 272, 310, 315, 317, 318, 320, 321, 325, 329, 330, 395, 401, 405, 445, 447, 452, 481, 485, 487, 489, 490		142, 143, 148−150, 175, 191, 269, 270, 315−317, 320, 322, 324, 325, 327, 329, 445, 481, 485	406	211	195, 196
4−5	74−84, 157−160, 164, 213, 214, 236, 276, 280−282, 310, 331, 338, 411	9	156, 197, 269	156, 197, 332		454
5−6	85−105, 112, 155, 161−164, 199, 200, 202, 204, 215, 235, 237−239, 283, 286, 287−291, 333, 337, 339, 343−345, 348, 408, 412−417, 421, 459, 461, 463, 466, 468, 470, 486, 495, 543, 545, 546, 551		154, 198, 235, 334−336, 348, 409, 462, 482, 488			201, 435, 436, 437
6−7	106−114, 161, 164−166, 200, 205−207, 216, 217, 219, 236, 241, 242, 292−302, 340, 346, 347, 349, 351−357, 418−420, 422, 424, 426, 438, 461, 477, 478, 491, 495, 498, 500, 503, 504, 525, 526, 528−530, 534, 536, 544		438, 499			201, 203, 207
7−8	115−117, 167, 168, 176, 208, 220, 244−246, 303, 305, 306, 355, 358−360, 427, 479, 516−523, 525, 527					
8−9	304, 428, 512, 514, 515, 524					
10	118, 513					

			Streak			
blue–bluish	green–greenish	brown–brownish	grey	green–black	grey–black	black
09, 221, 223, 25	225, 247, 249 – 251, 253, 254, 313, 362	442	2, 39, 361, 362, 441			221, 361, 441, 442
26, 228, 265	136, 228, 249, 257 – 267, 400, 404	267, 307, 326	3, 4, 7, 39, 172, 364, 365, 367, 369, 370, 372, 374, 383, 400, 404, 444		307, 366, 375	222, 367, 371, 373, 374, 376 – 380, 429, 430, 432
30, 243, 265, 71	123, 243, 264, 265, 268, 269, 271, 273, 275, 314, 448, 449	142, 191, 315, 316, 324, 328, 406, 445, 451	8, 270, 325, 381, 407, 447, 452, 481, 489, 490	124	123, 128, 308, 382, 446	124, 379, 384, 431, 446, 449, 483
77, 278	269, 277, 279, 284, 443, 456	279, 332, 453, 454, 460	385, 388, 454		12, 387	179, 379, 388, 443, 450, 453, 456, 460
238, 547	285, 342, 443, 467, 470	154, 180, 201, 334, 335, 341, 348, 386, 409, 434 – 437, 455, 457, 458, 460 – 462, 464, 465, 468, 469, 482, 488	215, 333, ·337, 343, 344, 459, 463, 464, 466 – 468, 470, 488	342	10, 11, 13, 14, 16, 387, 390 – 392	15, 180, 342, 379, 386, 389, 433, 443, 455, 458, 460, 469
	474, 478	201, 203, 341, 435, 436 – 438, 440, 461, 472, 473, 476	295, 340, 349, 351 – 353, 356, 473, 474, 491	125, 127	471	379, 425, 440
	475		358, 478			

Trans-parency	Colour					
	colourless	white–whitish	yellow–yellowish	orange	red–reddish–pink	violet
transparent	17, 25, 29−31, 33, 35, 36, 39, 40, 42−46, 50, 51, 55, 57−59, 61, 66, 71, 73, 75−79, 85−89, 91, 93−95, 98, 99, 101−104, 107−109, 113, 115, 116−118, 142, 161, 205, 213, 232, 236, 237, 281, 283, 286, 291, 309, 312, 355, 402, 405, 419, 427	17, 25, 29, 30, 31, 33, 35, 36, 40, 42−47, 51, 55−59, 61, 66, 71, 72, 75−79, 85−91, 93−95, 99, 101−104, 107, 108, 110, 113, 115, 116, 140, 153, 157, 161, 162, 165, 205, 211, 213, 232, 236−238, 281, 291, 294, 309, 312, 321, 349, 393, 402, 405, 416, 419	17, 25, 31, 33, 35, 36, 39, 42−47, 51, 55, 56, 57, 59, 61, 72, 73, 75−79, 85, 86, 88−91, 94, 98, 103, 107, 113, 115, 116−118, 129, 131, 136, 140, 142, 153, 157, 161, 162, 165, 167, 172, 176, 188, 198, 205, 232, 236, 238, 246, 252, 281, 283, 286, 291, 304, 305, 309, 311, 312, 321, 328, 349, 355, 393, 403, 405, 427, 428, 518, 529	33, 129, 140, 172, 176, 181, 188, 355	31, 33, 36, 39, 40, 44−47, 51, 57−59, 61, 71−73, 75−78, 85, 88−90, 102, 103, 107, 116−118, 142, 157, 162, 172, 176, 181, 183−185, 188, 189, 198, 199, 202, 205, 208, 211, 213, 219, 232, 238, 246, 281, 283, 291, 305, 347, 349, 355, 428, 519, 527, 530	33, 46, 58, 61, 73, 208, 211, 213, 217, 219, 244, 281, 357, 530
translucent	17, 25, 29, 30, 31, 33, 35−40, 42−46, 48, 51, 55, 57−59, 61, 66, 67, 71, 73, 75−81, 84−89, 91−94, 99, 101−105, 107, 108, 113, 115−118, 139, 142, 161, 205, 213, 232, 236, 237, 276, 281, 283, 286, 291, 309, 312, 355, 402, 405, 427	17, 18, 20, 23, 25, 27−31, 33, 35−38, 40−49, 51, 55−61, 63, 66−68, 70−72, 74−81, 83−94, 99−108, 110−113, 115, 116, 134, 139, 140, 146, 152, 153, 157, 159, 161, 162, 165, 193, 205, 206, 211, 213, 232, 236−239, 249, 255, 256, 272, 280, 281, 288, 291, 294, 301, 309, 312, 321, 349, 393, 395, 397−399, 402, 405, 414, 416, 486, 487, 495, 498, 501	17, 18, 23, 25, 27, 28, 31, 33, 35, 36, 38, 39, 41−48, 51, 55−57, 59−61, 67, 68, 70, 72−81, 84−86, 88−91, 94, 100, 103, 106, 107, 111−113, 115−118, 129, 131−134, 136−143, 146−150, 152, 153, 155−157, 159, 161−163, 165, 166, 168, 171, 172, 175, 176, 193, 197, 198, 203, 205, 232, 235, 236, 246, 248, 252, 255, 256, 270, 272, 280, 281, 283, 286, 291, 292, 295, 301, 304, 305, 309, 311, 312, 317, 321, 326, 328, 331, 332, 337, 349, 351, 355, 393, 397−399, 403, 405, 415, 417, 418, 420, 422, 427, 428, 438, 486−489, 495, 501	33, 129, 133, 140, 141, 143, 146, 147, 156, 170−172, 175, 176, 181, 280, 326, 332, 337, 355	28, 31, 33, 36, 39, 40, 44−49, 51, 57−59, 61, 67, 70−73, 75−78, 80, 81, 85, 88−90, 100, 102, 103, 107, 111, 112, 116−118, 142, 157, 162, 171, 172, 176, 181−186, 189, 192−194, 196−200, 202, 203, 205, 206, 208, 210, 211, 213, 219, 232, 235, 238, 246, 270, 280, 281, 283, 289, 291, 292, 295, 305, 324, 326, 337, 347, 349, 350, 351, 355, 395, 415, 417, 418, 420, 428, 486, 489, 495, 519, 536.	33, 46, 58, 61, 73, 208−211, 213, 215−217, 219, 244, 281, 317, 544
opaque		1−5, 7−16, 19−22, 24, 26, 62, 63, 65, 69, 82, 92, 96, 97, 103, 111, 112, 154, 160, 179, 239, 249, 293, 310, 318, 320, 364, 380, 381, 387, 388, 392, 396, 399, 486, 487, 500	7, 19−22, 24, 62, 69, 97, 103, 111, 112, 118, 119, 123−125, 127, 128, 135, 141, 142, 149, 154, 155, 160, 166, 197, 203, 235, 292, 320, 322, 326, 329, 330, 332, 335−337, 341, 384, 396, 399, 415, 418, 420, 438, 459, 481, 486−489, 491, 499, 500	135, 141, 169, 326, 332, 337	4, 19, 21, 22, 103, 111, 112, 118, 135, 142, 154, 177, 179, 180, 184, 187, 189, 195, 197, 201, 203, 207, 219, 235, 292, 293, 324, 326, 337, 350, 371, 386, 406, 415, 418, 420, 429, 435, 486, 489, 499, 500	209, 215, 219, 371

Colour				
blue-bluish	**green-greenish**	**brown-brownish**	**grey**	**black-blackish**
3, 57, 58, 61, 3, 79, 87, 93, 07, 117, 118, 29, 232, 236 — 38, 244, 246, 50, 305, 355, 16, 428, 470, 17	36, 61, 73, 78, 79, 90, 93, 94, 98, 101, 103, 104, 108, 117, 118, 136, 142, 153, 157, 162, 165, 172, 211, 213, 236 — 238, 250, 252 — 254, 257 — 259, 262, 266, 268, 269, 277, 281, 283 — 286, 290, 291, 294, 299, 300, 302 — 306, 311, 313, 344, 349, 355, 357, 402, 403, 407, 444, 517, 518, 529, 551	25, 31, 36, 39, 40, 47, 51, 57, 59, 61, 71, 72, 79, 90, 91, 116, 129, 140, 142, 157, 161, 162, 176, 189, 198, 205, 219, 246, 269, 283, 291, 299, 309, 311, 312, 313, 321, 328, 344, 347, 349, 355, 357, 359, 393, 403, 416, 427, 428, 444, 477, 534	31, 35, 36, 39, 42, 43, 44, 56 — 59, 61, 66, 71, 76, 79, 85 — 87, 89, 93, 94, 102, 107, 108, 113, 118, 142, 153, 165, 172, 184, 185, 205, 211, 236 — 238, 244, 283, 290, 294, 309, 311 — 313, 321, 357, 393, 402, 403, 405, 407, 416, 419, 427, 428, 534	39, 118, 142, 162, 184, 198, 219, 246, 269, 286, 299, 313, 321, 344, 359, 402, 405, 407, 416, 444, 470, 477
3, 57, 58, 61, 3, 73, 79, 87, 3, 105, 107, 17, 118, 209, 16, 223, 225 — 30, 232, 235 — 39, 244 — 246, 50, 263, 265, 72, 280, 305, 38, 351, 355, 16, 422, 428, 70, 495, 501, 44	23, 28, 36, 61, 68, 73, 78, 79, 90, 93, 94, 101, 103, 104, 108, 112, 117, 118, 136, 138, 139, 142, 146, 153, 157, 159, 162, 163, 165, 166, 168, 171, 172, 175, 206, 209, 211, 213, 216, 228, 236 — 239, 248 — 259, 261 — 263, 265 — 273, 275 — 281, 283 — 292, 294 — 306, 311, 313, 317, 324, 333, 338, 344, 349, 351, 353, 355 — 357, 398, 402, 403, 407, 412, 414, 415, 444, 452, 467, 488, 489, 495, 545	25, 31, 36, 39, 40, 47, 49, 51, 57, 59 — 61, 68, 71, 72, 79, 81, 90, 91, 106, 111, 112, 116, 129, 132, 139 — 143, 146 — 148, 150, 152, 157, 161 — 163, 166, 170, 171, 175, 176, 189, 192, 198, 200, 203, 205, 206, 219, 246, 255, 256, 265, 267, 269, 270, 272, 283, 288, 291, 295, 299, 309, 311 — 313, 316, 317, 321, 324, 326, 328, 331 — 334, 337, 338, 340, 341, 344, 345, 347, 349 — 353, 355 — 359, 393, 394, 399, 403, 408, 412, 415, 416, 420, 424, 426, 427, 428, 438, 444, 447, 454, 462, 464, 477, 486 — 489, 501, 544	23, 31, 35, 36, 39, 41 — 44, 49, 56 — 61, 66, 67, 70, 71, 76, 79, 80, 83 — 87, 89, 92 — 94, 102, 107, 108, 111 — 113, 118, 142, 146, 153, 165, 171, 172, 184 — 186, 192, 205, 206, 210, 211, 228, 236 — 238, 244, 270, 280, 283, 290, 292, 294, 295, 301, 309, 311 — 313, 317, 321, 331, 340, 345, 357, 393 — 395, 397 — 399, 402, 403, 405, 407, 408, 412, 414 — 418, 420, 422, 424, 426 — 428, 438, 452, 486, 487, 495, 498, 501, 544	39, 112, 118, 142, 162, 184, 186, 198, 203, 209, 219, 235, 246, 269, 273, 275, 286, 295, 299, 313, 317, 321, 324, 332, 340, 341, 344, 356, 358, 359, 402, 405, 407, 416, 418, 424, 434, 438, 444, 447, 448, 452, 454, 462, 465, 467 — 470, 477, 489, 498
4, 69, 118, 9, 221, 222, 40, 235, 239, 41 — 243, 245, 5, 546, 547	19 — 22, 24, 103, 112, 118, 142, 160, 166, 209, 239, 247 — 249, 264, 265, 273, 278, 279, 282, 292, 293, 298, 314, 324, 329, 333, 343, 353, 356, 400, 406, 412, 413, 415, 443, 467, 475, 488, 489	19, 20, 60, 111, 112, 119, 123, 128, 135, 141, 142, 154, 166, 169, 180, 189, 201, 203, 207, 219, 265, 293, 307, 310, 314, 316, 318 — 320, 322, 324, 326, 330, 332 — 337, 340 — 343, 350, 352, 353, 356, 358, 396, 399, 404, 409, 412, 413, 415, 420, 424, 426, 429, 435, 438, 442, 449, 454, 455, 459, 462, 464, 473, 481, 486 — 489, 491, 499, 500	5, 8, 9, 12 — 16, 19, 20, 24, 82, 92, 111, 112, 118, 142, 160, 179, 180, 184, 195, 201, 222, 241, 292, 307, 319, 330, 340, 343, 361, 362, 364 — 367, 369 — 388, 392, 396, 399, 400, 404, 406, 409, 412, 413, 415, 418, 420, 424 — 426, 431, 432, 435, 438, 441, 443, 446, 451, 473, 481, 486, 487, 491	5, 112, 118, 142, 169, 184, 201, 203, 209, 219, 221, 235, 246, 273, 307, 310, 314, 324, 329, 332, 340 — 343, 356, 358, 365, 367, 372, 373, 376, 379, 380, 383, 400, 404, 406, 409, 413, 418, 424, 425, 429 — 435, 438, 440 — 443, 446, 448, 449 — 451, 453 — 462, 467 — 469, 471 — 476, 478, 479, 481, 489, 491

Index of Minerals

Figures in italics indicate text pages; Roman figures refer to numbers of minerals.

Acicular Iron Ore   462
Adularia   101
Agate   *14, 26,* 504, 505, 507, 509, 510, 511, 538
Alabandite   449
Albite   *17,* 100
Alexandrite   *25,* 524
Allanite   464
Allemontite   8
Almandine   219, 526
Alstonite   74
Alum Stone   67
Aluminiferous Strengite   160
Aluminite   18
Alumocalcite   97
Alunite   67
Alunogen   27
Amazonite   545
Amazonstone   545
Amber   *12, 28,* 140, 552
Amethyst   *25, 31,* 217, 218, 533
Ammonium Alum   29
Ammonium Chloride   17
Amosite   288
Amphibole   *12, 31, 172, 173,* 290, 468
Amphibole Family   414, 415, 470, 488, 549
Amphibolite   575
Amygdaloidal Basalt   *172,* 559
Analcite   89
Anatase   *18,* 235
Andalusite   426, 491
Andesite   *172,* 103
Andradite   300, 356, 525
Anglesite   402
Anhydrite   58, 190
Ankerite   60
Annabergite   249, 254
Anorthite   102, 204
Anthophyllite   345, 408
Anthophyllite Asbestos   408
Antigorite   489
Antimonite   *25,* 367, 368
Antimony   381
Antimony Bloom   49
Antimony Glance   367, 368
Antimony Ochre   154
Apatite   *17, 22, 25, 31,* 82, 158, 214, 281, 310, 338
Apjohnite   28
Apophyllite   213
Aquamarine   *170,* 517
Aragonite   *14, 18, 20,* 61, 62, 63, 320, 485
Arfvedsonite   470
Argentiferous Grey Copper Ore   382
Argentite   *24,* 365
Argyrodite   307
Arsenic   380
Arsenical Nickel   180
Arsenical Pyrites   15, 389

Arsenolite   38
Arsenopyrite   *28,* 15, 389
Asbestos   *27,* 255, 490
Asteriated Quartz   111
Asteriated Sapphire   514
Astrophyllite   328
Atacamite   266
Augite   *17, 31,* 467
Aurichalcite   225
Autunite   138, 260
Aventurine   289, 542
Aventurine Felspar   500
Aventurine Quartz   542
Axinite   *17,* 357
Azurite   *15,* 230, 231

Baddeleyite   473
Barrandite   160
Barytes   *17, 31,* 57, 144, 145, 234
Barytocalcite   153
Basalt   *172,* 558, 559
Bauxite   *173,* 568
Bell Metal Ore   384
Benitoite   241
Bentonite   396
Berthierite   222
Beryl   *14, 17, 25,* 305, 306, 516, 517, 518, 519
Betafite   329
Beudantite   269
Biotite   *172,* 444
Bismuth   4
Bitter Salt   45
Bitter Spar   405
Black Jack   142, 445
Black Tellurium   361
Blue Carbonate of Copper   230, 231
Blue Iron Earth   209
Blue Lead   366
Blue Spar   239, 240
Bohemian Garnet   527
Boleite   243
Boracite   114
Borax   43
Bornite   429
Botryogen   183
Boulangerite   378
Bournonite   383
Braunite   440
Breccia   *173,* 561
Breithauptite   386
Breunnerite   331
Brittle Silver Ore   373
Bromlite   74
Bronzite   333
Brookite   *18,* 198, 348
Brown Haematite   409, 410, 482
Brown Iron Ore   409, 410, 482
Brown Ironstone   409, 410, 482
Brown Manganese Ore   451
Bundle Zeolite   72

Byssolite   290

Cabrerite   254
Cacoxenite   148
Calamine   79, 280
Calcareous Spar   51, 52, 53, 54, 170
Calcite   *15, 17, 18, 22, 24, 25, 27, 28, 31, 173,* 51, 52, 53, 54, 170, 319, 561
Calcium Tungstate   157
Caledonite   262
Callaite   546
Calomel   393
Camphylite   327
Carnallite   36
Carnotite   149
Carpholite   163
Cassiterite   *17, 20, 26, 27, 30, 31,* 438, 439
Cat's Eye   488, 543
Ceruse   401
Cerussite   321, 401
Ceylonite   475
Chabazite   77
Chalcanthite   *17,* 227
Chalcedony   *11, 14,* 422, 423, 501, 502, 506, 508, 539, 540
Chalcocite   370
Chalcolite   258
Chalcophyllite   253
Chalcopyrite   *15, 30,* 124
Chalcotrichite   196
Chalk   *23, 28, 31, 173,* 26
Chalybite   317
Chamosite   *15,* 404
Chiastolite   491
Chile Saltpetre   25
Chloanthite   *14,* 390
Chlorargyrite   39
Chlorite Family   *25,* 248
Chondrodite   349
Chrome Iron Ore   457
Chromic Iron   457
Chromite   *14, 30,* 457
Chrysoberyl   304, 524
Chrysocolla   265
Chrysolite   299, 354, 528
Chrysoprase   297, 540
Chrysotile   255, 256, 490
Cinnabar   184
Cinnabarite   184
Citrine   *26, 170,* 167, 532
Clausthalite   372
Claystone   *173,* 564
Clinochlore   248
Clinozoisite   292
Cobalt Bloom   210
Coelestine   232
Colemanite   66
Columbite   469
Common Garnet   356
Comptonite   90

Conglomerate 562
Copper *12, 28*, 177, 178
Copper Glance 370
Copper Protoxide 196
Copper Pyrites 124
Copper Uranite 258, 261
Copper Vitriol 227
Copperas 252
Cordierite *25*, 244
Cornelian 539
Cornelian Onyx 502
Cornwallite 278
Coronadite 450
Corundum *17, 22*, 428, 512, 514, 515
Covellite 221
Crocidolite 488, 543
Crocoite 188
Cronstedtite 448
Cross Stone *75*, 76
Cryolite 40
Cubic Zeolite 77
Cuprite 195, 196
Cuprodescloizite 324
Cuprosklodowskite 251
Curite 156
Cyanite 164, 492
Cyanotrichite 223
Cylindrite 377
Cyprine 242

Danburite 427
Datolite 86
Delvauxite 169
Demantoid 300, 525
Descloizite 406
Desmine 72
Devilline 257
Diallage 452
Diamond *12, 18, 22, 26, 168, 170*, 118, 513
Diaspore 107
Dichroite 244
Diopside 215, 286
Dioptase 284
Diorite *172*, 555
Disthene 164, 236, 492
Dolomite *173*, 59, 151, 318, 561
Dravite 359
Dumortierite 216

Egeran 352
Eisenkiesel 207, 499
Emerald *25, 168, 170, 171*, 306, 516
Emerald Nickel 268
Endellionite 383
Enstatite 412
Epidote 295, 296
Epsomite *28*, 45
Erinite 278
Erythrite 210
Eucairite 3
Euchroite 271
Eudidymite 99
Euxenite 341
Evansite 69

Fahlerz 431, 483

Fassaite 344
Fayalite 418
Feather Alum 139
Feather Ore 375
Felspar Family *12, 15, 22, 31, 172*, 100, 101, 102, 103, 104, 105, 204, 205, 346, 420, 544
Ferberite 453
Fergusonite 461
Ferruginous Quartz 207
Fibrolite 206
Fibrous Zeolite 70, 88, 90, 91, 199
Fire Clay 566
Fire Opal 202
Firestone 424
Flint 424
Flos Ferri 63
Fluor Spar *24, 25*, 73, 212, 233
Fluorite *20, 22, 24, 27, 31*, 73, 212, 233
Forsterite 165
Fowlerite 200
Francolite 159
Franklinite 476
Freibergite 382

Gabbro *172*, 556
Gadolinite 474
Galena *24, 27*, 366
Galmei 79, 411
Garnet Family *15, 173*, 176, 219, 300, 303, 356, 478, 525, 526, 527
Garnierite 264
Gaylussite 42
Gedrite 415
Germanite 371
Gersdorffite 13
Geyserite *14*, 486
Gilbertite 398
Glassy Opal 95
Glauber Salt 30
Glauberite 44
Gneiss *173*, 569
Goethite 335, 462
Gold *12, 170*, 119, 120, 121, 122
Granite *172*, 553
Granulite *173*, 571
Graphite *12, 18, 24, 28*, 441
Green Earth 247
Green Lead Ore 270, 325
Green Schist 574
Green Vitriol 252
Greenockite 143
Greenstone *173*, 574
Grey Antimony 367, 368
Grey Copper 431
Grey Nickel Pyrites 13
Gummite 135
Gypsum *15, 17, 20, 22, 23, 24, 25, 27, 28, 31, 173*, 31, 32

Haematite *26, 28*, 201, 435, 436, 437
Hair Pyrites 123
Hair Salt 139
Halite *16*, 33, 34, 224
Halotrichite 139
Hambergite 115

Harmotome 76
Hausmannite 434
Hauyne 238
Haüynite 238
Heavy Spar 57, 144, 145, 234
Hedenbergite 343, 466
Heliodor 518
Helvite 166
Hemimorphite *17*, 79
Herrengrundite 257
Hessite 369
Heteromorphite 374
Heulandite 71, 194
Hiddenite 529
Hopeite 47
Horn Lead 309
Horn Quicksilver 393
Horn Silver 39
Hornblende 468
Hübnerite 454
Humite 106
Hyalite 95
Hydromagnesite 65
Hydroxylapatite 82
Hydrozincite 41
Hypersthene 413

Ilmenite 458
Ilvaite 342
Indigo Copper 221
Indigolite 245
Inyoite 37
Iolite 244
Iron 385
Iron Alum 139
Iron Glance 435
Iron Mica 437, 444
Iron Pyrites 125, 126
Iron Tourmaline 479

Jachymovite 251
Jadeite 301, 550
Jamesonite 375
Jarosite 322
Jasper 503, 537
Jordanite 432

Kainite 46
Kakoxen 148
Kampylite 175, 327
Kaolinite *28, 31, 173*, 21
Kascholong 96
Keramohalite 27
Kerargyrite 39
Kermesite 182
Krennerite 7
Kröhnkite 229
Kunzite 530
Kyanite *15, 17, 23, 173*, 236

Labradorite 544
Lamellar Zeolite 71
Langite 263
Lapis Lazuli 547
Laumontite 70
Lazulite 239, 240
Lazurite 547
Lead Glance 366
Lead Vitriol 402

Lechatelierite 161
Lepidocrocite 335
Lepidolite 211
Lettsomite 223
Leucite *172*, 92
Leucopyrite 11
Levynite 78
Libethenite 275
Lievrite 342
Lime Uranite 138, 260
Limonite *15, 173*, 409, 410, 482
Linarite 226
Linnaeite 387
Liroconite 228
Lithionite 311
Lithium Mica 211
Löllingite 10, 11
Ludwigite 456
Lumachel 484

Macle 491
Magnesite 405
Magnesium Silicate 403
Magnetic Pyrites 128, 308
Magnetite *14, 19, 28, 30,* 433
Malachite *15, 25,* 273, 274, 548
Mandelstone 559
Mangan-Blende 449
Mangancalcite 193
Manganese Alum 28
Manganese Spar 192, 200
Manganiferous Epidote 350
Manganite 451
Marble 573
Marcasite *15,* 127
Margarite 395
Marl *173,* 565
Maucherite 179
Meerschaum 24
Meionite 87, 421
Melanite 478
Melanterite 252
Mercury *11,* 1
Mercury Fahlore 446
Mesitine Spar 152, 331
Mesitite 152, 331
Mesolite 84
Metacinnabarite 430
Mica Family *12, 14, 15, 21, 24, 25, 27,* 211, 312
Mica Schist *173,* 570
Micaceous Iron Ore 444
Microcline *172,* 545
Miemite 318
Miesite 487
Milarite 98
Milky Quartz 110
Millerite 123
Mimetesite 146, 174, 175, 327
Mimetite 146, 174
Minium 187
Mirabilite 30
Mispickel 15, 389
Mock Lead 445
Mock Ore 445
Moldavite *171,* 551
Molybdenite 362
Molybdenum Ochre 134, 362
Molybdite 134

Monazite 337
Montmorillonite *173,* 19
Moonstone 105
Morganite 519
Morion 477
Moroxite 338
Mossy Opal 498
Mottramite 324
Muscovite *172,* 312

Nacrite 397
Nagyagite 361
Natrocalcite 42
Natrolite 88, 199
Needle Ironstone 462
Nepheline *17, 172,* 291
Nephrite 287, 549
Neptunite 465
Niccolite 180
Nickel Bloom 249
Nickel Glance 13
Niobite 469
Nitronatrite 25
Nosean 416
Noumeite 264
Nussierite 147

Obsidian 560
Olivenite 267
Olivine *12, 15, 17, 172,* 299, 354, 528
Olivine Family 418
Omphacite 285
Onyx 506, 508
Opal *10, 15, 24,* 112, 202, 424, 486, 495, 496, 497, 498, 535
Orpiment 131
Orthite 464
Orthoclase *17, 172,* 205, 346

Palygorskite 399
Pea Grit 62
Pea Stone 62
Pectolite 83
Pelosiderite 330
Periclase 94
Pericline 104
Peridot 299, 354, 528
Perovskite 459
Pharmacolite 48
Phenakite 116
Phillipsite 75
Phlogopite 403
Phosgenite 309
Phosphomimetite 175
Phosphorite *15,* 310
Phyllite *173,* 572
Picrosmine 256
Piedmontite 350
Pisolite 62
Pistacite 296
Pitch Blende 443
Pitch Ore 443
Plagioclase Family *172,* 500
Plasma 298
Platinum 9
Pleonast 475
Plumbo-Calcite 55
Polianite 425

Pollucite 419
Polycrase 341
Polysphaerite 487
Porphyry *172,* 557
Precious Opal 495, 496, 497, 535
Prehnite 294
Proustite *25,* 185
Pseudomalachite 277
Psilomelane 460
Pycnite 168
Pyrantimonite 182
Pyrargyrite *25,* 186
Pyrite *15, 18, 21, 24, 26, 27, 30,* 125, 126
Pyrochlore 334
Pyrolusite 379
Pyromorphite 147, 270, 325
Pyrope 527
Pyrophyllite 23
Pyrosmalite 279
Pyroxene Family *12, 172,* 285, 286, 412, 452, 466, 467, 550
Pyrrhotite *17, 28,* 128, 308

Quartz *12, 14, 17, 18, 19, 20, 21, 22, 24, 26, 27, 170, 172, 173,* 109, 110, 207, 289, 297, 298, 477, 499, 531, 532, 533, 534, 536, 542
Quicksilver 1

Radial Blende 316
Rammelsbergite 392
Realgar 181
Red Antimony 182
Red Haematite 201
Red Lead Ore 188
Red Oxide of Copper 195
Red Oxide of Iron 201, 435
Red Oxide of Lead 187
Red Oxide of Zinc 197
Red Silver Ore 185, 186
Remolinite 266
Rhaetizite 164
Rhodochrosite 192
Rhodonite *17,* 200
Riebeckite Asbestos 488, 543
Rock Crystal *25, 27, 170,* 109, 531
Rock Salt *15, 16, 24, 25, 27, 173,* 33, 34, 224
Romeite 154
Rose Beryl 519
Rose Quartz *25,* 536
Rubellan 189
Rubellite 208, 220
Ruin Marble 319
Rutile *18, 27, 170,* 203, 347, 541

Safflorite 388
Sagenite 347, 541
Samtblende 335
Sandstone *173,* 563
Sanidine 420
Saponite 22
Sapphire *26, 168, 170,* 514
Satin Spar 132
Scapolite 87
Scapolite Family 421
Scheelite *17, 27,* 157

Schorl 479
Schroeckingerite 137
Schwazite 446
Scolezite 91
Scorodite 407
Seladonite 247
Selenite 132
Semseyite 376
Sepiolite 24
Serpentine *15*, 489, 576
Shell Marble 484
Siderite *14*, 317, 330
Silicate of Zinc 79
Siliceous Sinter 486
Sillimanite *173*, 206
Silver 5, 6, 363
Silver Fahlerz 382
Silver Glance 365
Silver Telluride 369
Skutterudite 16, 391
Smaltite 16, 388, 391
Smithsonite 280, 411
Smoky Quartz *26, 170*, 534
Soap-Stone 22
Soda Nitre 25
Sodalite *172*, 93, 237
Soddite 150
Spathose Iron 317
Spear Pyrites 127
Specularite 435
Spessartite 176
Sphalerite *27, 30, 31*, 142, 191, 315, 445
Sphene 162, 463
Spinel *170*, 246, 360, 522
Spinel Family 475
Spodumene 108, 529, 530
Sprudelstein 320, 485
Staffelite 159
Stannine 384
Stassfurtite 114
Staurolite 358
Steatite 20
Stellerite 194
Stephanite 373
Stibnite 367, 368
Stilbite 71, 72
Stilpnomelan 314
Stolzite 171, 323

Strontianite 64
Strüverite 471
Struvite *17*, 394
Succinite 140, 552
Sulphur *12, 15, 17, 25, 28*, 129, 130
Sulphuric Pyrites 125, 126
Sunstone 500
Syenite *172*, 554
Sylvanite 2
Sylvite *28*, 35

Table Spar 80
Talc *22, 24, 28, 173*, 20
Tantalite 472
Tarnowitzite 81
Tellurium 364
Tetrahedrite 431, 483
Thomsonite 90
Thorite 332
Thortveitite 340
Thuringite 400
Tiger's Eye 488, 543
Tin Pyrites 384
Tin White Cobalt 388
Tincal 43
Tinsel 131
Tinstone 438, 439
Titanite *17*, 162, 339, 463
Titanoferrite 458
Topaz *22, 26, 27*, 117, 168, 523
Torbernite 258, 261
Tourmaline *14, 21, 25, 31*, 245, 302, 359, 479, 480, 493, 494, 520
Tourmaline Family 208, 220, 359
Travertine 567
Tremolite 414
Tridymite *18*, 113
Troostite 417
Tschermigite 29
Turquoise 546
Tyrolite 250

Ullmannite 12
Uran Ochre 133, 135
Uraninite 443
Uranite 259
Uranium Mica 136, 137, 259
Uranocircite 136, 259

Uvarovite 303

Valentinite 49
Vanadinite 326
Variscite 276
Verdelite 302
Vermiculite 313
Vesuvianite *17*, 242, 351, 352, 353
Violane 215
Vivianite 209

Wad 442
Wagnerite 85
Walchovite 141
Wardite 282
Warwickite 447
Wavellite 68, 272
Wheel Ore 383
Whewellite *12*, 50
White Arsenic 38
White Lead Ore 321, 401
White Nickel 14, 390
Willemite *27*, 283
Wiluite 353
Witherite 56
Wolframite *17, 26*, 455
Wollastonite 80
Wood Opal 155
Wulfenite *17, 172*, 173
Wurtzite 316

Xanthosiderite 336

Yellow Lead Ore 172, 173
Yenite 342

Zaratite 268
Zeolite Family 78, 84, 88, 90, 91, 194, 199
Zinc Blende 191, 315, 445, 481
Zinc Bloom 41
Zinc Spar 280
Zincite *17*, 197
Zinnwaldite 311
Zippeite 133
Zircon *17*, 355, 521
Zircon-favas 473
Zirconia 473
Zoisite *173*, 293

General Index

Accompanying minerals   15
Acidic rocks   172
Adamantine lustre   27
Aggregates   19–20
Alkaline rocks   172
Allochromatic minerals   25
Alteration rocks   173
Amorphous minerals   10
Anisotropic minerals   21
Aplitesv   172
Arkoses   173
Associated minerals   15
Axis of symmetry   16

Basic rocks   172
Biochemical origin of minerals   15
Biogenic sediments   173
Breccias   173
Brittle minerals   24
Brilliant cut   169

Cabochon cut   169
Carat   169
Centre of symmetry   16
Changes of colour   26
Chemical properties   28
Chemical sediments   173
Chemico-sedimentary processes   15
Classification of minerals   12–13
Classification of rocks   172
Clastic sediments   173
Clays   173
Cleavage   24
Cleavage fragments   24
Cleavafe rifts   24
Cohesion properties   22
Collecting equipment   32
Collecting of minerals   31
Colour of minerals   25
Colourless minerals   25
Conglomerates   173
Contact metamorphism   15
Cryptocrystalline minerals   11
Crystal, definition   16
Crystal faces   20
Crystal forms   17
Crystal lattice   16
Crystal symmetry   16
Crystal systems   18
Crystalline schists   173
Crystallization   14
Crystallographic axes   18
Cutting form   169

Dendrites   20
Deposited rocks   173
Distortions   19

Double refraction   27
Doublet   170
Druses   20
Ductile minerals   24
Dull lustre   27

Elastic minerals   25
Epitaxis   20
Eruptive rocks   172
Extrusive rocks   172

Facets   169
Feel   28
Flexible minerals   25
Form   18
Fracture   24

Gemstones   168
Geodes   20
Glyptography   169
Greasy lustre   27
Greywackes   173

Habit   18
Hardness   22
Hardness scale   22
Heat conductivity   28
Hydrothermal minerals   14

Identification of minerals   29
Identification of precious stones   170
Identification of rocks   174
Idiochromatic   25
Igneous rocks   172
Imitation precious stones   169
Intrusive rocks   172
Isotropic minerals   21

Law of constancy of angle   16
Luminescence   27–28
Lustre   26–27

Magma   13–14
Magmatic differentiation   14
Magmatic formation of minerals   13–14
Magmatic rocks   172
Magnetism   28
Malleable minerals   24
Metallic lustre   26
Metamorphic mineral formation   15
Metamorphic rocks   173
Metasomatic mineral formation   14
Mineral collecting   31
Mineral identification   29
Mirror plane   16

Modifications   18
Mohs' scale of hardness   22

Non-metallic lustre   26

Opaque   27
Ores   11
Organic sediments   173

Paragenesis   15
Pearly lustre   27
Pegmatites   14
Physical properties   21
Plane of symmetry   16
Play of fire   169
Pleochroic minerals   25
Plutonic rocks   172
Pneumatolysis   14
Polymorphs   18
Precious stones   168 ff.
Pseudomorphs   21
Pseudo-symmetry   20

Reflection plane   16
Refraction of light   27
Rock-building minerals   12
Rocks   172 ff.

Sandstones   173
Scratch hardness   22
Sedimentary rocks   173
Silky lustre   27
Soft minerals   24
Space angles   16
Space lattice   16
Specific gravity   21–22
Streak   26
Streak plate   26
Structure of rocks   174
Submetallic lustre   27
Syntaxis   20
Synthetic precious stones   169

Taste   28
Texture of rocks   174
Thermoluminescence   28
Translucent   27
Transparency   27
Transparent   27
Triboluminescence   28
Twin crystals   20
Twinning striation   20

Veinstones   172
Verneuil process   170
Vitreous lustre   27
Volcanic rocks   172

Weathering processes   14–15

Localities of Minerals

Figures indicate numbers of minerals found in the given locality; bold figures refer to localities of illustrated minerals.

Europe

Austria

Ankogel, Salzburg   572
Bleiberg, Carinthia   41, 55, 79, 172, 280, **484**
Eisenerz, Styria   **63**
Greiner in Zemmtal, Tyrol   164, 395
Greiner Wald, Upper Austria   **331**
Gulsen near Kraubath, Styria   256, **457**
Habachtal, Salzburg   306
Hallein near Salzburg   44, **190**
Hallstatt, Salzkammergut   **30**, 44, 132, **224**
Hüttenberg, Carinthia   60, **96**, 383
Knappenwand in Untersulz-bachtal, Salzburg   **290, 295**
Kogel near Brixlegg, Tyrol   **446**
Kraubath, Styria   65
Krieglach, Styria   239
Leoben, Styria   276
Leogang, Salzburg   56
Lisenz Alps, Sellrain, Tyrol   **426**
Lölling near Hüttenberg, Carinthia   10, 407
Mariazell, Styria   **542**
Mitterberg, Salzburg   15
Modriach, Styria   **541**
Obergurgl, Ötztal, Tyrol   219
Oberpinzgau, Salzburg   339
Obirberg near Kappel, Carinthia   326, 406
Ötztal, Tyrol   **285**
Pfunders, Tyrol   104, 162
Prägraten-on-Isel, East Tyrol   198, 348
Rauris, Pinzgau, Salzburg   293
Rothenkopf, Zillertal, Tyrol   **104, 286**
Saualpe, Carinthia   293
Schellgaden, Salzburg   157
Schladming, Styria   **180**
Schmirn near Matrei, Tyrol   100
Schwarzenbach near Bleiburg, Carinthia   402
Schwaz, Tyrol   **250**
Sonnblick, Salzburg   119, **235**
Spittal-on-Drau, Carinthia   108
Sticklberg, Lower Austria   **240**
Sulzbachtal, Oberpinzgau, Salzburg   162, 339
Teufelsmühle, Habachtal, Salzburg   **339**
Trieben, Styria   **405**
Veitsch, Styria   405
Weisseck, Salzburg   **233**
Werfen, Salzburg   **85**, 152, **239**
Zillertal, Tyrol   20, **248**, 295, 359, **395**

Belgium

Berneau near Liège   169
Vielsalm, Ardennes   176, 275

Czech Republic

Bělá, Bohemia   **562**
Besednice, Bohemia   **551**
Blatno, Bohemia   **201**
Březová, Bohemia   **464**
Cerhovice, Bohemia   **68**
Čermníky near Kadaň, Bohemia   **29**
Česká Lípa, Bohemia   **88**
Chabičov, Moravia   **314**
Chuchle, Bohemia   **18**
Cínovec, Bohemia   168, **171**, 207, 267, **311, 323, 455**
Dědova Hora, Bohemia   **234**
Dolní Bory, Moravia   **244**
Doubice, Bohemia   **90**
Duchcov, Bohemia   **31**
Hauenštejn, Bohemia   **84**
Hazlov, Bohemia   **352**
Heřmanov, Moravia   **345**
Hořenec, Bohemia   **61**
Horní Blatná, Bohemia   **425**
Horní Slavkov, Bohemia   **163, 214**, 258, 261, **281, 438, 439, 454**
Hrbek, Bohemia   **148**
Hrubšice, Moravia   24, **298**
Jáchymov, Bohemia   **38, 48, 133, 137, 185, 249, 251**, 365, **373**, 443, **565**
Jílové, Bohemia   **120**
Kadaň, Bohemia   **247**
Karlovy Vary (Carlsbad), Bohemia   62, **320, 485**
Kaznějov, Bohemia   **252**
Kladno, Bohemia   **50, 123**
Komořany, Bohemia   **127**
Kopanina, Bohemia   **564**
Kozákov, Bohemia   96, **559**
Kralupy, Bohemia   18
Kraslice, Bohemia   **354, 574**
Křepice, Bohemia   **121**
Krkonoše (Giant Mountains), Bohemia   **553**
Krupka, Bohemia   **4, 362, 444**
Kunštát, Moravia   **569**
Kutná Hora, Bohemia   193, 448
Levín u Nové Paky, Bohemia   **507, 538**
Lukov, Bohemia   **467, 468**
Maršíkov, Moravia   293, 304
Meclov, Bohemia   **305**
Měděnec, Bohemia   **510**
Mořina, Bohemia   **170**
Nučice, Bohemia   **169, 404**
Obří důl, Giant Mountains, Bohemia   **157**
Oloví, Bohemia   **325, 401**

Paškopole, Bohemia   467
Peřimov, Bohemia   **111**
Podbořany, Bohemia   **21**
Podmoklice, Bohemia   **528**
Podsedice, Bohemia   **527**
Příbram, Bohemia   **6, 8**, 143, **145, 175, 316, 321, 327, 335, 374**, 375, **378, 379**, 381, **443, 448, 460, 462**, 477
Ratibořice, Bohemia   **110**
Řepčice, Bohemia   **77**
Rožná, Moravia   **208**, 211, **245**
Sedlec near Karlovy Vary, Bohemia   21
Smrkovec, Bohemia   **261**
Šternberk, Moravia   **400**
Stříbro, Bohemia   153, **487**
Stupava, Moravia   **575**
Tátobity, Bohemia   **557**
Ústí nad Labem, Bohemia   **199**
Valchov, Moravia   **141**
Valeč, Bohemia   **95**
Vinařická hora, Bohemia   **75**
Vrchlabí, Bohemia   **563, 570**
Zaječov, Bohemia   **499**
Zbirov, Bohemia   **160**

Denmark

Faroe Islands, Nólsoy (Skútin Cave)   **22**, 78, 84, 91, 202, 213

Germany

Altenberg near Aachen   **47**, 79, 280, 283, 411
Altenberg, Ore Mountains   134, **168**
Annaberg, Ore Mountains   249
Arnsberg, Westphalia   367, 374
Aschaffenburg, Spessart   358, 458
Auerbach a. d. Bergstrasse   351, 433
Bad Ems near Koblenz   270
Bad Grund, Harz   64, 73, 127, 315
Bad Harzburg, Harz   70, 287, 333, 452
Badenweiler, Black Forest   146, 153, 187, 270, 325
Baste near Harzburg, Harz   333
Berchtesgaden, Salzburg Alps   129
Bergen in Vogtland   136, 259
Betzdorf (Sieg), Siegerland   273
Black Forest   57
Blaue Kuppe near Eschwege   61, 62, 63
Bleialf, Eifel   187
Bodenmais, Bavarian Forest   76, 103, 206, **209**, 244, 308, 345, **472**

Brand-Erbisdorf, Saxony **397**
Brandholz near Goldmühl,
  Fichtelgebirge 119, 389
Bräunsdorf near Freiberg,
  Saxony **182**, 222
Breitenbrunn, Ore Mountains
  456
Buggingen near Müllheim,
  Baden 33, 35, 36, 224
Bühl near Kassel 385
Burgk near Dresden 50
Celle, Lower Saxony 33, 35, 36,
  224
Charlotte Mine, Clausthal-
  Zellerfeld, Harz 372
Christian Levin Mine near
  Essen-Borbeck, Nordrhein-
  Westphalia 309
Clara Mine near Wolfach, Black
  Forest 73, 144, 212, 234
Clausthal-Zellerfeld, Harz 325,
  378
Dernbach, Westerwald **269**
Diethendorf, Ore Mountains **452**
Dollart, Lower Saxony 42
Dornburg-on-Saale 232
Drachenfels, Pfälzer Wald 113,
  420
Drensteinfurt, Münsterland 64
Dudweiler near Saarbrücken 17
Duingen near Hildesheim 89
Dünsberg near Giessen,
  Hessen 68, 272
Ehrenfriedersdorf near Annaberg,
  Ore Mountains **453**
Eibenstock, Ore Mountains **97**,
  359
Eifel 420, 444
Eisleben, Harz 137, **179**
Elbingerode, Harz 201
Eleonora Mine near Siegen,
  Siegerland 148
Elgersburg near Ilmenau,
  Thuringia 379, 451
Epprechtstein near Kirchenlamitz,
  Fichtelgebirge 117, 346
Erbendorf, Fichtelgebirge **296**
Erzgebirge (Ore Mountains) 157,
  249, 311, 380, 439, 443
Eschersheim near Frankfort-on-
  Main 159
Falkenstein, Vogtland **136, 259**
Feldberg, Black Forest 142
Fichtelgebirge 400, 439
Freiberg, Ore Mountains 5, **15**,
  124, 182, 186, 206, **307**, 365, **382**,
  389
Freudenstadt, Black Forest 278
Friedrichssegen Mine near Bad
  Ems 321
Gefrees, Fichtelgebirge **333**
Gengenbach, Black Forest 80
Gersdorf near Chemnitz **571**
Giershagen near Stadtberge 232
Göda near Bautzen, Saxony **555**
Göpfersgrün, Fichtelgebirge 111,
  352
Graul Mine near Schwarzenberg,
  Saxony **407**

Hagendorf, East Bavaria 47
Hagendorf, Upper Palatinate 158,
  469
Hamburg **394**
Harzgerode, Harz 12, **13**
Haslach, Black Forest 86, 213
Hegau, Deckentuffe 444, 467
Heilbronn, Württemberg 33, 224
Heligoland **26**
Henneberg near Meiningen,
  Thuringia 98
Herdorf, Siegerland **409**
Himmelsfürst Mine near Freiberg,
  Saxony 307
Hof, Bavaria **556**
Hofsgrund, Black Forest **270**
Hohenkrähen, Hegau 95
Hohentwiel, Hegau 88, 420
Homboll, Hegau 22
Horhausen, Westerwald 269
Höwenegg, Hegau 75, 299, 360
Idar-Oberstein, Nahe 217
Ilfeld, Harz 434, **447, 451**
Ilmenau, Thuringia **434**
Johanngeorgenstadt,
  Ore Mountains 135, 137, **146**,
  260
Jusi, Schwäbische Alb 299
Kaiserstuhl 80, 92, 213, 291
Katzenbuckel, Odenwald 291
Käusersteimel Mine, Siegerland
  177
Kinzigtal, Black Forest 415, 464
Kropfmühl near Passau 441
Laacher See, Eifel 82, 92, 93,
  162, **189**, 237, 238, **416**, 467
Laasphe, Siegerland 200
Lahn-Dill area 201
Landshut, Bavaria 19, 396
Lautenthal, Upper Harz 200
Lauterberg, Harz 57, 58, 144,
  234, 273
Leisnig, Saxony 97
Leuchtenberg, Upper Palatinate
  212
Lindebach near Bad Ems 316
Lüderich near Bensberg 143
Lüneburg, Lower Saxony **114**
Lützelburg, Kaiserstuhl 75, 95,
  299
Mansfeld, Harz 14, 180, 370
Mechernich, Eifel 366, 401
Messbach near Plauen,
  Vogtland 276
Moschellandsberg, Rhine-
  Palatinate 1, 184, **393**
Müsen, Schwaben Mine,
  Siegerland **387**
Nahe area 83
Neubulach near Calw, Black
  Forest 230, 273
Neudorf near Quedlinburg,
  Harz **317, 383**, 455
Niedermendig, Eifel **187, 238**,
  355, 416
Nieder-Ramstadt, Bergstrasse
  388
Nördlinger Ries 161
Oberrotweil, Kaiserstuhl 478

Oberstein, Nahe 70, 71, 77, 247
Odenwald 155
Öhrenstock, Thuringia **440**
Pechtelsgrün, Vogtland 455
Penig, Saxony 211
Pflasterkaute near Eisenach,
  Thuringia 84, 90, 199
Plauenscher Grund near Dresden,
  Saxony **554**
Radautal near Harzburg, Harz
  415, 418
Rammelsberg near Goslar
  227, 252
Rauschermühle near Nieder-
  kirchen, Palatinate 294
Recht, Eifel 23
Reichenbach, Odenwald 177
Rheinbreitbach near
  Bad Honnef-on-Rhine 196
Richelsdorf, Hessen **392**
Röhrenhof, Fichtelgebirge 313
Rosenegg, Hegau 123
Rüdersdorf near Berlin 123
Rügen Island **424**
Saalfeld, Thuringia 400
Sangerhausen, Harz **42**
Sasbach, Kaiserstuhl 61, 62, 63
Sayda near Freiberg,
  Saxony 253
Schapbach, Black Forest 402
Schelingen, Kaiserstuhl 165,
  334
Schneckenstein near Falkenstein,
  Ore Mountains 117, **523**
Schneeberg, Ore Mountains 4,
  14, 185, **210**, 250, 365, **388, 390**,
  392, **425**, 460
Schwarzenberg, Ore Mountains
  148, **166**, 322, 357, 407, **573**
Sendenhorst, Münsterland **64**
Sennelager near Paderborn 161
Siegerland 12, 13, 124, 128,
  317, 335, 370, 379, 429
Solnhofen, Fränkische Alb **442**
Spechtshausen near Freital,
  Saxony **558**
Spessart 312
St. Andreasberg, Harz 8, 10, 11,
  38, **54**, 58, 71, 72, 76, 89, 128,
  186, 213, 308, 363, 373, **380**,
  381, 386
St. Wendel, Saar **505**
Staffel-on-Lahn
Stassfurt, Saxony **35, 36, 46**, 114
Stolberg, Harz 3, 372
Stolberg near Aachen 142, 316,
  481
Sundwig near Iserlohn,
  Westphalia 207
Thannhausen, Bavaria 396
Tiefengrün-on-Saale 342
Tilkerode, Harz 3, 372
Tittling near Passau 98
Treseburg, Harz 357
Upper Harz 401
Upper Palatinate 20, 21
Vogelsberg, Oberhessen 77
Waldgirmes near Wetzlar-on-
  Lahn 272

Waldsassen, Bavarian Forest 209, 375
Warnemünde, Mecklenburg 552
Weenzen near Elze-on-Leine 129
Weilburg, Lahn 314
Weiler near Lahn, Black Forest 269
Wiesloch near Heidelberg 41, 127, 280, 411, 432
Wippra, East Harz 163
Wittichen, Black Forest 4, 38, 48, 180, 185, 210, 363, 380, 390, 443
Wolfach-on-Kinzig, Black Forest 373
Wolfsberg near Sangerhausen, Harz 49, 367, 376
Wölsendorf-on-Naab, Bavaria 133, 136, 233, 443
Wurlitz, Fichtelgebirge 300
Zorge near Harzburg, Harz 372
Zwiesel, Bavarian Forest 158, 305

Finland

Pargas 394, 441
Pusunsaari in Impilaks 87
Vuohijärvi 459

France

Adervielle in Vallée du Louron, Pyrenees 279
Allemont 294, 381
Auteuil 18
Autun near Limoges 138
Beaujeu, Dep. Rhône 147
Bourg d'Oisans, Dauphiné 109, 235, 295, 357
Chazelle near Pontgibaud, Auvergne 222
Chessy near Lyon 195, 231, 271
Esterel 103
Gèdres, Pyrenees 415
Ile d'Aix near La Rochelle 141
Ile de Groix, Brittany 350
La Garonne near Carqueiranne, Dep. Var 223
Markirch, Vosges 8, 48, 124, 185, 380, 431
Minette, Lotharingia 404
Mont Doré 67, 413
Montmorillon, Dep. Vienne 19
Pontgibaud 383
Quimper 358
St. Yrieux near Limoges 260

Great Britain

Alston Moor, Westmorland 56, 74, 153, 212
Bishoptown near Paisley, Scotland 143
Botallack Mine near St. Just, Cornwall 451
Carrarach Mine, Cornwal 278
Cornwall 15, 261, 263, 275, 311, 317, 375, 384, 439, 448
Cumberland 52, 175, 191, 315, 327, 330, 445
Dry Gill Mine, Cumberland 174

Durham 318
Egremont, Cumberland 53
Fallowfield, Cumberland 74
Huel Basset, Cornwall 196
Kilpatrick near Dumbarton, Scotland 194
Lancaster, Lancashire 491
Leadhills, Scotland 55, 262, 401
Lizard, Cornwall 483, 489
Lostwithiel, Cornwall 336, 425
Red Gill near Keswick, Cumberland 226, 262
Redruth, Cornwall 228, 253, 258, 370
Snowdon near Tremadoc, North Wales 198, 348
St. Agnes, Cornwall 209
St. Day, Cornwall 267
St. Just, Cornwall 398
Strontian, Argyll 76
Tavistock, Devon 126

Greece

Kassandra, Chalkidiki 125
Laurion 225, 254, 322, 411
Náxos 107, 395, 428
Sérifos 342
Tinos 561

Greenland

Blaafjeld near Ovifak 385
Disko 78
Igalik 465
Ivigtut 40
Kangek 544
Kangerdluarsuk 470
Kap Farewell 461

Hungary

Gánt 568
Tokod 29

Iceland

Grákollur (Hill), Reydarfjördur 423
Helgustadir, Reydarfjördur 51
Stóra Geysir 486
Teigarhorn, Berufjördur 71, 72, 91

Ireland

Antrim 385
Benyevenagh 78

Italy

Agrigento, Sicily 130
Ala, Piedmont 525
Alatal, Piedmont 248
Alghero, Sardinia 221
Albanian Mountains 444
Alto Adige (Val di Vizze, Pfitsch) 164, 203, 256, 433
Aosta, Piedmont 350, 414

Ariccia 92
Baveno, Lago Maggiore 72, 346
Bolzano 27
Brosso near Traversella, Piedmont 125, 344
Campiglia, Tuscany 343
Capo di Bove 92
Cianciana, Sicily 129
Colli Euganei 113
Craveggia, Piedmont 471
Cyclopen Islands 102, 204
Domodossola, Piedmont 171, 323
Elba 410
Etna 17, 29
Fassatal, Piedmont 71, 89, 247, 286, 344
Florence 319
Frascati, Albanian Mountains near Rome 300
Gavorrano, Tuscany 125
Grosseto near Pereta, Tuscany 182
Grotta d'Oggi, Elba 494, 520
Iglesias, Sardinia 280, 315
La Spezia 287
La Tolfa near Civitavecchia 67
Lipari 560
Monte Amiata, Tuscany 1, 184
Monte Mulatto, South Tyrol 157
Monte Narba, Sardinia 12, 386
Monte-Poni, Sardinia 225, 309, 321, 402, 411
Monte Somma, Vesuvius 90, 94, 102, 106, 165, 344, 349, 351
Monte Vulture near Melfi 416
Monzoni in Fassatal, South Tyrol 475
Parre in Val Sarentina 73
Perticara near Rimini 232
Pfitschtal near Vipiteno (Sterzing) 59
Rio Marina, Elba 125, 342, 435
San Giovanni Mine, Laorca, Sardinia 41
San Piero in Campo, Elba 208, 220, 419
Sarrabus, Sardinia 373
Seiser Alm, South Tyrol 86, 89
Solfatara near Pozzuoli 27
St. Marcel in Val d'Aosta, Piedmont 154, 215, 440
Toal della Foja, Trentino 204
Traversella, Piedmont 152, 157
Val di Susa, Piedmont 301
Vesuvius 17, 65, 87, 93, 181, 291, 421
Vipiteno (Sterzing), South Tyrol 358

Norway

Arendal, Aust-Agder 86, 295, 332, 341, 356, 461, 463
Bamle near Oedegården 85, 403, 412, 415
Bodö, Nordland 219
Brevik on Langesundsfjord 332

Ekersund near Stavanger   458
Frederiksvärn near Larvik,
   Oslofjord   334, 500
Hitterö Island   474
Iveland, Aust-Agder   337, 340,
   474
Kongsberg-on-Lågenelf   5, 363
Kragerö-on-Langesund   244,
   458
Langesundsfjord   99, 115, 328
Moss   469
Narvik   105
Övre Arö Island in Langesunds-
   fjord   99, 166
Skutterud in Kirchspiel Modum
   16, 391
Slangsvold near Moss   362
Snarum   82, 165, 391
Souland   242
Strömsheien-on-Ströms Sea in
   Sätersdal   242
Tvedestrand, Aust-Agder   289

Poland

Bochnia near Cracow   58
Jordanów, Silesia   370, 429
Mirsk, Silesia   80
Strzegom, Silesia   100, 205, 346
Szklary, Silesia   297, 540
Tarnowice   81
Wieliczka near Cracow   33
Wilcza Poręba near Karpacz   216
Złoty Stok, Silesia   10, 11, 389

Portugal

Fayal Island, Azores   418
Madeira   112
Sabugal   138, 149

Romania

Baia de Aries   2
Baia Sprie (Felsöbánya)   57, 139,
   144, 181
Botesti (Botesbánya)   369
Capnic   181, 368, 431, 533
Ciclova   356, 389
Ditrău   93, 237
Dognecea   34
Fata Bai   364
Herja (Chiuzbaia, Kisbánya)
   128, 222, 376
Moldova, Banat   178, 223, 273
Moravica, Banat   456
Roşia Montană (Verspatak)   119,
   122, 449
Săcărâmb (Nagvág)   3, 7, 192,
   361, 449
Uroiu (Aranya Hill)   113

Slovakia

Banská Štiavnica   59, 107, 142, 151,
   186, 193, 218
Červenica   202
Dobšiná   13, 14, 180, 576
Donovaly   437

Dubník   139, 535
Handlová   566
Kremnica   45, 57, 409
Kuzmice   19
Lovinobaňa   399, 405
Ľubietová   271, 275, 277
Magurka   367
Mlynky   60, 124
Prešov   32, 33
Sliač   567
Špania Dolina   45, 228, 232, 257,
   263, 273
Tajov near Banská Bystrica   131
Tri Vody   422
Železník   69, 482

Spain

Almaden, Sierra de Castillejo
   393
Barranco Jaroso in Sierra
   Almagrega   322
Cap Ortegal, North-West Spain
   268
Huelva on Gulf Cadiz   391
Linares, South Spain   226, 402
Rio Tinto   227, 252
Sierra Cabrera   254
Sierra de Ronda, Andalusia   106
Villa Rubia de los Ojos   44

Sweden

Åker, Södermanland   246
Bastnäs Mine near Riddarhyttan
   387
Broddebo, Kalmar   279
Falun, Kopparberg, Svealand
   183, 219, 372
Grängesberg, Kopparberg,
   Svealand   362
Jakobsberg, Värmland   154, 215,
   350, 440
Kiruna, Norrbotten   433
Långban   94, 434, 466
Norberg   456
Nordmark, Värmland   314, 434
Sala   381
Småland   433
Utö   245
Varuträsk, Västerbotten   8, 108,
   302, 419, 461, 469, 474
Ytterby near Waxholm   461, 474

Switzerland

Amsteg-on-Reuss, Uri   198
Binnatal, Wallis   181, 203, 235,
   337, 432
Campolungo, Tessin   164, 358,
   403, 414, 428
Chamoson, Wallis   404
Fleschhorn, Wallisian Alps   458
Gotthard area   72, 101, 436, 534
Grimsel   101
Intschitobel near Amsteg   100
Lago Tremorgio, Tessin   87
Piz Vallatscha, Graubünden   427
Pizzo Forno, Tessin   236, 492

Riedertobel near Amsteg   348
Ripmfischwäng, Zermatt   459
Scopi, Graubünden   357
Tavetsch, Bündner Oberland
   162
Val Giuv, Graubünden   98
Val Strem near Sedrun,
   Tavetsch   98
Wallis   392
Zermatt   23, 239, 293

Turkey

Alabanda Ruins, Anatolia   449
Anatolia   546
Eskischehir   24
Guleman, East Anatolia   457

USSR (former) - European Part

Akhmatov Mine near Zlatoust,
   Urals, Russia   459
Berezovsk, Urals, Russia   188,
   262
Biser, Central Urals, Russia   303
Crimea, Ukraine   24
Chibiny Tundra, Kola Peninsula,
   Russia   328
Děražnja, Podolien, Ukraine   310
Ilmen Mountains, Southern
   Urals, Russia   355
Kaluš near Stanislav, Ukraine   46
Klaipeda, Lithuania   140
Kuban, Caucasus, Russia   131
Maikop, Caucasus, Russia   50
Miass near Zlatoust, Southern
   Urals, Russia   40, 116, 428
Murzinka, Urals, Russia   426
Mužijevo near Beregovo,
   Ukraine   67
Nevyansk near Yekaterinburg,
   Urals, Russia   490
Nikopol, Ukraine   451
Nizhni Tagil, Central Urals,
   Russia   9, 253, 267, 277,
   300
Sysertsk, Central Urals, Russia
   303
Tokovaya River, Central Urals,
   Russia   116, 176, 304, 306,
   395, 524
Urals, Russia   255
Yantarny (Palmnicken), Baltic
   Coast   140
Yekaterinburg, Central Urals,
   Russia   132
Zlatoust, Southern Urals, Russia
   246, 248, 360

USSR (former) - Asiatic Part

Altyn Tyube Mount, Kazakhstan
   284
Baikal on Lake Baikal, Russia
   547
East Siberia, Russia   384
Nerchinsk, Transbaikal, Russia
   79, 378, 518
Siberia, Russia   479

Vilyui River, Yakutia, Russia 118, **353**
Zavodskoi, Altai   369

Yugoslavia (former)

Allchar near Mrežičko, Macedonia 127, **131**, 181
Bor, Serbia   221
Cetinje, Montenegro   **49**
Dobrova, Slovenia   **359**
Dravograd, Slovenia   **302**
Idrija, Slovenia   **1**, 45, 184, **430**
Krešovo near Sarajevo, Bosnia 181, 367
Mežica, Slovenia   **172**, 325
Prilep, Macedonia   164, 236
Trepća (Stantrg)   128, 142, 308, 342, 366, 378
Tržić, Slovenia   **184**

North America

Canada

Athabaska Sea, Saskatchewan 251
Cobalt, Ontario   5, 13, 179, 386, 388, 392
Peter's Point, Nova Scotia   **70**
Renfrew, Quebec   **338**, 355
St. Paul Island, Labrador   **413**
Thetford Mines, Quebec   **255**
Timiskaming, Ontario   14, 390
Timmins, Ontario   **237**

USA

Alum Cave, Unaka Mountains, Sevier Co., Tennessee   **28**
Amity, New York   **360**
Arizona   155
Badin, Cotton Stone Mountains, North Carolina   **23**
Bergen Hill (Tunnel), New Jersey **83**
Bisbee, Arizona   177, **195**
Boulder, Colorado   453
Buena Vista, Colorado   **134**
Butte, Montana   221, 370, 429
California   25
Cedar Valley, Tooele County, Oquirrh Mountains, Utah   282
Celebes, Douglas County, Oregon 264
Chesterfield, South Carolina   **108**
Clear Lake near San Francisco, California   43
Climax Mine near Leadville, Colorado   362
Clover Creek, Lincoln Co., Idaho 155
Copper Queen Mine near Morenci, Graham Co., Arizona 223
Cripple Creek, Colorado   2, 7, 361, 364
Danbury, Connecticut   427

Death Valley, Inyo Co., California 37, **66**
Dell Norte County, California **308**
Edenville, New York   447
Flat Rock Mine, Mitchell Co., North Carolina   **135**
Franklin, New Jersey   **197**, **200**, 279, **283**, 349, 476, 478
Goshen, Massachusetts   245
Haddam, Connecticut   **304**
Hot Springs, Arkansas   **531**
Houghton Co., Michigan   177
Joplin, Missouri   **366**
Juneau, Alaska   194
Kansas near Collyer, Trego Co. **498**
Keystone, South Dakota   305
Leadville, Colorado   321
Lewiston, Clay Canyon, Utah **282**
Llano Co., Texas   471
Massachusetts   **408**
Middletown, Connecticut   **312**
Mine La Motte, Missouri   387
Montana   **480**
Montgomery Co., Arkansas   68, 272, **276**
Mount Blanco-on-Furnace Creek near Death Valley, California 37
Mount Spokane, Washington 283, 260
Nevada   43
Pala Chief, San Diego Co., California   208, **220**, **519**, **530**
Paradox Valley, Long Park, Colorado   149
Pikes Peak, Colorado   40, **545**
Providence, Rhode Island   **20**
Red Cloud Mine, Boulder Co., Colorado   369
Redington Mine, Knoxville, California   **183**
Riverside Co., California   216
Rock River, Wyoming   **396**
Russel, St. Lawrence Co., New York   **427**
Salt Lake, Utah   30
San Benito County, California 88, **241**, **465**
Sterling Hill near Ogdensburg, New Jersey   **197**, **417**
Table Mountain near Golden, Colorado   91
Tampa Bay, Florida   **501**
Terlingua, Brewster Co., Texas 393
Texas (Wood's Chrome Mine), Lancaster Co., Pennsylvania **268**
Tiger, Arizona   243
Total Wreck Mine, Bisbee, Arizona   **406**
Treasury Hill in Beaver, Salt Lake Co., Utah   39
Westchester, Pennsylvania   **313**
West Mine on Snake River, Summit Co., Colorado   449

West Patterson, New Jersey **294**
Yuma, Arizona   **216**

Central and South Amerika

Antofagasta, Chile   **25**
Atacama, Chile   229
Boleo near Santa Rosalia, Baja California, Mexico   **243**
Brazil   **289**, 347, 502, **539**
Chuquicamata, Chile   229
Copiapoó, Chile   265, 284
Coquimbo, Chile   **265**
Durango, Mexico   **158**
Figueira, Brazil   **529**
Itambacuri, Brazil   **517**
Los Lamentos, Mexico   **173**
Matto Perro, Uruguay   **217**
Minas Gerais, Brazil   **473**, **493**, **506**
Minas Novas, Brazil   302
Morococha, Peru   450
Muzo in Boyaca State, north of Bogotá, Colombia   **306**
North Chile   266
Oruro, Bolivia   **384**
Ouro Preto, Brazil   272
Poopó, Bolivia   **377**
Rio Grande do Sul, Brazil   **167**, **532**
Salta, Argentina   37
San Miguel on Rio Jequetinonha, Minas Gerais, Brazil   **536**
San Miguel di Piracicaba, Minas Gerais, Brazil   **116**
Serra do Grão Mogol, Minas Gerais, Brazil   116
Serra do Mar, Brazil   218
Uruguay   **508**
Zacatecas, Mexico   **39**
Zimapan, Mexico   **202**, **225**

Africa

Abenab, South-West Africa   326, 406
Algeria   49
Ambatofotsikely, Madagascar **337**
Ambositra, Madagascar   **428**
Ampandandrava, Madagascar **292**, **403**
Ampangabe, Madagascar   **341**, **471**
Antsirabé, Madagascar   176
Befanamo, east of Ankazobe, Madagascar   **340**
Betafo, Madagascar   **329**
Bou Azzer, Morocco   **16**, 179, 210
Broken Hill, Rhodesia   47, 174, 283, 406
Bushveld, Transvaal, Union of South Africa   303
Cairo, Egypt   **503**

Delagoabai, Union of South Africa   28
Djebel Mahser, Morocco   **326**
Djelfa, Algeria   59, 151
Egypt   30
Friesenberg, Otavibergland, South-West Africa   **324**
Griquatown, Union of South Africa   **488**
Imalo, Madagascar   **115**
Imini near Varzázat, Mine, Bou Tazoult, Antiatlas, Morocco   **450**
Kabamby, Madagascar   **537**
Kasolo, Katanga, Congo   156
Katanga (now Shaba), Congo   251, 263, **274**, 275, 387, **548**
Kimberley, Union of South Africa   **118, 513**
Libian Desert **161**
Los Island, Kassa, West Africa   **328**
Lydenburg, Transvaal   **288**
Machakos, Kenya (Brit.)   236
Madeira   **112**
Maharitra, Madagascar   **211**
Merensky Reef, Rustenburg, Union of South Africa   9
Messina, Transvaal, Union of South Africa   **429**
Morocco   310
Otavi, South-West Africa   265, 284
Otjosondu, South-West Africa   440

Palabora, Murchison Range, East Transvaal, Union of South Africa   313
Renéville, Congo   **284**
Shinkolobwe, Katanga (now Shaba), Congo   **150, 156,** 258
Sierra Leone   1í8
St. John's Island (Zebirget), Red Sea, Egypt   **299**
Union of South Africa   **543**
Upper Egypt   25
Transvaal, Union of South Africa   9
Tsumeb, South-West Africa   **81,** 146, 174, 226, **230**, 262, **280,** 309, 324, 327, **371**, 431
Windhuk, South-West Africa   414

Asia

Burma   439
China   **550**
Ichinokawa Mine (Iyo Province), Japan   **367**
India   **504, 509, 526**
Israel   310
Kandy, Sri Lanka   **105**
Kotaki River in Niigata Pref., Japan   **301**
Kyurazawa Mine (Ashio-machi), Tochigi Pref., Japan   279
Mijako, Japan   102, 204
Mogok, north-east of Mandalary, Upper Burma   301

Mutsu, Japan   432
Obira Mine, Province Bungo, Japan   427
Ratnapura, Sri Lanka   **511**
Sabaragamuva, Sri Lanka   **514**
Sri Lanka   244, 246, 403, **441, 512,** 521
Tibet   **43**
Ting-Tuc near Cao Bang, Tonkin, Vietnam   **260**
Tonokamiyama, Omi Province Japan   **117**

Australia

Adelaide   27
Broken Hill, New South Wales   39, 171, 323, 450
Bulls Creek, Queensland   **496,** 497
Bura-Bura Mine near Adelaide   266
Cooper Creek, Queensland   **495**
Dundas, Tasmania   **188**
Goyamin Pool, Chittering Valley, South West Division   **206**
Kawa-Kawa, New Zealand   287
Labo, Luzón, Philippines (USA)   188
New Zealand   **549**
Nouméa, New Caledonia   **264**
Wallaroo, South Australia   266
West Australia   7, 364

List of Reference Books

Anderson, B. W.: Gem Testing. Heywood & Comp., Ltd, London 1947

Bloss, F. Donald: An Introduction to the Methods of Optical Crystallography. Holt, Rinehart & Winston, New York 1961

Bunn, Charles: Crystals – Their Role in Nature and in Science. Academic Press, New York – London 1964

Dake, H. C., Fleener Frank L., Wilson Ben Hur: Quartz Family Minerals. A Handbook for the Mineral Collector. Whittlesey House, McGraw-Hill, New York – London 1938

Dana, E. S.: A Textbook of Mineralogy. John Wiley, New York 1932

Dana, L., Hurlbut, S.: Manual of Mineralogy. Wiley, New York 1952

Deer, W. A., Howie, R. A., Zussman, J.: Rock Forming Minerals. 1962–1964

Kraus, E. H., Hunt, W. F., Ramsdell, L. S.: Mineralogy - An Introduction to the Study of Minerals and Crystals. McGraw-Hill, New York – London 1936

Kraus, E. H.: Tables for the Determination of Minerals. McGraw-Hill, New York – London 1930

Kraus, E. H., Slawson, C. B.: Gems and Gem Materials. McGraw-Hill, New York – London 1941

Lindgren, W.: Mineral Deposits. McGraw-Hill, New York – London 1933

McCarthy, J. R.: Fire in the Earth – The Story of the Diamond. Robert Hale Ltd, London 1946

Phillips, F. C.: An Introduction to Crystallography, Longmans, Green & Co., London, New York, Toronto 1949

Read, H. H.: Elements of Mineralogy. Woodbridge Press, Ltd, Guilford 1939

Rogers, A. F., Kerr, P. F.: Optical Mineralogy. MacGraw-Hill, New York – London 1942

Rogers, A. F.: Introduction to the Study of Minerals. McGraw-Hill, New York – London 1937

Taylor, H. E.: Wonders of the Earth's Crust. Sir Isaac Pitman & Sons, Ltd, London 1932

Wahlstrom, E. E.: Optical Crystallography. John Wiley & Sons, Inc., New York – London 1960

Webster, Robert: The Gemmologists Compendium. N.A.G. Press, Ltd, London 1947

Webster, Robert: Gems. Their Sources, Descriptions and Identification. London 1962

Winchel, A. N., Winchel, H.: Elements of Optical Mineralogy. John Wiley & Sons, Inc., New York – London 1951